A-Level
Biology

Exam Board: Edexcel A (Salters-Nuffield)

Revising for Biology exams is stressful, that's for sure — even just getting your notes sorted out can leave you needing a lie down. But help is at hand...

This brilliant CGP book explains **everything you'll need to learn** (and nothing you won't), all in a straightforward style that's easy to get your head around. We've also included **exam questions** to test how ready you are for the real thing.

There's even a free Online Edition you can read on your computer or tablet!

How to get your free Online Edition

Go to **cgpbooks.co.uk/extras** and enter this code...

1880 3477 7462 2051

This code only works for one person. If somebody else has used this book before you, they might have already claimed the Online Edition.

A-Level revision? It has to be CGP!

Published by CGP

From original material by Richard Parsons.

Editors:
Charlotte Burrows, Katherine Faudemer, Rachel Kordan, Christopher McGarry, Ciara McGlade,
Sarah Pattison, Claire Plowman, Rachael Rogers, Camilla Simson, Hayley Thompson.

Contributors:
Sophie Anderson, Gloria Barnett, Jessica Egan, Mark Ellingham, James Foster,
Paddy Gannon, Julian Hardwick, Derek Harvey, Liz Masters, Adrian Schmit.

ISBN: 978 1 78294 298 6

With thanks to Lauren Burns and Christopher Lindle for the proofreading.
With thanks to Laura Jakubowski for the copyright research.

Clipart from Corel®
Printed by Elanders Ltd, Newcastle upon Tyne.

Contents

If you're revising for the **AS exams**, you'll need The Scientific Process, Topics 1-4, and the Practical Skills section at the back. If you're revising for the **A-level exams**, you'll need the **whole book**.

The Scientific Process

These pages are all about the scientific process — how we develop and test scientific ideas. It's what scientists do all day, every day (well, except at coffee time — never come between a scientist and their coffee).

Scientists Come Up with *Theories* — Then *Test Them...*

Science tries to explain **how** and **why** things happen — it **answers questions**. It's all about seeking and gaining **knowledge** about the world around us. Scientists do this by **asking** questions and **suggesting** answers and then **testing** them, to see if they're correct — this is the **scientific process**.

1) **Ask** a question — make an **observation** and ask **why or how** it happens. E.g. why is trypsin (an enzyme) found in the small intestine but not in the stomach?

2) **Suggest** an answer, or part of an answer, by forming a **theory** (a possible **explanation** of the observations) e.g. pH affects the activity of enzymes. (Scientists also sometimes form a **model** too — a **simplified picture** of what's physically going on.)

3) Make a **prediction** or **hypothesis** — a **specific testable statement**, based on the theory, about what will happen in a test situation. E.g. trypsin will be active at pH 8 (the pH of the small intestine) but inactive at pH 2 (the pH of the stomach).

4) Carry out a **test** — to provide **evidence** that will support the prediction (or help to disprove it). E.g. measure the rate of reaction of trypsin at various pH levels.

The evidence supported Quentin's Theory of Flammable Burps.

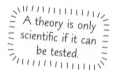

A theory is only scientific if it can be tested.

...Then They *Tell* Everyone About Their *Results...*

The results are **published** — scientists need to let others know about their work. Scientists publish their results in **scientific journals**. These are just like normal magazines, only they contain **scientific reports** (called papers) instead of the latest celebrity gossip.

1) Scientific reports are similar to the **lab write-ups** you do in school. And just as a lab write-up is **reviewed** (marked) by your teacher, reports in scientific journals undergo **peer review** before they're published.

2) The report is sent out to **peers** — other scientists that are experts in the **same area**. They examine the data and results, and if they think that the conclusion is reasonable it's **published**. This makes sure that work published in scientific journals is of a **good standard**.

3) But peer review **can't guarantee** the science is **correct** — other scientists still need to **reproduce** it.

4) Sometimes **mistakes** are made and bad work is published. Peer review **isn't perfect** but it's probably the best way for scientists to self-regulate their work and to publish **quality reports**.

...Then *Other Scientists* Will *Test* the Theory Too

Other scientists read the published theories and results, and try to **test the theory** themselves. This involves:

* Repeating the **exact same experiments**.
* Using the theory to make **new predictions** and then testing them with **new experiments**.

If the *Evidence* Supports a Theory, It's *Accepted* — for Now

1) If all the experiments in all the world provide good evidence to back it up, the theory is thought of as **scientific 'fact'** (for now).

2) But it will never become **totally indisputable** fact. Scientific **breakthroughs or advances** could provide new ways to question and test the theory, which could lead to **new evidence** that **conflicts** with the current evidence. Then the testing starts all over again...

And this, my friend, is the **tentative nature of scientific knowledge** — it's always **changing** and **evolving**.

The Scientific Process

So scientists need evidence to back up their theories. They get it by carrying out experiments, and when that's not possible they carry out studies. But why bother with science at all? We want to know as much as possible so we can use it to try and improve our lives (and because we're nosy).

Evidence Comes from Lab Experiments...

1) Results from **controlled experiments** in **laboratories** are **great**.
2) A lab is the easiest place to **control variables** so that they're all **kept constant** (except for the one you're investigating).
3) This means you can draw valid **conclusions**.

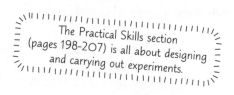

The Practical Skills section (pages 198-207) is all about designing and carrying out experiments.

...and Well-Designed Studies

1) There are things you **can't** investigate in a lab, e.g. whether stress causes heart attacks. You have to do a study instead.
2) You still need to try and make the study as controlled as possible to make it **valid**. But in reality it's **very hard** to control **all the variables** that **might** be having an effect.
3) You can do things to help, e.g. have **matched groups** — **choose two groups** of people (those who have quite stressful jobs and those who don't) who are **as similar as possible** (same mix of ages, same mix of diets etc.). But you can't easily rule out every possibility.

Having a control reduced the effect of exercise on the study.

Society Makes Decisions Based on Scientific Evidence

1) Lots of scientific work eventually leads to **important discoveries** or breakthroughs that could **benefit humankind**.
2) These results are **used by society** (that's you, me and everyone else) to **make decisions** — about the way we live, what we eat, what we drive, etc.
3) All sections of society use scientific evidence to make decisions, e.g. politicians use it to devise policies and individuals use science to make decisions about their own lives.

Other factors can **influence** decisions about science or the way science is used:

Economic factors

- Society has to consider the **cost** of implementing changes based on scientific conclusions — e.g. the **NHS** can't afford the most expensive drugs without **sacrificing** something else.
- Scientific research is **expensive** so companies won't always develop new ideas — e.g. developing new drugs is costly, so pharmaceutical companies often only invest in drugs that are likely to make them **money**.

Social factors

- **Decisions** affect **people's lives** — E.g. scientists may suggest **banning smoking** and **alcohol** to prevent health problems, but shouldn't **we** be able to **choose** whether **we** want to smoke and drink or not?

Environmental factors

- Scientists believe **unexplored regions** like remote parts of rainforests might contain **untapped drug** resources. But some people think we shouldn't **exploit** these regions because any interesting finds may lead to **deforestation** and **reduced biodiversity** in these areas.

So there you have it — that's how science works...

Hopefully these pages have given you a nice intro to how the world of science is run, e.g. what scientists do to provide you with 'facts'. You need to understand this, as you're expected to know all about the scientific process for the exams.

Water and Transport

Your body needs all sorts of different molecules to stay alive. It also needs to be able to transport these molecules around the body. That's where good old water comes in — read on...

Water is Vital to Living Organisms

Water makes up about 80% of a cell's contents. It has some important **functions**, inside and outside cells:

As her legs slowly dissolved, Jenny cursed her holiday.

1) Water is a **solvent**, which means some substances **dissolve** in it. Most biological reactions take place **in solution**, so water's pretty essential.

2) Water **transports** substances. Substances can be transported **more easily** if they're **dissolved** in a solvent. So the fact that water's a **liquid** and a **solvent** means it can easily transport all sorts of materials, like glucose and oxygen, around plants and animals.

Water Molecules have a Simple Structure

Examiners like asking you to relate **structure** to **properties** and **function**, so make sure you know the structure of water.

1) A molecule of **water** (H_2O) is **one atom** of **oxygen** (**O**) joined to **two atoms** of **hydrogen** (H_2) by **shared electrons**.

2) Because the **shared negative** hydrogen electrons are **pulled towards** the oxygen atom, the other side of each hydrogen atom is left with a **slight positive charge**.

3) The **unshared** negative electrons on the oxygen atom give it a **slight negative charge**.

4) This makes water a **dipolar** molecule — it has a **partial negative** ($\delta-$) charge on one side and a **partial positive** ($\delta+$) charge on the other.

unshared electron

nucleus of oxygen (O) atom

shared electrons

nucleus of hydrogen (H) atom

'δ' is the Greek letter 'delta'. So you read '$\delta-$' as 'delta negative.'

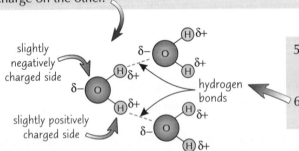

slightly negatively charged side

slightly positively charged side

hydrogen bonds

5) The slightly negatively-charged **oxygen atoms attract** the slightly positively-charged **hydrogen atoms** of other water molecules.

6) This attraction is called **hydrogen bonding** and it gives water some of its useful properties.

Water's Dipole Nature Makes it Good at Transporting Substances

Having a slight **negative charge** on one side and a slight **positive charge** on the other makes water **cohesive** and a **good solvent**. These properties make water good at **transporting substances**.

Water is Very Cohesive

1) Cohesion is the **attraction** between molecules of the same type (e.g. two water molecules). Water molecules are **very cohesive** (they tend to stick together) because they're **dipolar**.

2) This helps water to **flow**, making it great for **transporting substances**.

Water and Transport

Water is a **Good Solvent**

1) A lot of important substances in biological reactions are **ionic** (like **salt**, for example). This means they're made from **one positively-charged** atom or molecule and **one negatively-charged** atom or molecule (e.g. salt is made from a positive sodium ion and a negative chloride ion).

2) Because water is dipolar, the **slightly positive end** of a water molecule will be attracted to the **negative ion**, and the **slightly negative end** of a water molecule will be attracted to the **positive ion**.

3) This means the ions will get **totally surrounded** by water molecules — in other words, they'll **dissolve**.

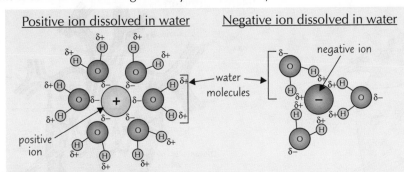

The dipolar nature of bears sometimes results in unexpected hydrogen bonding.

4) Water's **dipole nature** makes it useful as a **solvent** in living organisms. E.g. in **humans**, important **ions** can dissolve in the water in **blood** and then be transported around the body.

Multicellular Organisms Need *Mass Transport Systems*

1) All cells **need energy** — most cells get energy via **aerobic respiration**. The raw materials for this are **glucose** and **oxygen**, so the body has to make sure it can deliver enough of these to all its cells.

2) In single-celled organisms, these materials can **diffuse directly** into the cell across the cell membrane. The diffusion rate is quick because of the **short distance** the substances have to travel (see page 28).

3) In **multicellular** organisms (like us), diffusion across the outer membrane would be **too slow** because of the **large distance** the substances would have to travel to reach **all** the cells — think of how far it is from your skin to your heart cells.

4) So, multicellular organisms have **mass transport systems**:

> 1) The **mass transport systems** are used to **carry raw materials** from specialised **exchange organs** (e.g. the lungs and the digestive system) to the body cells, and to **remove metabolic waste** (e.g. carbon dioxide).
>
> 2) In mammals, the mass transport system is the **circulatory system**, where the heart is used to pump **blood** around the body.
>
> 3) Individual cells in tissues and organs get **nutrients** and **oxygen** from the blood and dispose of **metabolic waste** into the blood.

Richard had a different idea of mass transport to his biology teacher.

Practice Questions

Q1 Briefly describe what is meant by a dipolar molecule.

Q2 Why do multicellular organisms need mass transport systems?

Exam Question

Q1 Explain how the structure of water enables it to transport substances. [3 marks]

Pssssssssssssssssssssssssssssssssssssssssssssss — *need the loo yet?*

Water is pretty darn useful really. It looks so, well, dull — but in fact it's scientifically amazing, and essential for all kinds of jobs — like transporting things around the body. You need to learn its structure so that you can relate its solvent properties to its function as a transport molecule. Right, I'm off — when you gotta go, you gotta go.

The Heart and Blood Vessels

As I'm sure you know already, your heart is the 'pump' that gets oxygenated blood to your cells. It's very important, so unsurprisingly, you need to know how it works. You'll find that these pages definitely get to the heart of it... groan...

The **Heart** Consists of **Two Muscular Pumps**

The diagrams below show the **internal** and **external structure** of the heart. The **right side** of the heart pumps **deoxygenated blood** to the **lungs** and the **left side** pumps **oxygenated blood** to the **rest of the body**. Note — the **left and right sides** are **reversed** on the diagram, cos it's the left and right of the person that the heart belongs to.

External Structure

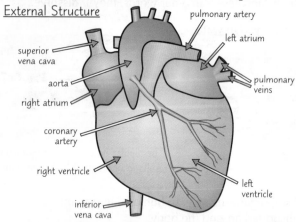

Internal Structure

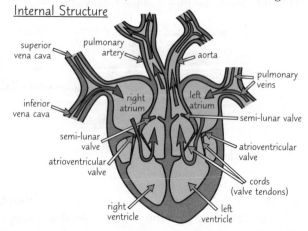

Heart Dissection Shows How the **Heart's Structure** Relates to its **Function**

You may get to carry out a heart dissection or you may get to watch one being carried out.

External examination: If you look at the outside of the heart you will see the **four main vessels** attached to it. The feel of the vessels can be used to help identify each one — arteries are thick and rubbery, whereas veins are much thinner (see next page).

You will also be able to see the right and left **atria**, the right and left **ventricles** and the **coronary arteries**.

Internal examination: The ventricles can be cut open using a scalpel so you can see inside each one. You should be able to see that the wall of the left ventricle is **thicker** than the wall of the right ventricle.

The **atria** can also be cut open. If you look at the atria walls, you should notice that they are **thinner** than the ventricle walls.

You can also look at the structures of the **atrioventricular valves** and **semi-lunar valves**.

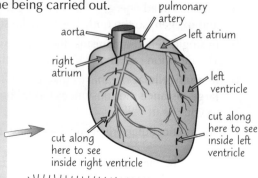

The differences you can see in the thicknesses of the walls of each ventricle, and between the ventricles and the atria are due to their different functions. See below for more.

When using a scalpel, you need to take precautions to avoid injuring yourself or others, e.g. by cutting in a direction away from yourself. Make sure you wash your hands and disinfect work surfaces once you're finished.

You Need to **Know What** the **Different Parts** of the **Heart Do**

Each bit of the heart is adapted to do its job effectively.

1) The **left ventricle** of the heart has **thicker**, more muscular walls than the **right ventricle**, because it needs to contract powerfully to pump blood all the way round the body. The right side only needs to get blood to the lungs, which are nearby.

2) The **ventricles** have **thicker walls** than the **atria**, because they have to push blood out of the heart whereas the atria just need to push blood a short distance into the ventricles.

3) The **atrioventricular (AV) valves** link the atria to the ventricles and **stop blood flowing back** into the atria when the ventricles contract. **Cords** attach the atrioventricular valves to the ventricles to stop them being forced up into the atria when the ventricles contract.

4) The **semi-lunar (SL) valves** link the ventricles to the pulmonary artery and aorta, and **stop blood flowing back** into the heart after the ventricles contract.

The Heart and Blood Vessels

Valves Help the Blood to Flow in One Direction

The **valves** only **open one way** — whether they're open or closed depends on the relative **pressure** of the heart chambers. If there's higher pressure **behind** a valve, it's forced **open**, but if pressure is higher **in front** of the valve it's forced **shut**. This means blood only flows in **one direction** through the heart.

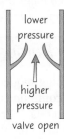
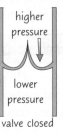

Substances are Transported Around the Body in Blood Vessels

The heart pumps the blood around the body through the blood vessels. You need to know about **three** types of blood vessel — **arteries**, **veins** and **capillaries**. Read on...

1) **Arteries** carry blood from the heart **to the rest of the body**. They're thick-walled, **muscular** and have **elastic tissue** in the walls to cope with the **high pressure** caused by the heartbeat. The inner lining (**endothelium**) is **folded**, allowing the artery to **expand** — this also helps it to cope with high pressure.

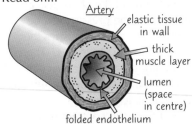

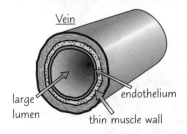

2) **Veins** take blood **back to the heart**. They're **wider** than equivalent arteries, with very little elastic or muscle tissue as the blood is under **lower pressure**. Veins contain **valves** to stop the blood flowing backwards. Blood flow through the veins is helped by contraction of the **body muscles** surrounding them.

3) **Capillaries** are the **smallest** of the blood vessels. They are where **metabolic exchange** occurs — substances are **exchanged** between cells and the capillaries. There are networks of capillaries in tissue (called **capillary beds**), which **increase** the **surface area** for exchange. Capillary walls are only **one cell thick**, which speeds up **diffusion** of substances (e.g. glucose and oxygen) into and out of cells.

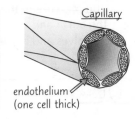

Practice Questions

Q1 Why is the left ventricle wall more muscular than the right ventricle wall?

Q2 Describe the structure of an artery.

Exam Questions

Q1 The diagram on the right shows the internal structure of the heart. What is the structure labelled **X**?

    A Aorta   **B** Left ventricle   **C** Right atrium   **D** Vena cava   [1 mark]

Q2 Explain how valves in the heart stop blood going back the wrong way.   [3 marks]

Q3 Explain how the structure of capillaries enables them to carry out metabolic exchange efficiently.   [2 marks]

Apparently an adult heart is the size of two fists. Two whole fists! Huge!

You may have noticed that biologists are obsessed with the relationship between structure and function, so whenever you're learning about the structure of something, make sure you know how this relates to its function. And what better place to start than the heart. Oh and don't forget the arteries, veins and capillaries...

Cardiac Cycle

The cardiac cycle is all the changes that happen in the heart during one heart beat. There's lots of contracting and relaxing and opening and closing of valves. You just need to know what is happening when. Easy.

The **Cardiac Cycle** Pumps Blood Round the Body

The cardiac cycle is an ongoing sequence of **contraction (systole)** and **relaxation (diastole)** of the atria and ventricles that keeps blood **continuously** circulating round the body. The **volume** of the atria and ventricles **changes** as they contract and relax. **Pressure** changes also occur, due to the changes in chamber volume (e.g. decreasing the volume of a chamber by contraction will increase the pressure in a chamber). The cardiac cycle can be simplified into three stages:

(1) Ventricular diastole, atrial systole

The **ventricles are relaxed**. The **atria contract**, decreasing the volume of the chambers and **increasing the pressure** inside the chambers. This **pushes** the blood into the **ventricles**. There's a slight **increase in ventricular pressure** and **chamber volume** as the **ventricles receive the ejected blood** from the contracting atria.

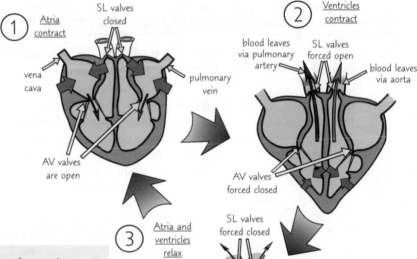

(2) Ventricular systole, atrial diastole

The **atria relax**. The **ventricles contract**, decreasing their volume and **increasing their pressure**. The pressure becomes **higher** in the ventricles than the atria, which forces the **AV valves shut** to prevent back-flow. The **pressure in the ventricles** is also **higher** than in the **aorta** and **pulmonary artery**, which forces **open** the **SL valves** and blood is forced out into these arteries.

(3) Cardiac diastole

The **ventricles and the atria both relax**. The higher pressure in the pulmonary artery and aorta closes the SL valves to prevent back-flow into the ventricles. Blood returns to the heart and the **atria fill again** due to the higher pressure in the vena cava and pulmonary vein. In turn this starts to **increase the pressure** of the atria. As the ventricles continue to **relax**, their **pressure falls below the pressure of the atria** and so the **AV valves open**. This allows blood to flow **passively** (without being pushed by atrial contraction) into the ventricles from the atria. The atria contract, and the whole process begins again.

You Might be Asked to **Interpret Data** on the **Cardiac Cycle**

You may well be asked to analyse or interpret **data** about the changes in **pressure** and **volume** during the cardiac cycle. Here are some examples of the kind of things you might get:

Example 1

You may have to describe the changes in pressure and volume shown by a **diagram**, like the one on the right. In this diagram the **AV valves** are open. So you know that the **pressure** in the atria is **higher** than in the **ventricles**. So you also know that the **atria are contracting** because that's what causes the **increase in pressure**.

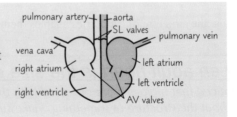

Cardiac Cycle

Example 2

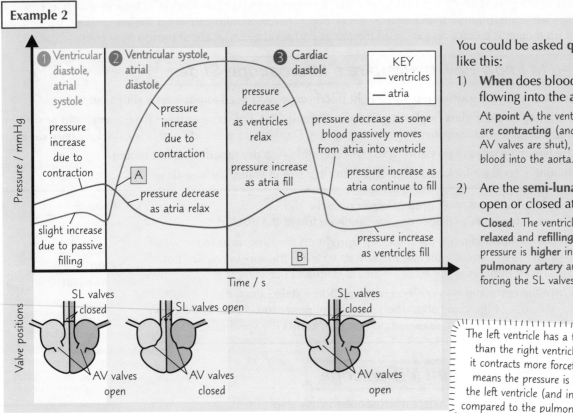

1 Ventricular diastole, atrial systole

pressure increase due to contraction

slight increase due to passive filling

2 Ventricular systole, atrial diastole

pressure increase due to contraction

pressure decrease as atria relax

A

3 Cardiac diastole

pressure decrease as ventricles relax

pressure increase as atria fill

pressure decrease as some blood passively moves from atria into ventricle

pressure increase as atria continue to fill

pressure increase as ventricles fill

B

KEY
— ventricles
— atria

Pressure / mmHg

Time / s

Valve positions

SL valves closed

AV valves open

SL valves open

AV valves closed

SL valves closed

AV valves open

You could be asked **questions** like this:

1) **When** does blood start flowing into the **aorta**?

   At **point A**, the ventricles are **contracting** (and the AV valves are shut), forcing blood into the aorta.

2) Are the **semi-lunar valves** open or closed at **point B**?

   Closed. The ventricles are **relaxed** and **refilling**, so the pressure is **higher** in the **pulmonary artery** and **aorta**, forcing the SL valves **closed**.

The left ventricle has a thicker wall than the right ventricle and so it contracts more forcefully. This means the pressure is higher in the left ventricle (and in the aorta compared to the pulmonary artery).

Example 3

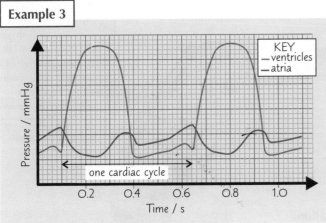

KEY
— ventricles
— atria

Pressure / mmHg

one cardiac cycle

0.2   0.4   0.6   0.8   1.0

Time / s

Or you could be asked a **question** like this:

1) **What** is the **heart rate** of this person in beats per minute?

   It takes **0.54 seconds** to complete **one cardiac cycle** (or one heartbeat). In one minute there will be: 60 ÷ 0.54 = 110 beats (2 s.f.). So the heart rate is **110 beats per minute**.

Practice Questions

Q1 Which valves open during ventricular systole?

Q2 Describe what happens to the ventricles and atria during cardiac diastole.

Exam Question

Q1 The table to the right shows the blood pressure in two heart chambers at different times during part of the cardiac cycle.

	Blood pressure / kPa	
Time / s	Left atrium	Left ventricle
0.0	0.6	0.5
0.1	1.3	0.8
0.2	0.4	6.9
0.3	0.5	16.5
0.4	0.9	7.0

a) Between what times are the AV valves shut? [1 mark]

b) Between what times do the ventricles start to relax? [1 mark]

c) Calculate the percentage increase in left ventricle blood pressure between 0.0 s and 0.3 s. [3 marks]

The cardiac cycle — a bewilderingly complicated pump-action bicycle...

Two whole pages to learn here, all full of really important stuff. If you understand all the pressure and volume changes then whether you get a diagram, graph or something else in the exam, you'll be able to interpret it, no probs.

Investigating Heart Rate

There are lots of things that affect heart rate, but when it comes to testing the effect of substances such as caffeine, we sometimes use animals rather than humans. A common choice of animal to use is the see-through water flea. Lovely. First up though is a quick lesson on all the things you need to know about using a light microscope...

You Need to Know How to **Prepare** a **Microscope Slide**...

1) If you want to look at a specimen under a **light microscope**, you need to put it on a **slide** first.

2) A slide is a strip of **clear glass** or **plastic**. Slides are usually **flat**, but some of them have a small **dip** or **well** in the centre (useful if your specimen's relatively big, e.g. *Daphnia*, or a liquid) — this is called a **cavity slide**.

3) There are **two main ways** of preparing a microscope slide — a **dry mount** or a **wet mount**.

4) A **wet mount** is good for looking at tiny organisms that live in water, such as algae.

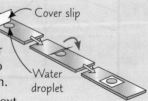
Cover slip

Water droplet

- Start by pipetting a small **drop of water** onto the slide. Then use **tweezers** to place your specimen on top of the water drop.

- To put the **cover slip** on, stand the slip **upright** on the slide, next to the water droplet. Then carefully **tilt** and lower it so it covers the specimen. Try **not** to get any **air bubbles** under there — they'll obstruct your view of the specimen.

- Once the cover slip is in position, you can add a **stain**. Put a drop of stain next to one edge of the cover slip. Then put a bit of **paper towel** next to the opposite edge. The stain will get **drawn** under the slip, **across** the **specimen**.

With a dry mount, you take the specimen, or slice of specimen and place it on the slide with a cover slip on top. No water or stain is added.

...and How to Use a **Light Microscope**

You're expected to be able to use a light microscope to view a specimen.

1) Start by clipping the **slide** containing the specimen you want to look at onto the **stage**.

2) Select the **lowest-powered objective lens** (i.e. the one that produces the lowest magnification).

3) Use the **coarse adjustment knob** to bring the stage up to just below the objective lens.

4) Look down the **eyepiece** (which contains the **ocular lens**). Use the **coarse adjustment knob** to move the stage downwards, away from the objective lens until the image is roughly in focus.

5) Adjust the **focus** with the **fine adjustment knob**, until you get a **clear image** of whatever's on the slide.

6) If you need to see the slide with **greater magnification**, swap to a **higher-powered objective lens** and refocus.

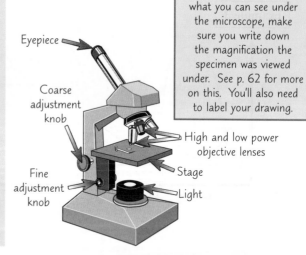
Eyepiece

Coarse adjustment knob

Fine adjustment knob

High and low power objective lenses

Stage

Light

If you're asked to draw what you can see under the microscope, make sure you write down the magnification the specimen was viewed under. See p. 62 for more on this. You'll also need to label your drawing.

You Can **Investigate** the Effect of **Caffeine** on the **Heart Rate** of **Daphnia**

Daphnia are tiny aquatic **invertebrates**. They're **transparent**, so you can see their internal organs. This means you can monitor their **heart rate** (the **number of heartbeats** in a **minute**) by observing them through a **microscope**.

1) Make up a **range** of caffeine solutions of **different concentrations** and a **control** solution that has no caffeine in it at all.

You could use a serial dilution technique to make up your solutions (see p. 199 for more).

2) Transfer **one** *Daphnia* into the dimple on a **cavity slide**.

3) Using a pipette, place a few drops of **caffeine solution** onto the *Daphnia*. Wait for 5 minutes while the caffeine is absorbed.

4) Place the slide onto the stage of a **light microscope** and adjust the **focus** so you can see the **beating heart** of the *Daphnia*. You can find the heart to the back side of the gut and above the brood pouch.

5) **Count** the number of **heartbeats** in **20 seconds**, timed using a stopwatch, and multiply this by **three** to calculate beats per minute (**heart rate**).

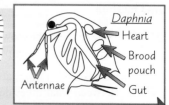
Daphnia
Heart
Brood pouch
Antennae
Gut

Investigating Heart Rate

6) **Repeat** this 10 times using the **same concentration** of caffeine but a **different** *Daphnia* individual each time.

7) Repeat the experiment using the **other concentrations** of caffeine solution and the **control** solution.

8) **Compare the results** to see how caffeine concentration affects heart rate.

Don't forget to keep all other factors constant (e.g. temperature and volume of caffeine solution).

Heart Rate *Increases* as Caffeine Concentration *Increases*

A good way to see the effect of caffeine concentration on heart rate is to draw a **graph** of the results of the *Daphnia* experiment.

1) Take the **average** of the 10 readings at each concentration and then graph your results — plot average heart rate (beats per minute) against concentration of caffeine.

2) Your results might look something like this.

3) This graph shows a **positive correlation** — as caffeine concentration **increases**, heart rate also **increases**.

See p. 206 for more on correlation.

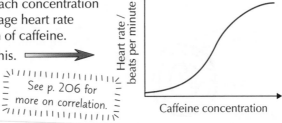

The result of the experiment — hooked on caffeine.

There are Some *Ethical Issues* Involved in Using *Invertebrates*

In the exam, you may have to discuss the **ethical issues** involved with using **invertebrates** in experiments. Here are some points to think about:

1) Experimenting on **animals** allows scientists to study things that would be **unethical** to study using humans. But many people believe that using animals is **also unethical** — they can't give **consent** and they may be subjected to **painful procedures**.

2) Some people believe it's **more acceptable** to perform experiments on **invertebrates** (like *Daphnia*, spiders and insects) than on **vertebrates** (like dogs and monkeys).

3) This is because they're considered to be **simpler organisms** than vertebrates. For example, they have a much **less sophisticated nervous system**, which could mean that they feel less pain (or no pain). Also, invertebrates are more **distantly related** to humans than other vertebrates.

4) But there are still ethical issues to consider when experimenting with invertebrates. For example, some people believe it's unethical to cause **distress** or **suffering** to **any living organism** — e.g. by subjecting them to **extremes of temperature** or depriving them of **food**.

Practice Questions

Q1 Describe how you would prepare a microscope slide to investigate the heart rate of *Daphnia*.

Exam Question

Q1 The graph shows the results of an experiment into the effects of caffeine on *Daphnia* heart rate.

a) Analyse the data to describe the relationship between caffeine concentration and heart rate in *Daphnia*. [1 mark]

b) Give two factors that would need to be kept constant during the experiment. [2 marks]

c) Discuss why some people may feel it's more acceptable to carry out experiments on invertebrates, such as *Daphnia*, than on vertebrates. [3 marks]

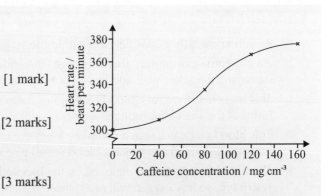

I reckon there are some ethical issues involved with sitting exams...

Breathe deeply, slow your heart rate, and concentrate on investigating the heart rates of Daphnia. *Make sure that you can outline how to set up the experiment and then put your debating hat on because it's time for some ethics.*

Cardiovascular Disease

No, your heart won't break if he/she (delete as appropriate) doesn't return your call... but there are diseases associated with the heart and blood vessels that you have to learn about...

Most **Cardiovascular Disease** Starts With **Atheroma** Formation

1) The wall of an **artery** is made up of **several layers** (see page 7).

2) The **endothelium** (inner lining) is usually smooth and unbroken.

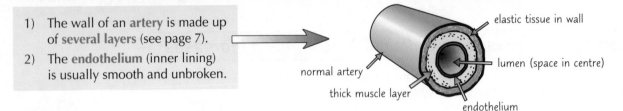

normal artery

elastic tissue in wall

lumen (space in centre)

thick muscle layer

endothelium

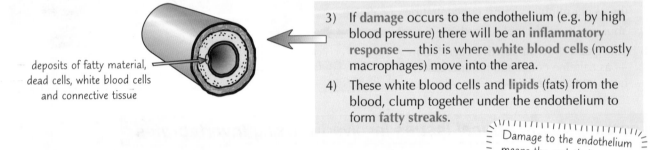

deposits of fatty material, dead cells, white blood cells and connective tissue

3) If **damage** occurs to the endothelium (e.g. by high blood pressure) there will be an **inflammatory response** — this is where white blood cells (mostly macrophages) move into the area.

4) These white blood cells and **lipids** (fats) from the blood, clump together under the endothelium to form **fatty streaks**.

Damage to the endothelium means the endothelium can't function normally — this is called endothelial dysfunction.

5) Over time, **more white blood cells, lipids** and **connective tissue** build up and harden to form a **fibrous plaque** called an **atheroma**.

6) This plaque **partially blocks** the lumen of the **artery** and **restricts blood flow**, which causes **blood pressure** to **increase**.

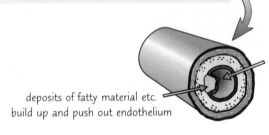

deposits of fatty material etc. build up and push out endothelium

lumen shrinks as artery wall swells, so it's more difficult for blood to pass through

7) The **hardening** of arteries, caused by atheromas, is called **atherosclerosis**.

Atheromas Increase the **Risk** of **Thrombosis** in **Arteries**

1) As you know, **atheromas** develop within the walls of **arteries** (see above).

2) An atheroma can **rupture** (burst through) the **endothelium** of an artery, **damaging** the artery wall and leaving a **rough** surface.

3) This triggers **thrombosis** (blood clotting) — a **blood clot** forms at the **site** of the rupture (see next page).

4) This blood clot can cause a complete **blockage** of the artery, or it can become **dislodged** and block a blood vessel elsewhere in the body.

5) The **blood flow** to **tissues** supplied by the blocked blood vessel will be severely **restricted**, so **less oxygen** will reach those tissues, resulting in damage.

6) **Heart attack, stroke** and **deep vein thrombosis** are three forms of **cardiovascular disease** that can be caused by blood clots — these are explained in more detail on the next page.

Cardiovascular Disease

You Need to Know *How a Blood Clot Forms*

Thrombosis is used by the body to **prevent** lots of blood being **lost** when a **blood vessel** is **damaged**.
A **series** of **reactions** occurs that leads to the formation of a **blood clot** (**thrombus**):

1) A **protein** called **thromboplastin** is **released** from the **damaged** blood vessel.

2) Thromboplastin, along with calcium ions from the plasma, triggers the **conversion** of **prothrombin** (a **soluble protein**) into **thrombin** (an **enzyme**).

3) Thrombin then catalyses the **conversion of fibrinogen** (a **soluble protein**) to **fibrin** (solid **insoluble fibres**).

4) The fibrin fibres **tangle together** and form a **mesh** in which **platelets** (**small fragments of cells** in the blood) and **red blood cells** get **trapped** — this forms the **blood clot**.

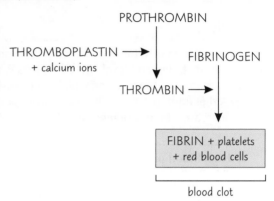

The **cardiovascular diseases** below can result from the formation of blood clots.

Blood Clots can Cause *Heart Attacks...*

① The **heart muscle** is supplied with **blood** by the **coronary arteries**.

② This blood contains the **oxygen** needed by heart muscle cells to carry out **respiration**.

③ If a coronary artery becomes **completely blocked** by a **blood clot** an area of the heart muscle will be totally **cut off** from its blood supply, so it **won't** receive any **oxygen**.

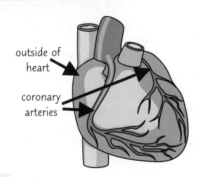

④ This causes a **myocardial infarction** — more commonly known as a **heart attack**.

⑤ A heart attack can cause **damage** and **death** of the **heart muscle**.

⑥ **Symptoms** include **pain** in the chest and upper body, **shortness of breath** and **sweating**.

⑦ If **large areas** of the heart are affected complete **heart failure** can occur, which is often **fatal**.

Coronary heart disease (CHD) is when the **coronary arteries** have lots of **atheromas** in them, which restricts blood flow to the heart. The atheromas also increase the risk of **blood clots** forming, leading to an increased risk of heart attack.

...Stroke...

1) A **stroke** is a **rapid loss** of **brain function**, due to a **disruption** in the **blood supply** to the **brain**.

2) This can be caused by a **blood clot** in an **artery** leading to the brain, which **reduces** the amount of blood, and therefore **oxygen**, that can reach the brain.

...and Deep Vein Thrombosis

1) **Deep vein thrombosis** (DVT) is the formation of a **blood clot** in a **vein** deep inside the body — it usually happens in **leg veins**.

2) It can be caused by **prolonged inactivity**, e.g. during **long-haul flights**, and the risk **increases** with **age**.

Cardiovascular Disease

Many **Factors** Can **Increase** the **Risk** of **Cardiovascular Disease (CVD)**

Lifestyle Factors:

Diet

A diet **high** in **saturated fat** (see p. 25) increases the risk of CVD. This is because it **increases blood cholesterol level**, which **increases atheroma formation**. Atheromas can lead to the formation of **blood clots**, which can cause a **heart attack**, **stroke** or **DVT**.
A diet **high in salt** also increases the risk of CVD because it increases the risk of **high blood pressure** (see below).

See page 25 for more on cholesterol.

High blood pressure

High blood pressure **increases** the **risk** of **damage** to the **artery walls**, which **increases** the **risk** of **atheroma formation**, which can lead to CVD. **Excessive alcohol consumption, stress** and **diet** can **all** increase blood pressure.

Smoking

- **Carbon monoxide** in cigarette smoke combines with **haemoglobin** (the protein that carries oxygen in the blood) and **reduces** the amount of **oxygen** transported in the **blood**. This **reduces** the amount of **oxygen available to tissues**. If the heart muscle doesn't receive enough oxygen it can lead to a **heart attack** and if the brain doesn't receive enough oxygen it can lead to a **stroke**.
- **Nicotine** in cigarette smoke makes **platelets sticky**, increasing the chance of **blood clots forming**, which increases the risk of CVD.
- Smoking also **decreases** the **amount** of **antioxidants** in the blood — these are important for **protecting cells** from damage. Fewer antioxidants means **cell damage** in the **artery walls** is more likely, and this can lead to **atheroma formation**, which increases the risk of CVD.

Inactivity

A **lack** of **exercise** increases the risk of CVD because it **increases blood pressure** (see above).

Factors Beyond Your Control:

Genetics

Some people inherit particular **alleles** (different versions of genes, see page 50) that make them **more likely** to have **high blood pressure** or **high blood cholesterol**, so they are **more likely** to suffer from CVD (see above).

Age

The risk of developing CVD **increases with age**. This is partly because **plaque** can **build up** very slowly over time, which can eventually lead to CVD.

Gender

Men are **three times more likely** to suffer from CVD than pre-menopausal women. This may be due to their different levels of **hormones** — for example, the hormone **oestrogen**, which is typically higher in females, increases levels of 'good' cholesterol (HDL) — see p. 25. The relatively low level of this hormone in men can lead to **higher levels** of total **blood cholesterol** and **increase** the **risk** of CVD.

Cardiovascular Disease

Perception of Risk Can be Different from Actual Risk

1) **Risk** can be defined as the **chance** of something **unfavourable** happening.
E.g. if you **smoke** you **increase** your chance of developing CVD.

2) The **statistical chance** of something unfavourable happening is supported by **scientific research**.
E.g. the actual risk of **dying** from **CVD** is **60%** higher for smokers than for non-smokers.

3) People's **perception** of risk may be very **different** from the actual risk:

- People may **overestimate** the risk — they may believe things to be a **greater risk** than they actually are. E.g. they may have **known someone** who **smoked** and **died** from CVD, and therefore think that if you smoke you **will** die of CVD. Also, there are often **articles** in the **media** about health issues, e.g. articles that highlight the link between smoking and CVD or the link between having a high BMI (see p. 27) and CVD. **Constant exposure** to information like this can make people **constantly worry** that they'll get CVD.

Melvin underestimated the risk of letting his mum dress him...

- Some people may **underestimate** the risk — they may believe things to be a **lower risk** than they actually are. This could be due to a **lack of information** making them **unaware** of the **factors** that contribute to diseases like CVD.

Practice Questions

Q1 Describe how an atheroma forms.

Q2 What is the role of fibrin in the blood clotting process?

Q3 Describe why high blood pressure increases the risk of CVD.

Q4 Give three factors that increase the risk of CVD but can't be controlled.

Q5 Give one reason why a person may underestimate the risk of developing CVD.

Exam Questions

Q1 Explain why people might overestimate the risk of developing CVD. [2 marks]

Q2 On the right is a diagram showing the process of blood clotting.

   PROTHROMBIN

   THROMBOPLASTIN⟶   FIBRINOGEN

a) Give the name of enzyme X. [1 mark]

   ENZYME X⟶

b) Name three things which make up a blood clot. [1 mark]

c) What type of ions are involved in the conversion of prothrombin to enzyme X? [1 mark]

d) People with the disorder called hypoprothrombinaemia have a reduced amount of prothrombin in their blood.
Explain the likely effect this will have on their blood clotting mechanism. [2 marks]

   blood clot

Q3 Describe how atheromas can increase the risk that a person will suffer from a heart attack. [4 marks]

Q4* Explain how smoking can increase the risk of developing CVD. [6 marks]

* You will be assessed on the quality of your written response in this question.

Atherosclerosis, thrombosis — more like a spelling test than biology...

I know there's a lot to take in here... but make sure you understand the link between atherosclerosis, thrombosis and CVD — basically an atheroma forms, which can cause thrombosis, which can lead to CVD. Also, practise writing down the flow diagram of all the proteins involved in blood clotting, 'cause you need to know it in detail.

Interpreting Data on Risk Factors

Those pesky examiners may ask you to analyse data on risk factors for other diseases too... do they know no limit?

You May Have to **Analyse** and **Interpret Data** About **Illness** or **Mortality**

In the **exam** you might have to analyse illness or mortality data (for any disease) to determine if something is a **risk factor**. Watch out for mixing up **correlation** and **causation** in any data you're given — just because results are correlated **doesn't prove** that a change in one causes a change in the other (see page 206).

STUDY ONE

A study was carried out to analyse data, gathered from **53 studies worldwide**, about the **link** between **smoking** and **breast cancer**. The study looked at **22 255** women **with** breast cancer and **40 832** women **without** breast cancer, all of whom reported **drinking no alcohol**. The results below show the **relative risk** of breast cancer for women with **different smoking histories**.

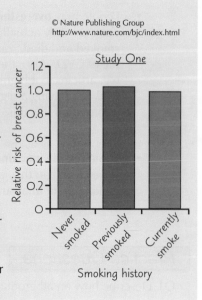

© Nature Publishing Group
http://www.nature.com/bjc/index.html

Here are some of the things you might be asked to do:

1) <u>Describe the data</u> — The results show that the **relative risk** of breast cancer for women who don't drink alcohol is **similar regardless of smoking history**.

2) <u>Draw conclusions</u> — The results show that for women who don't drink alcohol, smoking is **not associated** with an **increased risk** of breast cancer.

3) <u>Check any conclusions are valid</u> — This data appears to show **no link** between smoking history and the relative risk of breast cancer in women who don't drink, but you **can't** say that smoking **doesn't affect** breast cancer risk at all. The data **doesn't** take into account women who drink. Smoking and alcohol **together** could **affect the risk** of breast cancer. Also, the study doesn't take into account **other factors** that could affect risk of breast cancer such as the use of **hormone replacement treatment, physical activity**, etc.

You Need to be Able to **Recognise Conflicting Evidence**

1) The **evidence** from **one study** alone **wouldn't usually be enough** to conclude that a factor is a **health risk**.

2) **Similar studies** would be carried out to investigate the link. If these studies came to the **same conclusion**, the conclusion would become **increasingly accepted**.

3) Sometimes studies come up with **conflicting evidence** though — evidence that leads to a **different conclusion** than other studies. For example, one study may conclude that a factor **isn't** a **health risk**, whereas another study may conclude that the **same** factor **is a health risk**:

STUDY TWO

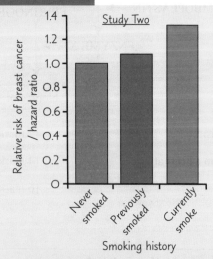

A study was carried out to determine if smoking is linked to an increased risk of breast cancer. **116 544** women without breast cancer in **California** were sent **questionnaires** to establish their **smoking history** and other personal information. The women were then followed for **5 years**. The results on the left show the **relative risk of breast cancer, adjusted for other factors** such as age and alcohol consumption, for women with **different smoking histories**.

1) <u>Describe the data</u> — The results show that the **relative risk** of breast cancer for women in California is **higher** for women who **previously smoked** or **still smoke** compared to those who have never smoked.

2) <u>Draw conclusions</u> — The results show that for women in California, smoking **is associated** with an **increased risk** of breast cancer.

3) <u>Comment on the conflicting evidence</u> — This second study shows that smoking **is linked** to an increased risk of breast cancer, which **conflicts** with the evidence from **study one** (see above). Because the two studies have produced conflicting evidence, **more results** would be needed in order to **fully assess** if smoking is an **important health risk** for the development of **breast cancer**.

Interpreting Data on Risk Factors

You May Have to Evaluate the Design of Studies

In the **exam** you could be asked to **evaluate** the **design** of a study they've given you. Here are some things to look out for:

1) **Sample size** — the **greater** the number of people used in a study, the **more reliable** the results.

There's more on reliability and validity in the Practical Skills section — see page 198.

   Selecting the sample should also be done carefully. The sample should be <u>representative</u> (i.e. it should reflect the variety of characteristics that are found in the population you're interested in studying) so that the results can be <u>generalised</u> to the whole population. A sample that is <u>unrepresentative</u> is <u>biased</u> and can't <u>reliably</u> be generalised to the whole population.

2) **Variables** — the **more variables** (other factors that could affect the results) that have been **controlled** in a study, the **more reliable** the results. This also makes the results more **valid** — by controlling the variables, you're making sure that you're only testing the thing you want to.

3) **Data collection** — the **less bias** involved in collecting the data, the **more reliable** the results.

4) **Controls** — the presence of controls **increases** the validity of the results.

5) **Repetition** by other scientists — if other scientists produce the **same results**, then the results are **more reliable**.

See page 207 for loads more on evaluating data.

EXAMPLE: STUDY ONE

1) **Sample size** — The study had a **large** sample size of **63 087 women** in total, which makes the results more reliable.

2) **Variables** — The study didn't take into account **some variables** that can affect the risk of breast cancer, like **hormone replacement therapy** and **physical activity**. This could have affected the results (decreasing their reliability and validity).

3) **Data collection** — The data was collected from **53 other studies** but we don't know how those other studies were designed.

4) **Controls** — There were a large number of controls, **40 832 women**. This increases the validity of the results.

5) **Repetition by other scientists** — Study two **doesn't agree** with the conclusion of study one.

EXAMPLE: STUDY TWO

1) **Sample size** — This study had a **really large** sample size of **116 544 women**, which makes the results more reliable.

2) **Variables** — This study took into account **other variables** like **hormone replacement therapy**, **physical activity**, alcohol consumption, etc. This **increases** the **reliability** and **validity** of the results.

3) **Data collection** — The data was collected from **questionnaires**, which can be biased. This **decreases** the **reliability** of the results.

4) **Repetition by other scientists** — Study one **doesn't agree** with the conclusion of study two.

Practice Questions

Q1 What is meant by conflicting evidence?

Q2 Why is it important to look at the data collection method when evaluating study design?

Exam Question

Q1 The results of a study involving 168 000 people in 63 countries have shown a strong correlation between waist measurement and risk of cardiovascular disease. Analysis of the results has shown that waist circumference is independently associated with cardiovascular disease.

   a) Give two reasons why the study provides strong evidence for a link between waist measurement and risk of cardiovascular disease. [2 marks]

   b) Give two ways that the results of this study could be made more reliable. [2 marks]

Exams — definitely a health risk...

These evaluating evidence questions come up quite a lot. The examiners like to see that you can analyse the data and that you can pick out the good and bad bits of a study. Luckily, I'm giving you plenty of examples of these types of questions. Make sure you look at the section at the back of this book on how to interpret data — then you'll be sorted.

Treatment of CVD

It's not all doom and gloom with CVD — there are some different treatments available.

Drugs *Can be Used to* Treat CVD

Although **prevention** is **better** than **cure**, there are some **treatments** for CVD.
You need to know **how** four of them work and be able to **describe** their **benefits and risks**.

1) Antihypertensives Reduce High Blood Pressure

These drugs include **beta-blockers** (which **reduce** the **strength** of the **heartbeat**) and **vasodilators** (which **widen** the **blood vessels**). They also include **diuretics**, most of which work by **reducing** the amount of **sodium** that's **reabsorbed** by the **blood** in the kidneys. This results in **less water** being reabsorbed (due to **osmosis**), which **reduces blood volume**.

See page 31 for more on osmosis.

All of these drugs **reduce blood pressure**, so there's **less chance** of **damage** occurring to the walls of the arteries. This **reduces** the risk of **atheromas** forming and **blood clots** developing (see p. 12-13).

BENEFITS:

The **different types** of antihypertensives work in **different ways**, so they can be given in **combination** to reduce blood pressure. Also, blood pressure can be **monitored at home**, so the patient can see if the drugs are **working**.

RISKS:

Palpitations (rapid beating of the heart), **abnormal heart rhythms, fainting, headaches** and **drowsiness** are all side effects of these drugs caused by the **blood pressure** becoming **too low**. Other side effects include **allergic reactions** and **depression**.

2) Statins Reduce Cholesterol in the Blood

Statins **reduce blood cholesterol** in humans by **reducing** the amount of 'bad' LDL cholesterol (see page 25) **produced** inside the **liver**. A lower blood cholesterol level **reduces atheroma formation**, which reduces the risk of CVD.

BENEFITS:

Statins reduce the risk of **developing CVD**.

RISKS:

Side effects include **muscle and joint pain**, **digestive system problems** and an **increased risk of diabetes**. **Nosebleeds, headaches** and **nausea** are also common side effects.

3) Anticoagulants Reduce the Formation of Blood Clots

Anticoagulants (e.g. warfarin and heparin) **reduce blood clotting**. This means blood clots are **less likely** to form at sites of **damage** in artery walls. So there's **less chance** of a **blood vessel** becoming **blocked** by a blood clot (see p. 12-13), reducing the risk of CVD.

BENEFITS:

Anticoagulants can be used to treat people who **already have blood clots** or **CVD** — they **prevent** any existing blood clots from **growing any larger** and prevent any **new** blood clots from **forming**. However, anticoagulants **can't get rid** of **existing** blood clots.

RISKS:

If a person taking these drugs is badly **injured**, the reduction in blood clotting can cause **excessive bleeding**, which can lead to **fainting** (and in serious cases **death**). Other side effects include **allergic reactions, osteoporosis** (weakened bones) and **swelling** of the tissues. These drugs can also **damage** the **fetus** if they're taken during pregnancy.

Treatment of CVD

4) Platelet Inhibitory Drugs Also Reduce the Formation of Blood Clots

Platelet inhibitory drugs (e.g. **aspirin**) are a type of **anticoagulant** (see previous page). They work by **preventing platelets clumping together** to form a blood clot. So, they **reduce** the formation of **blood clots**, reducing the chance of a blood vessel becoming **blocked** by a clot.

BENEFITS:

As with anticoagulants, these can be used to treat people who **already have blood clots** or **CVD**.

RISKS:

Side effects include **rashes, diarrhoea, nausea, liver function problems** and **excessive bleeding**, especially after a serious injury (see previous page).

These plate inhibitory drugs were doing a good job of preventing the plates from clumping together.

Practice Questions

Q1 How do anticoagulants work to reduce the risk of CVD?

Q2 State two benefits of treating CVD with antihypertensives.

Exam Questions

Q1 The graph below shows the numbers of prescriptions used in the prevention and treatment of CVD in England between 2006 and 2013.

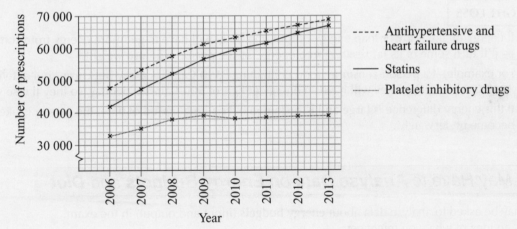

- - - - Antihypertensive and heart failure drugs
——— Statins
············· Platelet inhibitory drugs

a) Describe the general trend in the number of prescriptions of each treatment of CVD shown by the graph above. [2 marks]

b) State the least commonly prescribed treatment and give one benefit and one risk of that type of treatment. [2 marks]

c) Using values rounded to 2 significant figures, calculate the percentage increase in statin prescriptions between 2006 and 2011. Give your answer as a whole number. [1 mark]

d) Explain how statins reduce the risk of developing CVD. [2 marks]

Q2 A patient who is at risk of developing coronary heart disease (CHD) goes to see his doctor. The patient is obese and suffers from high blood pressure.

a) State one type of drug the doctor could prescribe to treat the patient's high blood pressure and explain how it reduces the risk of CHD. [2 marks]

b) Give one disadvantage of taking this drug. [1 mark]

I'd need several spoonfuls of sugar to help all these medicines go down...

These drugs don't cure the problem — they don't get rid of existing atheromas or blood clots, they just prevent them from getting any worse. Still, it's good to know that there are treatments out there. Now you just need to make sure you know the risks and benefits of each one. May I suggest writing yourself out a handy table...

Diet and Energy

Obesity is a risk factor for cardiovascular disease (CVD) and other diseases too, so it's important to maintain a healthy weight. Weight is affected by your diet as well as how much energy you use doing things like playing video games and stealing traffic cones*...

Organisms Take In and Use Up Energy

1) Organisms need a **supply** of **energy**, so that they can **grow**, **move**, **reproduce** etc. — in animals this energy is provided in the form of **food**.

2) **Energy budget** is a term used to describe the **amount of energy taken in** by an organism (in food) **and** the amount of energy **used up** by an organism (e.g. by moving).

Henri knew the cheese would push him over budget — but what harm could it do?

Energy Imbalance Causes Changes in Weight

Ideally, a person should **take in** the **same amount** of energy as **they use up** — their energy budget should be **balanced**. If there's an **imbalance** in the energy budget, it will **affect** the **person's weight**:

WEIGHT GAIN

1) If energy **intake** is **higher** than energy **output**, the **excess energy** will be turned into **fat reserves** by the body, so the person will **gain weight**.

2) For example, if a person **consumes** food containing **4000 Calories** a day and carries out **activities** that burn **3000 Calories** a day, there'll be an **excess of 1000 Calories** per day, so they'll put on weight.

3) If the energy difference is **a lot** and it's **sustained** over a **long period** of time, the person could become **obese**.

WEIGHT LOSS

1) If energy **intake** is **lower** than energy **output**, the body will have to **get** more energy from somewhere — it'll **turn** some of its **fat reserves** into energy, so the person will **lose weight**.

2) For example, if a person **consumes** food containing **2500 Calories** a day but carries out **activities** that burn **3000 Calories** a day, they will have an energy **deficit of 500 Calories** per day, so they'll lose weight.

3) If this energy difference is **large** and is **sustained** over a **long period** of time, the person is likely to become **underweight**.

You May Have to Analyse Data on Energy Budgets and Diet

You may be asked to analyse data about **energy budgets** (input and output) in the exam. Here's an idea of what you might get:

1) The **recommended daily intake** of Calories is **2000** for women and **2500** for men.

2) **Different activities** use up **different amounts** of Calories, as shown in the table. ⟹

3) You can use this information to **calculate** people's **energy budgets** — you'll need to use this formula: **energy input – energy output = energy budget**

Activity	Number of Calories used per hour
Cooking	159
Dog walking	224
Gardening	328
Swimming	513

- Ranjit takes in the recommended daily intake of Calories a day (**2500**). He swims for **one hour** and does **one hour** of **gardening** each day. He also **cooks** for **an hour** each day. His **bodily functions** (e.g. breathing) use up **1500 Calories** per day. So his energy budget is:
  Energy input – energy output = energy budget
  2500 – (1500 + 513 + 328 + 159) = **0**
  Ranjit's energy budget is **balanced** — he takes in as much as he uses up.

- Christina takes in **2000 Calories** a day. She **walks the dog** for **an hour** every **morning** and every **night**. Her **bodily functions** use up **1200** Calories per day. So her energy budget is:
  Energy input – energy output = energy budget
  2000 – (1200 + 224 + 224) = **352 Calories**
  Christina has an **excess of 352 Calories** per day.

You need to multiply these figures by the number of hours the activity lasts.

    * CGP does not condone the stealing of traffic cones

Diet and Energy

You Can **Measure** the **Amount** of **Vitamin C** in Your **Food**

1) You need to be able to carry out an **experiment** to find out **how much vitamin C** is in a **food sample**.
2) This can be done using a chemical called **DCPIP** — a **blue** dye that turns **colourless** in the presence of vitamin C.

Here's how you do it:

> You could make up the different concentrations using a serial dilution technique — see page 199.

First you need to make a **calibration curve**. To do this you need to:

1) Make up several **vitamin C solutions** of **different, known concentrations**. Ideally, you need about **six** different solutions.
2) Use a measuring cylinder to measure out a **set volume** of DCPIP (at a **set concentration**) into a test tube.
3) **Add** one of the **vitamin C solutions** to the DCPIP, **drop by drop**, using a pipette.
4) Gently **shake** the test tube for a **set length of time**, timed using a stopwatch, after each drop of vitamin C solution is added.
5) When the solution turns **colourless**, **record** the **volume** (no. of drops) of vitamin C solution that has been added.
6) **Repeat** the experiment **twice more**, with the **same** solution, and take an **average** of the three readings.
7) Make sure you keep **all** the other **variables** constant during the experiment, e.g. temperature.
8) **Repeat** the above procedure with **each solution**.
9) Use the results to draw a **curve of best fit**, showing volume of vitamin C solution against its concentration — this is the **calibration curve**.

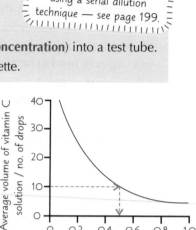

Then you can test the **unknown solution** in the same way as the known concentrations and use the calibration curve to find its concentration. E.g. 10 drops of an **unknown solution** is needed to turn DCPIP colourless. Reading **across** the calibration curve from a volume of **10 drops** shows that the concentration of vitamin C in the unknown solution is **0.5 mg cm^{-3}**.

Practice Questions

Q1 What is an energy budget?
Q2 Explain how an energy imbalance causes weight gain.

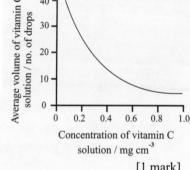

Exam Questions

Q1 The graph on the right shows a calibration curve for vitamin C concentration.

a) 25 drops of a food sample of unknown vitamin C concentration were needed to turn DCPIP colourless.
Use the calibration curve to work out the concentration of the solution. [1 mark]

b) State three variables that should be kept constant when making a calibration curve to test an unknown solution for vitamin C concentration. [3 marks]

Q2 A woman takes in 2000 Calories a day in food. She needs 1200 Calories each day to maintain her basic bodily functions. She also swims for two hours and does two hours of gardening each day.

a) i) Use the table on page 20 to calculate her energy budget. [1 mark]
ii) Explain what short-term effect this energy budget will have on her weight. [1 mark]

b) If the woman sustained this energy budget over a long period of time, what effect would it have on her weight? [1 mark]

Eat beans to increase the amount of Calories used for bodily functions...

If you've done an hour's revision you've used up around 120 Calories (which is 90 more than you'd use just sat on your bum watching telly)... well done you — go and have a biscuit to celebrate (and even up your energy balance).

Carbohydrates

Carbohydrates are the main energy supply in living organisms. Unfortunately they look a little bit boring, but don't let that put you off. Time to learn your monosaccharides from your polysaccharides. Let the good times roll...

Carbohydrates are Made from Monosaccharides

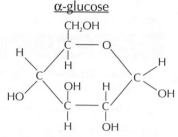

α-glucose

1) Most carbohydrates are **large**, complex molecules (polymers) composed of **long chains** of **monosaccharides** (monomers — small basic molecular units). For example, starch is a large carbohydrate composed of long chains of glucose.
2) **Single** monosaccharides are also called carbohydrates though.
3) **Glucose** is a monosaccharide with **six carbon** atoms in each molecule.
4) There are **two types** of glucose — **alpha** (α) and **beta** (β) — but you only need to learn about alpha-glucose for this section.
5) Glucose's **structure** is related to its **function** as the main **energy source** in animals and plants. Its structure makes it **soluble** so it can be **easily transported**, and its chemical bonds contain **lots of energy**.

Monosaccharides Join Together to Form Disaccharides and Polysaccharides

1) Monosaccharides are **joined together** by **glycosidic bonds** in a **condensation reaction** (a reaction where a molecule of **water** is **released**). A **hydrogen** atom on one monosaccharide bonds to a **hydroxyl** (OH) group on the other, releasing a molecule of water.
2) The **reverse** of this is a **hydrolysis reaction** — a molecule of water reacts with the glycosidic bond, **breaking it apart**.

'Mono' = 1, 'di' = 2, 'poly' = many and 'saccharide' = sugar.

3) When **two monosaccharides** join together, they form a **disaccharide**. Disaccharides are also **soluble** (though not as soluble as monosaccharides) and their chemical bonds store **more energy** than monosaccharides.

Two α-**glucose** molecules are joined together by a **glycosidic bond** to form **maltose**:

glucose + glucose ⇌ (condensation / hydrolysis) maltose + H_2O

H_2O is removed

glycosidic bond

Glycosidic bonds can form in **different places** in different molecules. E.g. in **maltose**, the bonds form between the **carbon 1** of the first monosaccharide and the **carbon 4** of the second, so it's called a **1-4 glycosidic bond**.

As well as maltose, you need to know how two other disaccharides are formed:
- **Lactose** — β-**glucose** and **galactose** with a **1-4 glycosidic bond**.
- **Sucrose** — α-**glucose** and **fructose** with a **1-2 glycosidic bond**.

1-4 glycosidic bond

4) A **polysaccharide** is formed when **more than two monosaccharides** join together:

Lots of α-glucose molecules are joined together by **1-4 glycosidic bonds** to form **amylose**:

glycosidic bonds

glucose   glucose   glucose   glucose   glucose

As well as amylose, you need to know how two other polysaccharides are formed:
- **Amylopectin** — α-**glucose** with **1-4 and 1-6 glycosidic bonds**, with lots of **side branches** (see next page).
- **Glycogen** — α-**glucose** with **1-4 and 1-6 glycosidic bonds** and **even more** side branches than amylopectin.

Carbohydrates

You Need to Learn About **Two Polysaccharides**

You need to know about the relationship between the **structure** and **function** of two polysaccharides:

1 **Starch** — the main **energy storage material** in **plants**

1) Cells get **energy** from **glucose**. Plants **store** excess glucose as **starch** (when a plant **needs more glucose** for energy it **breaks down** starch to release the glucose).

2) Starch is a mixture of **two** polysaccharides of **alpha-glucose** — **amylose** and **amylopectin**:

- **Amylose** — a long, **unbranched chain** of glucose joined together with **1-4 glycosidic bonds**. The angles of the glycosidic bonds give it a **coiled structure**, almost like a cylinder. This makes it **compact**, so it's really **good for storage** because you can **fit more in** to a small space.

- **Amylopectin** — a long, **branched chain** of glucose that contains **1-4 and 1-6 glycosidic bonds**. Its **side branches** allow the **enzymes** that break down the molecule to get at the **glycosidic bonds easily**. This means that the glucose can be **released quickly**.

3) Starch is also **insoluble** in water, so it **doesn't** cause water to enter cells by **osmosis** (see p. 31), which would make them swell. This makes it good for **storage**.

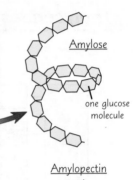
Amylose
one glucose molecule

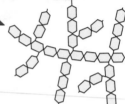
Amylopectin

2 **Glycogen** — the main **energy storage material** in **animals**

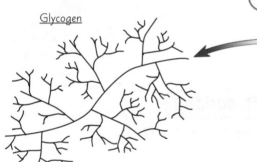
Glycogen

1) Animal cells get **energy** from **glucose** too. But animals **store** excess glucose as **glycogen** — another polysaccharide of **alpha-glucose**.

2) Its structure is very similar to amylopectin (it has **1-4** and **1-6 glycosidic bonds**), except that it has **loads** more **side branches** coming off it. Loads of branches means that stored glucose can be **released quickly**, which is **important for energy release** in animals.

3) It's also a very **compact** molecule, so it's good for storage.

4) Like starch, glycogen's also **insoluble** in water, so it doesn't cause cells to swell by osmosis.

5) It's a **large molecule**, so it can store **lots of energy**.

Practice Questions

Q1 What type of bonds hold monosaccharide molecules together in a polysaccharide?
Q2 Name the two monosaccharides that join together to form lactose.
Q3 What is the function of glycogen?

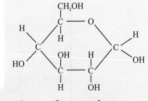

Exam Questions

Q1 The diagram above shows an α-glucose molecule. Two of these molecules can be joined together to form maltose.

a) Draw a diagram to show the products of this reaction. [2 marks]
b) Explain how maltose molecules are broken down. [1 mark]

Q2 Starch is made of two polysaccharides of alpha-glucose — amylose and amylopectin. Explain how the structure of starch relates to its function as an energy storage material in plants. [3 marks]

Mmmmm, starch... Tasty, tasty chips and beans... *dribble*. Ahem, sorry.
Remember that condensation and hydrolysis reactions are the reverse of each other. You need to learn how disaccharides and polysaccharides are formed and broken down by these reactions. And don't forget that starch is composed of two different polysaccharides — amylose and amylopectin (which is really similar to glycogen). Phew.

Lipids and Cardiovascular Disease

Right, that's carbohydrates covered. But there's another important kind of molecule you need to know about, and that's lipids, or 'fatty oily things' to you and me. First up, some fatty acid fun, then on to how a certain type of lipid called cholesterol can affect your cardiovascular health. Doesn't sound too thrilling, I know, but just go with it...

Triglycerides are a Kind of Lipid

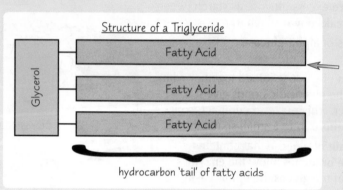

Structure of a Triglyceride

1) There are loads of kinds of **lipid**, but luckily, you only need to know about **triglycerides** (fats).

2) A triglyceride is made of **one** molecule of **glycerol** with **three fatty acids** attached to it.

3) Fatty acid molecules have long tails made of **hydrocarbons** (carbon chains with hydrogen atoms branching off).

4) The tails are **hydrophobic** (water-repelling).

5) These tails make lipids **insoluble** in water.

6) All **fatty acids** consist of the same basic structure, but the **hydrocarbon tail varies**. The tail is shown in the diagram with the letter **R**.

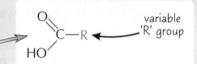

Contrary to popular belief, cows aren't hydrophobic.

Triglycerides are Formed by Condensation Reactions

1) Like carbohydrates, triglycerides are formed by **condensation reactions** and broken up by **hydrolysis reactions**.

2) Three **fatty acids** and a single **glycerol molecule** are joined together by **ester bonds**.

3) A **hydrogen** atom on the glycerol molecule bonds to a **hydroxyl** (OH) group on the fatty acid, **releasing** a molecule of **water**.

4) The **reverse** happens in **hydrolysis** — a molecule of water is added to **each ester bond** to break it apart, and the triglyceride **splits up** into three fatty acids and one glycerol molecule.

Each of the fatty acids in a triglyceride is attached to the glycerol molecule by an ester bond.

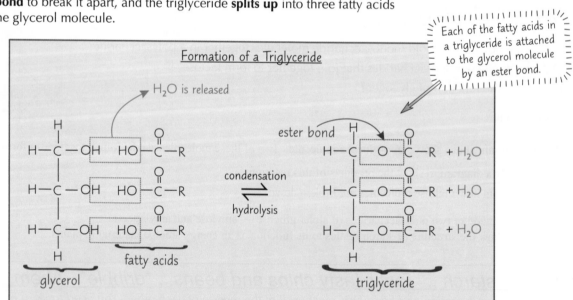

Lipids and Cardiovascular Disease

Lipids can be *Saturated* or *Unsaturated*

1) There are two types of lipids — **saturated** lipids and **unsaturated** lipids.

2) **Saturated** lipids are mainly found in **animal fats** (e.g. butter) and **unsaturated** lipids are mostly found in **plants** (e.g. olive oil).

3) Unsaturated lipids **melt at lower temperatures** than saturated ones.
That's why margarine's easier to spread than butter straight out of the fridge.

4) The difference between these two types of lipids is their **hydrocarbon tails**.

> **Saturated**
>
> Saturated lipids **don't** have any **double bonds** between the **carbon atoms** in their hydrocarbon tails — every carbon is attached to at least two **hydrogen** atoms. The lipid is 'saturated' with hydrogen.
>
> hydrocarbon tail

> **Unsaturated**
>
> Unsaturated lipids **do** have **double bonds** between the **carbon atoms** in their hydrocarbon tails. These double bonds cause the chain to kink. If they have **two or more** of them, the lipid is called **polyunsaturated**.
>
> hydrocarbon tail
>
> double bond between carbon atoms in the hydrocarbon tail causes a <u>kink</u> in the tail

Bruce was pretty sure his tail contained double bonds.

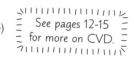

See pages 12-15 for more on CVD.

5) A diet high in **saturated fat** increases your risk of developing **CVD** (cardiovascular disease) because it increases your **blood cholesterol level** — see below.

High Blood Cholesterol Increases the Risk of CVD

1) **Cholesterol** is a type of **lipid** that is made in the body.

2) Some is **needed** for the body to **function normally**.

3) Cholesterol needs to be attached to **protein** to be moved around, so the body forms **lipoproteins** — substances composed of both **protein** and **lipid**. There are **two types** of lipoprotein:

HIGH DENSITY LIPOPROTEINS (HDLs)	LOW DENSITY LIPOPROTEINS (LDLs)
1) They are **mainly protein**.	1) They are **mainly lipid**.
2) They transport **cholesterol** from **body tissues** to the **liver** where it's **recycled** or **excreted**.	2) They transport cholesterol from the **liver** to the **blood**, where it circulates until needed by cells.
3) Their function is to **reduce total blood cholesterol** when the level is **too high**.	3) Their function is to **increase total blood cholesterol** when the level is **too low**.

4) **High total blood cholesterol level** (the level of HDL, LDL and other cholesterol) and **high LDL level** have both been linked to an **increased risk** of **CVD**.

5) As you saw on page 14, this is because an **increased cholesterol level** is thought to increase **atheroma formation**.

Lipids and Cardiovascular Disease

You May Have to **Interpret** Data on the **Link** Between **Cholesterol** and **CVD**

Take a look at the following example of the sort of study you might see in your **exam**:

Example: The graph shows the results of a study involving **27 939 American women**. The **LDL cholesterol level** was **measured** for each woman. These women were then **followed** for an average of **8 years** and the **occurrence** of **cardiovascular events** (e.g. heart attack, surgery on coronary arteries) or **death** from cardiovascular diseases was **recorded**. The **relative risk** of a cardiovascular event, **adjusted** for **other factors** that can affect cardiovascular disease, was then calculated.

Here are some of the things you might be asked to do:

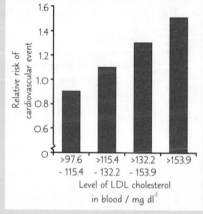

1) **Describe the data** — The **relative risk** of a cardiovascular event **increases** as the level of **LDL cholesterol** in the blood **increases**.

2) **Draw conclusions** — The graph shows a **positive correlation** between the **relative risk** of a cardiovascular event and the level of **LDL cholesterol** in the blood.

3) **Check any conclusions are valid** —
Make sure any conclusions **match** the data, e.g.
   - This data only looked at **women** — no males were involved, so you can't say that this trend is true for **everyone**.
   - You can't say that a high LDL cholesterol level is **correlated with** an increased risk of **heart attacks**, because the data shows **all** first cardiovascular events, including surgery on coronary arteries.
   - Also, you can't conclude that a high LDL cholesterol level **caused** the increased relative risk of a cardiovascular event — there may be other reasons for the trend.

There's more on correlation and cause on page 206.

4) **Other things to think about** — A **large sample size** was used (27 939). Data based on large samples is **better** than data based on small samples. This is because a large sample is **more representative** of the whole population (i.e. it shares more of the various **characteristics** of the population).

Practice Questions

Q1 What sort of reaction occurs during the formation of a triglyceride?

Q2 Describe how triglycerides are broken down.

Q3 What type of lipid is found in olive oil?

Q4 What is a polyunsaturated lipid?

Q5 What is a lipoprotein?

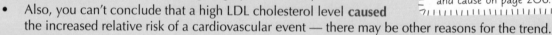

glycerol

fatty acid

Exam Questions

Q1 Triglycerides are formed from glycerol and fatty acid molecules. These molecules are shown in the diagrams on the right.

   a) Draw a diagram to show the structure of a triglyceride. [1 mark]

   b) What sort of bonds are formed between these molecules in a triglyceride? [1 mark]

Q2 Explain the difference in structure between a saturated lipid and an unsaturated lipid. [2 marks]

Q3 a) Describe the differences in structure and function between high density lipoproteins and low density lipoproteins. [3 marks]

   b) Low density lipoproteins are sometimes referred to as 'bad cholesterol'. Explain why low density lipoproteins are sometimes referred to in this way. [1 mark]

Hydrocarbon tails, unsaturated lipids... Whatever happened to plain old lard?

You don't get far in life without extensive lard knowledge, so learn all the details on these pages good and proper. Once you've got your HDLs sorted from your LDLs, make sure you know what to look for in data about the effect of cholesterol. You'll need to check if the conclusions are valid by going over the methods used with a fine-toothed comb.

Reducing Risk Factors of CVD

As you saw on the last couple of pages, and back on page 14, there are lots of potential risk factors for developing cardiovascular disease (CVD). Chin up though — there are some changes you can make to your lifestyle to reduce your risk of developing CVD...

Lifestyle Advice to Reduce the Risk of CVD is Based on Scientific Research

There've been loads of **scientific studies** carried out to **identify risk factors** (see page 14) for CVD. The **results** from these scientific studies are published in **scientific journals**. **Government organisations** (like the **NHS**) and the **media** report the findings to the **general public**. People can use this information to **make choices** about their **lifestyle**, so they can **reduce** their chance of developing CVD.

EXAMPLE: DIET

1) Scientific research has linked a **diet high in saturated fat** (see page 25) to an **increased risk** of CVD.
   - This information can be used to **educate people** about the risk of **certain diets** and to encourage them to **reduce** their saturated fat intake.
   - The **Food Standards Agency** encourages **food manufacturers** to label their products to show the amount of **saturated fat** in them, so people can make an **informed choice** about what they eat.

2) Scientific studies have also shown that **obese** people are **more likely** to develop CVD. **Obesity indicators** such as **waist-to-hip ratio** or **BMI (body mass index)** can be used to assess if people are **overweight** or **obese**.
   Waist-to-hip ratio is calculated using this formula:

   $$\text{Waist-to-hip ratio} = \frac{\text{waist (cm)}}{\text{hips (cm)}}$$

   BMI is calculated using this formula:

   $$BMI = \frac{\text{body mass (kg)}}{\text{height}^2 \text{ (m}^2)}$$

   A 'normal' BMI for adults is between 18 and 25.

   The results of these obesity indicators are compared to 'normal' values in a **published data table**. For example, if a male has a waist-to-hip ratio of more than 1.0, he is carrying too much weight around his abdomen. If someone is overweight or obese, then that person can make **choices** to **reduce** their **weight** and reduce their **risk** of CVD — e.g. they may go on a low-calorie **diet** or **increase** their **activity level**. These obesity indicators can then be used to **monitor** the **effects** any **changes in lifestyle** have on the person's weight.

   Example:
   Calculate the BMI of a person who weighs 63 kg and is 1.7 m tall.
   $$BMI = \frac{\text{body mass (kg)}}{\text{height}^2 \text{ (m}^2)}$$
   $$= 63 \div 1.7^2 = \textbf{21.8 kg m}^{-2}$$

EXAMPLE: SMOKING

1) Scientific research has linked **smoking** to an **increased risk** of CVD.
2) This research has led to **TV adverts** and **warnings** on **cigarette packets** about the risks of smoking. The NHS encourages people to give up by giving **free advice** and **prescribing nicotine patches**.
3) All of this encourages people to **stop** smoking and so reduce their risk of CVD.

EXAMPLE: EXERCISE

1) Scientific research has linked **inactivity** to an **increased risk** of CVD.
2) This research has led to campaigns that encourage people to **exercise more frequently** to reduce their risk of CVD.

Practice Questions

Q1 Why are obesity indicators useful?
Q2 Give two examples of how people can be encouraged to stop smoking.

$$\text{Waist-to-hip ratio} = \frac{\text{waist (cm)}}{\text{hips (cm)}}$$

$$BMI = \frac{\text{body mass (kg)}}{\text{height}^2 \text{ (m}^2)}$$

Exam Question

Q1 A person's hip measurement is 95 cm and their waist measurement is 76 cm. They are 1.68 m tall and they have a BMI of 18.9 kg m^{-2}.
   a) Use the formula shown above to calculate the person's waist-to-hip ratio. [1 mark]
   b) Use the BMI formula shown above to calculate the person's body mass. [2 marks]

Revise more to decrease the risk of exam failure...

There you go — some free lifestyle advice for you. In fact, I'd pay attention to all the lifestyle advice on this page. Taking it on board will be good for your health and good for your grades... It doesn't get much better than that.

Gas Exchange

All organisms need to exchange gases with their environment. Gas exchange involves diffusion...

Diffusion is the Passive Movement of Particles

1) Diffusion is the net movement of particles (molecules or ions) from an area of **higher concentration** to an area of **lower concentration**.

2) Molecules will diffuse **both ways**, but the **net movement** will be to the area of **lower concentration**. This continues until particles are **evenly distributed** throughout the liquid or gas.

3) The **concentration gradient** is the path from an area of higher concentration to an area of lower concentration. Particles diffuse **down** a concentration gradient.

4) Diffusion is a **passive process** — **no energy** is needed for it to happen.

Gas Exchange Surfaces are Adapted for Efficient Diffusion

All living organisms **respire** — they **take in oxygen** and **give out carbon dioxide**. These gases **diffuse** across a surface called the **gas exchange surface**.

Most gas exchange surfaces have two things in common:

1) They give gas exchange organs (like the lungs) a **large surface area to volume ratio** — see below.

2) They're **thin** (often just one layer of epithelial cells) — this provides a **short diffusion pathway** across the gas exchange surface.

The organism also maintains a **steep concentration gradient** of gases across the exchange surface.

All these features **increase the rate of diffusion**.

The rate of diffusion also increases with temperature because the molecules have more kinetic energy — they move faster.

Surface Area to Volume Ratios Always Affect Exchange

1) **Large objects** have **smaller surface area to volume ratios** than **small objects**. For example:

2) The **smaller** the surface area to volume ratio (sa:vol) the **slower** the **rate of exchange**. E.g. a substance would **diffuse more slowly** out of the **big cube** than the **small cube**. **Gas exchange organs** need a **large sa:vol** to exchange gases **quickly**.

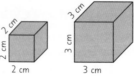

	Small cube	Big cube
Surface area (cm^2)	2 x 2 x 6 = 24	3 x 3 x 6 = 54
Volume (cm^3)	2 x 2 x 2 = 8	3 x 3 x 3 = 27
Surface area to volume ratio	24 : 8 = 3 : 1	54 : 27 = 2 : 1

The Lungs are Adapted for Efficient Gaseous Exchange

In mammals, the gas exchange surface is the **alveolar epithelium** in the **lungs**:

1) **Oxygen diffuses out of the alveoli, across the alveolar epithelium** (a layer of thin, flat cells) and the **capillary endothelium** (a type of epithelium that forms the capillary wall), and into the **blood**.

2) **Carbon dioxide diffuses into the alveoli from the blood and is breathed out.**

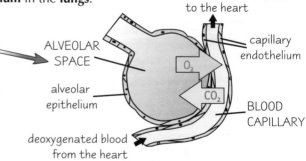

oxygenated blood to the heart

capillary endothelium

ALVEOLAR SPACE

O_2

CO_2

alveolar epithelium

BLOOD CAPILLARY

deoxygenated blood from the heart

The mammalian lungs have the following features, which all help to **increase** the **rate** of **gas exchange**:

1) Having **lots of alveoli** means there is a **large surface area** for diffusion to occur across.

2) The **alveolar epithelium and capillary endothelium** are each only **one cell thick**, giving a **short diffusion pathway**.

3) All the alveoli have a **good blood supply** from capillaries — they constantly **take away oxygen and bring more carbon dioxide**, maintaining the **concentration gradient**.

4) **Breathing in and out** refreshes the air in the alveoli, keeping the **concentration gradients** high.

Gas Exchange

Fick's Law Describes the Rate of Diffusion

Fick's Law relates the rate of diffusion to the **concentration gradient**, the **surface area** and the **thickness** of the **exchange surface**. It states that:

$$\text{rate of diffusion} \propto \frac{\text{area of diffusion surface} \times \text{difference in concentration}}{\text{thickness of diffusion surface}}$$

'∝' means 'is proportional to'.

The 'proportional to' bit means that the **rate of diffusion** will **double** if:

- the **surface area** or the **difference in concentration** <u>doubles</u>, OR
- the **thickness** of the surface <u>halves</u>.

You can write Fick's Law as an **equation**, which allows you to **calculate** the **rate of diffusion**. For example:

A fast rate of diffusion — not good in a swimming pool.

$$\text{Rate} = P \times A \times \frac{(C_1 - C_2)}{T}$$

Where: P = permeability constant
A = surface area
$(C_1 - C_2)$ = difference in concentration
T = thickness of the exchange surface

The units need to be the same throughout the equation. E.g. if the thickness is given in µm then the area should be in µm².

Example:

A section of alveolar epithelium has a **surface area** of **2.2 µm²** and is **1.0 µm** thick. The **permeability constant** of the alveolar epithelium for oxygen is **0.012 s⁻¹**. The **concentration** of oxygen on one side of the epithelium (C_1) is 2.3×10^{-16} **mol µm⁻³** and the concentration of oxygen on the other side (C_2) is 9.0×10^{-17} **mol µm⁻³**.

To calculate the **rate of diffusion of oxygen** across the alveolar epithelium, you need to put these values into the equation above:

$$\text{Rate of diffusion} = 0.012 \text{ s}^{-1} \times 2.2 \text{ µm}^2 \times \frac{(2.3 \times 10^{-16} \text{ mol µm}^{-3} - 9.0 \times 10^{-17} \text{ mol µm}^{-3})}{1.0 \text{ µm}}$$

$$= 3.7 \times 10^{-18} \text{ mol µm}^{-2} \text{ s}^{-1}$$

There are **different ways** of writing Fick's Law as an equation. **Don't worry** though — no matter what equation you're given in the exam, you'll also be given **all the information you need** to **use it**. Then it's just a case of popping the numbers into their correct places in the equation and running it all through your calculator.

Practice Questions

Q1 Diffusion is a passive process. What does this mean?

Q2 How does a thin gas exchange surface help the rate of diffusion?

Q3 What is Fick's Law?

Q4 According to Fick's Law, what will happen to the rate of diffusion if the surface area of a gas exchange surface is doubled?

Exam Questions

Q1 Efficient gas exchange surfaces have the following characteristics:

- large surface area
- short diffusion pathway
- high concentration gradient

Explain how these characteristics apply to human lungs. [4 marks]

Q2 Emphysema is a lung disease that destroys alveoli. Explain why a patient suffering from emphysema would have a decreased rate of gas exchange in their lungs. [2 marks]

I'll give you my gas, if you give me yours...

So gas exchange in mammals happens across the alveolar epithelium. Remember, like all gas exchange surfaces, it's really thin and has a large surface area (thanks to there being loads of alveoli). Both of these things, along with a high concentration gradient, help to keep up a fast rate of gas exchange — making sure you get plenty of oxygen for revision.

Cell Membranes

The cell membrane is basically the cell boundary. Small molecules, like oxygen and carbon dioxide, are able to cross this boundary by diffusion. Other substances enter and leave the cell in different ways. To understand how substances get across the cell membrane, you have to know its structure. Helpfully, it's all explained below...

Cell Membranes have a 'Fluid Mosaic' Structure

The **structure** of all membranes is basically the same. They're composed of **lipids** (mainly **phospholipids** — a type of lipid with a phosphate group attached to it), **proteins** and **carbohydrates** (usually attached to proteins or lipids).

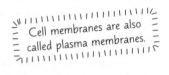
Cell membranes are also called plasma membranes.

1) In 1972, the **fluid mosaic model** was suggested to describe the **arrangement** of **molecules** in the membrane.

2) In the model, **phospholipid molecules** form a continuous, double layer (**bilayer**) — see below. This bilayer is **'fluid'** because the phospholipids are **constantly moving**.

> **Phospholipid molecules** have a 'head' and a 'tail'.
> - The **head** contains the **phosphate group**. It's **hydrophilic** — it **attracts water**.
> - The **tail** is made of two **fatty acids**. It's **hydrophobic** — it **repels water**.
> - Because of this, the molecules automatically **arrange** themselves into a **bilayer** — the **hydrophilic heads face out** towards the water on either side of the membrane. The **hydrophobic tails** are on the **inside**, making the centre of the bilayer **hydrophobic**. This means that the membrane doesn't allow water-soluble substances (like ions) through it.

phospholipid head
phospholipid bilayer
phospholipid tail
fatty acid

3) **Protein molecules** are scattered through the bilayer, like tiles in a **mosaic**. Because the phospholipid bilayer is fluid, the proteins can **move around** within it.

4) Some **proteins** have a **polysaccharide** (carbohydrate) **chain** attached — these are called **glycoproteins**.

5) Some **lipids** also have a **polysaccharide chain** attached — these are called **glycolipids**.

6) **Cholesterol** (a type of lipid) is also present in the membrane. It fits **in between** the phospholipids, forming **bonds** with them. This makes the membrane more **rigid**.

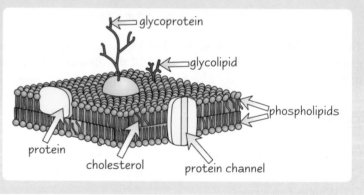
glycoprotein
glycolipid
phospholipids
protein
cholesterol
protein channel

The membrane is **partially permeable** — **small molecules** can move through **gaps** between the **phospholipids**, but **large molecules** and **ions** can only pass through special **membrane proteins** called **channel proteins** and **carrier proteins** (see page 32).

The Fluid Mosaic Model is Based on Scientific Evidence

1) Before the 1970s, most scientists believed cell membranes were composed of a **phospholipid layer** between **two continuous layers of proteins**. This was because **electron microscope** (EM) images appeared to show **three layers** in a cell membrane.

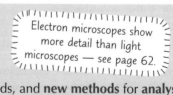
Electron microscopes show more detail than light microscopes — see page 62.

2) In time, **improved** EM techniques showed a **bilayer** of phospholipids, and **new methods** for **analysing proteins** showed that they were **randomly distributed** in cell membranes, not in a continuous layer.

3) Scientists also carried out experiments that proved the cell membrane is **fluid** — e.g. they fused a **mouse cell** with a **human cell**, and found that the mouse and human **membrane proteins** completely **intermixed** throughout the cell membrane — the proteins could only **mix** like this if the membrane was fluid.

4) All of this **new evidence** led to the **fluid mosaic model**.

Cell Membranes and Osmosis

You already know that some small molecules can diffuse across cell membranes.
Well, water can diffuse across cell membranes too — this is called osmosis.

Osmosis is the Diffusion of Water Molecules

1) Osmosis is the **diffusion** of free **water molecules** across a **partially permeable membrane**, (e.g. a cell membrane) from an area of **higher concentration** of water molecules to an area of **lower concentration** of water molecules.

2) Water molecules will diffuse **both ways** through the membrane, but the **net movement** will be to the side with the **lower concentration** of water molecules.

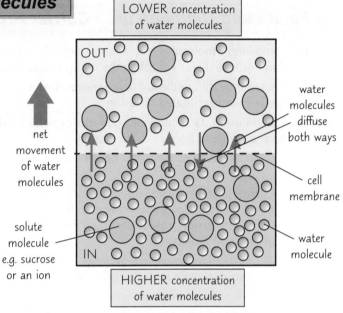

LOWER concentration of water molecules

OUT

net movement of water molecules

solute molecule e.g. sucrose or an ion

IN

HIGHER concentration of water molecules

water molecules diffuse both ways

cell membrane

water molecule

D'oh

Phew

Partially permeable membranes can be useful at sea.

A higher number of solute (e.g. sucrose) molecules means a lower concentration of water molecules and vice versa.

Practice Questions

Q1 How are phospholipids arranged in a cell membrane?

Q2 The membrane of a cell can be described as 'partially permeable'. What does this mean?

Q3 What is osmosis?

Exam Questions

Q1 Which of the following statements about the cell membrane is true?

A The cell membrane is mainly composed of glycolipids.

B The molecules that make up the cell membrane are constantly moving.

C Molecules can only pass through the cell membrane via channel proteins.

D Cholesterol makes the cell membrane less rigid. [1 mark]

Q2 Pieces of potato of equal mass were put into different concentrations of sucrose solution for three days. The difference in mass for each is recorded in the table on the right.

Concentration of sucrose / %	1	2	3	4
Mass difference / g	0.4	0.2	0	− 0.2

a) Explain why the pieces of potato in 1% and 2% sucrose solutions gained mass. [3 marks]

b) Give a reason why the mass of the piece of potato in 3% sucrose solution stayed the same. [1 mark]

c) What would you expect the mass difference for a potato in a 5% solution to be? Explain your answer. [2 marks]

Fluid Mosaic Model — think I saw one being sold at a craft fair...

Scientists are a bit annoying — they keep changing their minds about things like the structure of the cell membrane. But they don't do it on a whim — they need new experimental data that proves something isn't how they thought it was.

Transport Across the Cell Membrane

Like diffusion (and osmosis), facilitated diffusion is a passive transport process.
There's also an active transport process involving energy, which is imaginatively named 'active transport'.
Facilitated diffusion and active transport are actually quite similar — they both involve proteins.

Facilitated Diffusion uses Carrier Proteins and Channel Proteins

1) Some **larger molecules** (e.g. amino acids, glucose), and **charged particles** (e.g. ions) **don't diffuse directly through** the phospholipid bilayer of the cell membrane.

2) Instead they diffuse through **carrier proteins** or **channel proteins** in the cell membrane — this is called **facilitated diffusion**.

3) Like diffusion, facilitated diffusion moves particles **down** a **concentration gradient**, from a higher to a lower concentration.

4) It's also a passive process — it **doesn't** use **energy**.

Andy needed all his concentration for this particular gradient...

Carrier proteins move **large molecules** into or out of the cell, down their concentration gradient. **Different carrier proteins** facilitate the diffusion of **different molecules**.

1) First, a large molecule **attaches** to a carrier protein in the membrane.

2) Then, the protein **changes shape**.

3) This **releases** the molecule on the **opposite side** of the membrane.

Channel proteins form **pores** in the membrane for **charged particles** to diffuse through (down their concentration gradient). **Different channel proteins** facilitate the diffusion of **different charged particles**.

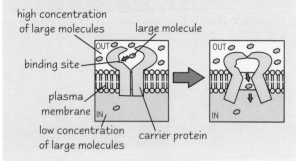

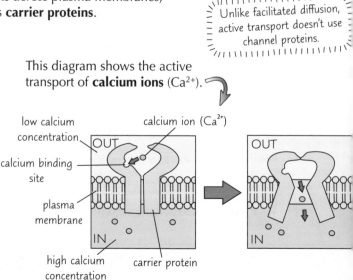

Active Transport Moves Substances Against a Concentration Gradient

Active transport uses **energy** to move **molecules** and **ions** across plasma membranes, **against** a **concentration gradient**. This process involves **carrier proteins**.

Unlike facilitated diffusion, active transport doesn't use channel proteins.

1) The process is pretty similar to facilitated diffusion — a molecule **attaches** to the carrier protein, the protein **changes shape** and this moves the molecule **across** the membrane, **releasing it** on the other side.

2) The only difference is that **energy** is used — this energy comes from **ATP**.
   - ATP is produced by **respiration**.
   - It acts as an **immediate** source of **energy** in the cell.
   - When ATP is **hydrolysed** (broken down) in the cell, energy is **released**. This energy is used to move the molecule against its concentration gradient.

This diagram shows the active transport of **calcium ions** (Ca^{2+}).

Transport Across the Cell Membrane

Cells can *Take in* Substances by *Endocytosis*

1) Some molecules are way too **large** to be taken into a cell by carrier proteins, e.g. proteins, lipids and some carbohydrates.

2) Instead a cell can **surround** a substance with a **section** of its **cell membrane**.

3) The membrane then **pinches off** to form a **vesicle** inside the cell containing the **ingested substance** — this is **endocytosis**.

4) Some cells also take in much **larger objects** by endocytosis — for example, some **white blood cells** (called phagocytes) use endocytosis to take in things like **microorganisms** and **dead cells** so that they can destroy them.

5) Like active transport, (see previous page), this process also uses **ATP** for **energy**.

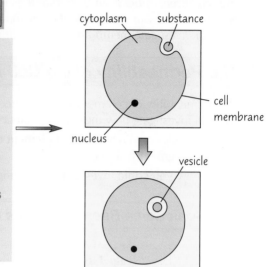

Cells can *Secrete* Substances by *Exocytosis*

1) Some substances **produced** by the cell (e.g. **digestive enzymes**, **hormones**, **lipids**) need to be **released** from the cell — this is done by **exocytosis**.

2) **Vesicles** containing these substances **pinch off** from the sacs of the **Golgi apparatus** (a structure that processes new proteins and lipids — see p. 59) and **move towards** the cell membrane.

3) The vesicles **fuse** with the **cell membrane** and **release** their contents **outside** the cell.

4) Some substances (like membrane proteins) **aren't** released outside the cell — instead they are **inserted** straight into the cell membrane.

5) Exocytosis uses **ATP** as an **energy source**.

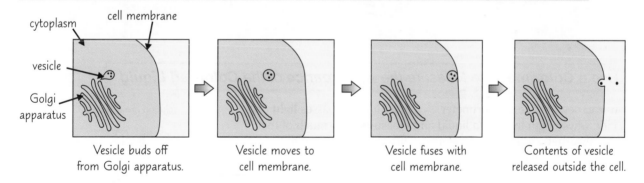

| Vesicle buds off from Golgi apparatus. | Vesicle moves to cell membrane. | Vesicle fuses with cell membrane. | Contents of vesicle released outside the cell. |

Practice Questions

Q1 When would facilitated diffusion take place rather than simple diffusion?

Q2 What is active transport?

Q3 Which molecule provides the energy for active transport?

Exam Questions

Q1 Describe the role of membrane proteins in facilitated diffusion. [3 marks]

Q2 Explain the difference between endocytosis and exocytosis. [4 marks]

Revision — like working against a concentration gradient...

Wouldn't it be great if you could revise by endocytosis — you could just stick this book on your head and your brain would slowly surround it and take it in... actually when I put it like that it sounds a bit gross. Maybe just stick to the good old 'closing the book and scribbling down the diagrams till you know them off by heart' method.

Investigating Cell Membrane Structure

You might remember from p. 30 that the cell membrane is partially permeable — it allows some molecules through it but not others. But changes in the environment can affect the structure of the membrane, and so how permeable it is. You can investigate membrane permeability using beetroot — a seriously under-appreciated vegetable if you ask me.

The **Permeability** of the **Cell Membrane** can be **Investigated** in the **Lab**

The permeability of cell membranes is affected by **different conditions**, e.g. **temperature** and **alcohol concentration**. You can investigate how these things affect permeability by doing an experiment using **beetroot**.

Beetroot cells contain a **coloured pigment** that **leaks out** — the **higher** the **permeability** of the membrane, the **more pigment** leaks out of the cell.

Here's how you could investigate how **temperature** affects **beetroot membrane permeability**:

1) **Soak** Some **Beetroot Cubes** in **Water** at **Different Temperatures**

1) Use a **scalpel** to carefully cut five **equal sized** pieces of beetroot. (Make sure you do your cutting on a **cutting board**.) **Rinse** the pieces to remove any pigment released during cutting.
2) Use a **measuring cylinder** or **pipette** to measure **5 cm³ of water** into five different test tubes.
3) Place the test tubes into **water baths** at **different temperatures**, e.g. 10 °C, 20 °C, 30 °C, 40 °C, 50 °C, for around 5 minutes to allow the water to reach the desired temperature.
4) Place the five pieces of beetroot into the five different **test tubes**, for the **same length of time** (measured using a **stopwatch**).
5) **Remove** the pieces of beetroot from the tubes, leaving just the **coloured liquid**.

2) Use a **Colorimeter** to Measure the **Absorbance** of the **Coloured Liquid**

Now you need to use a **colorimeter** — a machine that passes **light** of a specific wavelength through a liquid and measures **how much** of that light is **absorbed**. Many colorimeters use **filters** to make sure the light passing through the liquid is at the desired wavelength. Here's what you do...

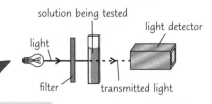

1) Firstly, switch the colorimeter on and allow **five minutes** for it to **stabilise**. Then set up the colorimeter so you're using a **blue filter** (or a wavelength of about **470 nm**) and use pure water to calibrate the machine to **zero**.
2) Next, use a **pipette** to transfer a **sample** of the liquid from the first of your beetroot test tubes to a **clean cuvette** — it should be about **three quarters full**.
3) Put the cuvette in the colorimeter and **record the absorbance** of the **coloured solution**.
4) **Repeat steps 2-3** for the liquids in the remaining four test tubes (using a clean pipette and cuvette each time).
5) You're now ready to analyse your results — the **higher** the **absorbance** reading, the **less light** is passing through the solution. This means **more pigment** has been **released**, so the **higher** the **permeability** of the membrane.

A cuvette is a small container that fits inside a colorimeter.

Depending on the resources you have available, you may be able to connect the colorimeter to a **computer** and use **software** to **collect the data** and **draw a graph** of the results.

Investigating Cell Membrane Structure

Increasing the Temperature Increases Membrane Permeability

Experiments like the one on the previous page have shown that membrane permeability changes with temperature:

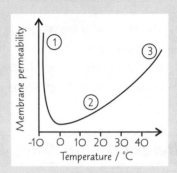

(1) Temperatures below 0 °C — the phospholipids don't have much energy, so they can't move very much. They're packed closely together and the membrane is rigid. But channel proteins and carrier proteins in the membrane deform, increasing the permeability of the membrane. Ice crystals may form and pierce the membrane making it highly permeable when it thaws.

(2) Temperatures between 0 and 45 °C — the phospholipids can move around and aren't packed as tightly together — the membrane is partially permeable. As the temperature increases the phospholipids move more because they have more energy — this increases the permeability of the membrane.

(3) Temperatures above 45 °C — the phospholipid bilayer starts to melt (break down) and the membrane becomes more permeable. Water inside the cell expands, putting pressure on the membrane. Channel proteins and carrier proteins deform so they can't control what enters or leaves the cell — this increases the permeability of the membrane.

Increasing the Alcohol Concentration Increases Membrane Permeability

1) You can also test the effect of alcohol concentration on membrane permeability.

2) The graph on the right shows that as alcohol concentration increases, the permeability of the cell membrane increases.

3) This is because alcohol dissolves the lipids in the cell membrane, so the membrane loses its structure.

Practice Questions

Q1 What is a colorimeter used for?

Q2 What happens to the permeability of a cell membrane at temperatures below 0 °C?

Q3 What happens to the permeability of a cell membrane as the temperature increases above 0 °C?

Exam Question

Q1 The table on the right shows the results of an investigation into the effect of alcohol concentration on the permeability of beetroot cell membranes.

Alcohol concentration (%)	Absorbance
0	0.14
25	0.22
50	0.49
75	1.03
100	1.28

a) Describe a suitable method that could have been used to obtain these results. [4 marks]

b) What conclusion can be drawn from the results? [2 marks]

c) Give an explanation for the results. [1 mark]

Perm-eability — it's definitely decreased since the 80s...

Ah beetroot. Works nicely in a salad, a chocolate cake (if you're feeling adventurous) and even the odd lab experiment. What more could you ask for from a vegetable..? You need to know a method for investigating membrane permeability in the lab and you need to be able to explain how temperature and alcohol concentration affect cell membranes.

Protein Structure

There are loads of different proteins with loads of different functions. But what are proteins? What do they look like? Well, for your enjoyment, here are the answers to these questions and many, many more...

Proteins are Made from Long Chains of Amino Acids

1) The **monomers** (see page 22) of proteins are **amino acids**.
2) A **dipeptide** is formed when **two** amino acids join together.
3) A **polypeptide** is formed when **more than two** amino acids join together.
4) **Proteins** are made up of **one or more polypeptides**.

Grant's cries of "die peptide, die" could be heard for miles around. He'd never forgiven it for sleeping with his wife.

Different Amino Acids Have Different Variable Groups

Amino acids have the same general structure — a **carboxyl group** (-COOH), an **amine** or **amino group** (-NH$_2$) and a **carbon-containing R group** (also known as a **variable** side group).

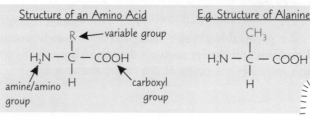

All living things share a bank of only **20 amino acids**. The only **difference** between them is what makes up their carbon-containing **R group**.

Glycine is the only amino acid that doesn't have carbon in its side group. Its R group consists of just one hydrogen atom.

Polypeptides are Formed by Condensation Reactions

Amino acids are linked together by **condensation** reactions to form polypeptides. A molecule of **water** is **released** during the reaction. The bonds formed between amino acids are called **peptide bonds**. The reverse reaction happens during digestion.

Proteins Have Four Structural Levels

Proteins are **big, complicated** molecules. They're much easier to explain if you describe their structure in four 'levels'. These levels are a protein's **primary**, **secondary**, **tertiary** and **quaternary** structures.

<u>Primary Structure</u> — this is the **sequence** of **amino acids** in the **polypeptide chain**.
<u>Secondary Structure</u> — the polypeptide chain doesn't remain flat and straight.
Hydrogen bonds form between the amino acids in the chain.
This makes it automatically **coil** into an **alpha** (α) **helix** or **fold** into a **beta** (β) **pleated sheet** — this is the secondary structure.
<u>Tertiary Structure</u> — the coiled or folded chain of amino acids is often **coiled** and **folded further**. More **bonds** form between different parts of the polypeptide chain, including **hydrogen bonds** and **ionic bonds** (see next page). **Disulfide bonds** can also form (see next page). For proteins made from a **single** polypeptide chain, the tertiary structure forms their **final 3D structure**.
<u>Quaternary Structure</u> — some proteins are made of **several different polypeptide chains** held together by **bonds**. The **quaternary structure** is the way these polypeptide chains are assembled together. For proteins made from more than one polypeptide chain (e.g. haemoglobin, insulin, collagen), the quaternary structure is the protein's **final 3D structure**.

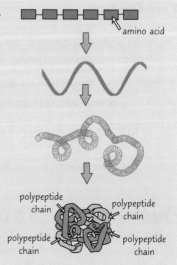

Protein Structure

Different Bonds Hold Different Structural Levels Together

The four structural levels of a protein are held together by **different kinds** of **bonds**:

1) **Primary structure** — held together by the **peptide bonds** between amino acids.
2) **Secondary structure** — held together by **hydrogen bonds** (see previous page).
3) **Tertiary structure** — this is affected by a few different kinds of bonds:
   - **Ionic bonds.** These are **attractions** between **negative** and **positive** charges on different parts of the molecule.
   - **Disulfide bonds.** Whenever two molecules of the amino acid **cysteine** come close together, the **sulfur atom** in one cysteine bonds to the sulfur in the other cysteine, forming a disulfide bond.
   - **Hydrophobic** and **hydrophilic interactions.** When **hydrophobic** (water-repelling) groups are close together in the protein, they tend to **clump together.** This means that **hydrophilic** (water-attracting) groups are more likely to be pushed to the **outside**, which affects how the protein **folds up** into its final structure.
   - **Hydrogen bonds.**
4) **Quaternary structure** — this tends to be determined by the **tertiary structure** of the individual polypeptide chains being bonded together. Because of this, it can be influenced by **all the bonds** mentioned above.

> Hydrogen bonds are weak bonds between a slightly positively-charged hydrogen atom in one molecule and a slightly negatively-charged atom in another molecule.

A Protein's Primary Structure Determines its 3D Structure and Properties

1) The **amino acid sequence** of a protein determines what **bonds** will form and how the protein will **fold up** into its 3D structure. E.g. if there are many cysteines, these will form **disulfide bonds** with each other, so the protein folds up in a certain way.
2) The **3D structure** of a protein determines its **properties**. Its properties relate to its **function** in the body.

Proteins Can Have a Globular or Fibrous 3D Structure

GLOBULAR

1) Globular proteins are **round, compact** proteins made up of **multiple polypeptide chains**.
2) The chains are **coiled up** so that **hydrophilic** (water-attracting) parts of chains are on the **outside** of the molecule and **hydrophobic** (water-repelling) parts of chains face **inwards**.
3) This makes the proteins **soluble**, so they're **easily transported** in fluids.
4) E.g. **haemoglobin** is a globular protein made of **four** polypeptide chains. It **carries oxygen** around the body in the blood. It's **soluble**, so it can be easily transported in the blood. It also has iron-containing **haem groups** that **bind** to oxygen.

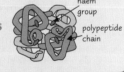
haem group
polypeptide chain

FIBROUS

1) Fibrous proteins are made up of **long, insoluble polypeptide chains** that are **tightly coiled** round each other to form a **rope shape**.
2) The chains are held together by **lots of bonds** (e.g. disulfide and hydrogen bonds), which make the proteins **strong**.
3) Because they're strong, fibrous proteins are often found in **supportive tissue**.
4) E.g. **collagen** is a **strong, fibrous protein** that forms connective tissue in **animals**.

Practice Questions

Q1 Draw the basic structure of an amino acid.
Q2 Name four types of bond that determine the 3D structure of a protein.

Exam Question

Q1 Proteins, such as keratin, are made of polypeptides. Describe how a polypeptide is formed. [3 marks]

The name's Bond — Peptide Bond...

Heating a protein to a high temperature will break up its ionic and hydrogen bonds and hydrophobic/hydrophilic interactions. In turn this will cause a change in the protein's 3D shape, which can lead to it becoming non-functional.

Enzymes

Enzymes crop up loads in biology — they're really useful 'cos they make reactions work quickly. So, whether you feel the need for some speed or not, read on — because you really need to know this basic stuff about enzymes.

Enzymes *are* Biological Catalysts

Enzymes **speed up chemical reactions** by acting as **biological catalysts**.

> A catalyst is a substance that speeds up a chemical reaction without being used up in the reaction itself.

1) Enzymes catalyse **metabolic reactions** — both at a **cellular level** (e.g. **respiration**) and for the **organism** as a **whole** (e.g. **digestion** in mammals).

2) Enzymes can affect **structures** in an organism (e.g. enzymes are involved in the production of **collagen**, see previous page) as well as **functions** (like **respiration**).

3) Enzymes can be **intracellular** (catalyse reactions **inside** cells) or **extracellular** (produced and secreted by cells to catalyse reactions **outside** cells).

4) Enzymes are **proteins** (see pages 36-37).

5) Enzymes have an **active site**, which has a **specific shape**. The active site is the part of the enzyme where the **substrate** molecules (the substance that the enzyme interacts with) **bind to**.

6) Enzymes are **highly specific** due to their tertiary structure (see next page).

Enzymes *Lower* the *Activation Energy* of a *Reaction*

In a chemical reaction, a certain amount of **energy** needs to be supplied to the chemicals before the reaction will **start**. This is called the **activation energy** — it's often provided as **heat**. Enzymes **lower** the amount of activation energy that's needed, often making reactions happen at a **lower temperature** than they could without an enzyme. This **speeds up** the **rate of reaction**.

When a substrate fits into the enzyme's active site it forms an **enzyme-substrate complex** — it's this that lowers the activation energy. Here are two reasons why:

1) If two substrate molecules need to be **joined**, being attached to the enzyme holds them **close together**, **reducing** any **repulsion** between the molecules so they can bond more easily.

2) If the enzyme is catalysing a **breakdown reaction**, fitting into the active site puts a **strain** on bonds in the substrate, so the substrate molecule **breaks up** more easily.

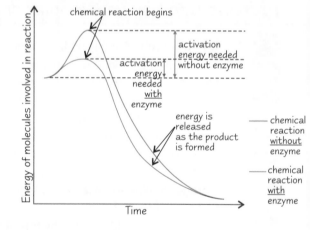

The '*Lock and Key*' Model is a Good Start...

Enzymes are a bit picky — they only work with substrates that fit their active site. Early scientists studying the action of enzymes came up with the '**lock and key**' model. This is where the **substrate fits** into the **enzyme** in the same way that a **key fits** into a **lock**.

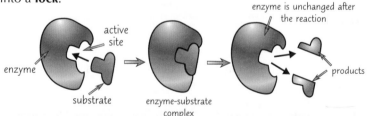

Scientists soon realised that the lock and key model didn't give the full story. The enzyme and substrate do have to fit together in the first place, but new evidence showed that the **enzyme-substrate complex changed shape** slightly to complete the fit. This **locks** the substrate even more tightly to the enzyme. Scientists modified the old lock and key model and came up with the '**induced fit**' model.

Enzymes

...but the 'Induced Fit' Model is a **Better Theory**

The '**induced fit**' model helps to explain why enzymes are so **specific** and only bond to one particular substrate. The substrate doesn't only have to be the right shape to fit the active site, it has to make the active site **change shape** in the right way as well. This is a prime example of how a widely accepted theory can **change** when **new evidence** comes along. The 'induced fit' model is still widely accepted — for now, anyway.

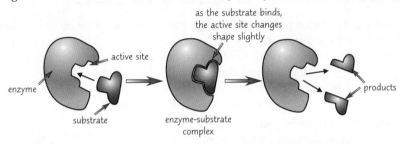

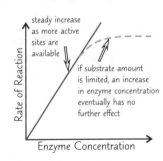

The 'Luminous Tights' model was popular in the 1980s but has since been found to be grossly inappropriate.

Enzyme **Properties** Relate to Their **Tertiary Structure**

1) Enzymes are **very specific** — they usually only catalyse **one** reaction, e.g. maltase only breaks down maltose, sucrase only breaks down sucrose.

2) This is because **only one complementary substrate will fit** into the active site.

3) The active site's **shape** is determined by the enzyme's **tertiary structure** (which is determined by the enzyme's **primary structure**).

4) Each **different enzyme** has a **different tertiary structure** and so a **different shaped active site**. If the substrate shape doesn't match the active site, an enzyme-substrate complex **won't** be formed and the reaction won't be catalysed.

5) If the tertiary structure of the enzyme is **altered** in any way, the **shape** of the active site will **change**. This means the **substrate won't fit** into the active site, an enzyme-substrate complex **won't** be formed and the enzyme will no longer be able to carry out its function.

6) The tertiary structure of an enzyme may be **altered** by changes in **pH** or **temperature**.

7) The **primary structure** (amino acid sequence) of a protein is determined by a **gene**. If a mutation occurs in that gene (see page 50), it could change the tertiary structure of the enzyme **produced**.

Enzyme Concentration Affects the Rate of Reaction

1) The **more enzyme molecules** there are in a solution, the **more active sites** are present and therefore the more likely a substrate molecule is to **collide** with an **active site** and form an **enzyme-substrate complex**. So increasing the concentration of the enzyme **increases** the **rate of reaction**.

2) But, if the amount of **substrate** is **limited**, there comes a point when there's more than enough enzyme molecules to deal with all the available substrate, so adding more enzyme has **no further effect**. Substrate concentration has become a **limiting factor**.

steady increase as more active sites are available

if substrate amount is limited, an increase in enzyme concentration eventually has no further effect

Rate of Reaction

Enzyme Concentration

Substrate Concentration Affects the Rate of Reaction **Up to a Point**

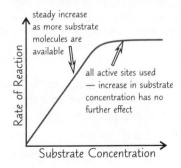

steady increase as more substrate molecules are available

all active sites used — increase in substrate concentration has no further effect

Rate of Reaction

Substrate Concentration

1) The **higher** the substrate concentration, the **faster** the reaction — more substrate molecules means a **collision** between substrate and enzyme is **more likely** and so more active sites will be used. This is only true up until a '**saturation**' point though. After that, there are so many substrate molecules that the enzymes have about as much as they can cope with (all the **active sites are full**), and adding more **makes no difference**.

2) Substrate concentration **decreases** with **time** during a reaction (unless more substrate is added to the reaction mixture), so if no other variables are changed, the **rate of reaction will decrease over time** too. This makes the **initial** rate of reaction (the reaction rate at the **start**) the **highest** rate of reaction.

TOPIC 2B — PROTEINS AND GENETICS

Enzymes

You can **Measure** the **Rate** of an **Enzyme-Controlled** Reaction

There are **two** ways to measure the **rate** of a reaction. Using these, you can **investigate** the effect of changing the **enzyme** or **substrate concentration** on the **initial rate** of a reaction.

1) You Can Measure **How Fast** the **Product** of the Reaction is **Made**

Catalase catalyses the **breakdown** of **hydrogen peroxide** into **water** and **oxygen**. It's easy to measure the volume of oxygen produced and to work out **how fast** it's given off. Using this reaction, you can **investigate** the effect of **changing the enzyme concentration** on the **initial rate** of reaction — the diagram below shows the **apparatus** you'll need. (You'll also need a **stand** and **clamp** to hold the cylinder upside down, as well as a **stopwatch**.) During the experiment, the oxygen released **displaces** the water from the measuring cylinder. You'll need to **decide** on a **range** of **catalase concentrations** to investigate before you start.

1) Add a **set volume** and **concentration** of **hydrogen peroxide** to a boiling tube. To keep the pH constant, add a set amount of a suitable **buffer solution** to the tube. (A buffer solution is able to resist changes in pH when small amounts of acid or alkali are added.)

2) Set up the rest of the **apparatus** as shown in the diagram.

3) Use a pipette to add a **set volume** of one of the **concentrations** of **catalase** to the boiling tube. Then **quickly attach** the **bung** and **delivery tube**.

4) **Record** the volume of oxygen **produced** in the measuring cylinder **every ten seconds** for the **first minute** (60 s) of the reaction. Use a **stopwatch** to measure the time.

5) **Repeat** the experiment twice more, and find the **average volume of oxygen produced** at **each** ten second interval.

6) Plot your data on a **graph** of **volume of oxygen produced** (cm³) against **time** (seconds) and draw a **tangent** (see next page) to determine the **initial rate** of the reaction.

7) **Repeat** the **whole** experiment at **each** of the other **catalase concentrations** under investigation. You can then **compare** the **initial rate** of the reaction for **each** **concentration** to determine the **effect** of **changing the enzyme concentration** on the initial rate of reaction.

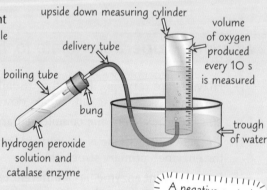

upside down measuring cylinder

volume of oxygen produced every 10 s is measured

delivery tube

boiling tube

bung

trough of water

hydrogen peroxide solution and catalase enzyme

A negative control reaction, using a boiling tube that doesn't contain any catalase, should also be carried out.

2) You Can Measure **How Fast** the **Substrate** is **Removed**

Amylase catalyses the breakdown of **starch** to **maltose**. This experiment shows you how to investigate the **effect** of **changing** the **starch concentration** on the **initial rate** of the **reaction**. It uses a **colorimeter** (see page 34) to measure the **colour change** of a **solution** in response to **enzyme activity**. The **rate** of this **colour change** indicates the **rate** of the **reaction**. You'll need to decide on a **range** of **starch concentrations** to investigate before you start.

1) Set up a **colorimeter** with a **red filter** and **zero** it using a **cuvette** (see page 34) containing **iodine dissolved in potassium iodide solution**. This will have a browny-orange colour.

2) Into **another** cuvette, pipette a set volume of one of the **concentrations** of **starch** that you're investigating, as well as a set volume of **iodine dissolved in potassium iodide solution**, and **mix** the contents together. The presence of starch causes the solution to turn a **dark blue-black colour**. Place the cuvette in the zeroed colorimeter and **record** the **absorbance**.

3) Now **add** a set volume and concentration of **amylase** enzyme to the cuvette and immediately **start** a **stopwatch**.

4) Every **ten seconds** for a set amount of time (e.g. 5 minutes), **record** the **absorbance** shown by the colorimeter.

5) **Repeat steps 1-4** twice more and use the data to calculate an **average absorbance** reading for **each** ten second interval.

6) **Plot** the data on a **graph** of **absorbance against time** and draw a **tangent** (see next page) to estimate the **initial rate of reaction**. Absorbance is unitless — it **doesn't** have its own proper **unit** of measurement, so it can be described in **arbitrary units**. The unit of the rate will be **arbitrary units per second** (arbitrary units s⁻¹).

A negative control experiment should also be carried out for each of the starch concentrations. For this, no amylase should be added to the cuvette. The absorbance should stay the same throughout the experiment, supporting that it is the enzyme that's breaking down the starch.

7) **Repeat** the **whole** experiment at **each** of the other **starch concentrations** and **calculate** an **average initial rate** for **each**. You can then **compare** these figures to determine the effect of changing substrate concentration.

TOPIC 2B — PROTEINS AND GENETICS

Enzymes

You Can Use a *Tangent* to *Calculate* the *Initial Rate of Reaction*

The **initial** rate of reaction is the rate right at the **start** of the reaction, close to **time equals zero** ($t = 0$) on the graph. To work out the initial rate of reaction carry out the following steps:

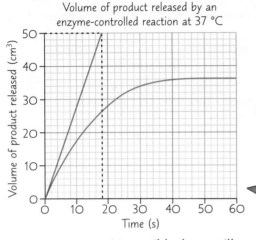

Volume of product released by an enzyme-controlled reaction at 37 °C

1) **Draw** a **tangent** to the curve at **$t = 0$**, using a ruler. Do this by positioning the ruler so it's an **equal distance** from the curve at **both sides** of where it's touching it. Here you'll have to **estimate** where the curve would **continue** if it carried on **below zero**. Then draw a **line** along the ruler. (For more on drawing tangents see p. 205.)

2) Then calculate the **gradient** of the **tangent** — this is the **initial rate of reaction**. Gradient = change in y axis ÷ change in x axis On this graph it's: 50 cm³ ÷ 18 s = **2.8 cm³ s⁻¹**.

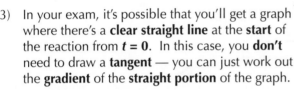

3) In your exam, it's possible that you'll get a graph where there's a **clear straight line** at the **start** of the reaction from **$t = 0$**. In this case, you **don't** need to draw a **tangent** — you can just work out the **gradient** of the **straight portion** of the graph.

4) Gradient = 0.50 arbitrary units ÷ 12 s
   = **0.042 arbitrary units s⁻¹**

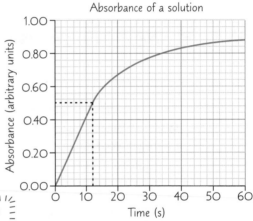

Absorbance of a solution

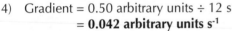

If you're comparing the initial rate of reaction for two different reactions, you can work out the ratio of the rates to give you a quick and easy comparison.

Practice Questions

Q1 What is an enzyme?

Q2 What is the name given to the amount of energy needed to start a reaction?

Q3 What is an enzyme-substrate complex?

Q4 Why can an enzyme only bind to one substance?

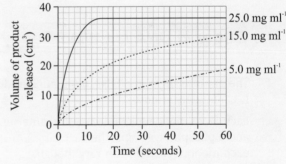

Exam Question

Q1 A student investigated the effect of enzyme concentration on the rate of an enzyme-controlled reaction. The product of the reaction was a gas. A tube was set up containing some substrate solution. A set volume of 5.0 mg ml⁻¹ enzyme solution was then added to the tube, and a bung with a hose connected to a gas syringe was put in the top. The amount of gas collected was recorded every 10 seconds for 1 minute. The experiment was then repeated using two different concentrations of enzyme. The volume and concentration of substrate solution was kept the same.

a) Draw a tangent to find the initial rate of reaction when using 25.0 mg ml⁻¹ enzyme solution. Show your working. [2 marks]

b) Analyse the graph to explain how the enzyme concentration affects the initial rate of reaction. [2 marks]

c) Give a negative control that should have been included in the investigation. Explain your answer. [2 marks]

d) When the substrate is broken down, the solution changes from blue to colourless. State how this experiment could be adapted to measure the colour change instead of the volume of product released. [2 marks]

But why is the enzyme-substrate complex?

There's plenty to sink your teeth into here, but it's all worth remembering for the exams. Make sure you know all about how enzymes work, and make sure you know how to investigate the initial rate of an enzyme-controlled reaction. If you've got a few spare minutes after that, spend some time arguing with your friends about how to pronounce 'scone'.

DNA and RNA Basics

These two pages are all about nucleic acids — DNA and RNA. These molecules are needed to build proteins, which are required for the cells in living organisms to function. They're right handy little things.

DNA and RNA Carry Important Information

DNA and RNA are both types of **nucleic acid**. They're found in **all living cells** and they both carry **information**.

1) **DNA** (deoxyribonucleic acid) is used to store **genetic information** — that's **all the instructions** an organism needs to **grow and develop** from a fertilised egg to a fully grown adult.

2) **RNA** (ribonucleic acid) is similar in structure to DNA. One of its main functions is to **transfer** genetic information from the **DNA** to the **ribosomes**. Ribosomes are the body's **'protein factories'** — they read the RNA to make **polypeptides** (proteins) in a process called **translation** (see page 47). Ribosomes themselves are made from **RNA** and **proteins**.

DNA and RNA are Polymers of Mononucleotides

1) A **mononucleotide** is a type of biological molecule. It's made from:

- a **pentose sugar** (that's a sugar with **5** carbon atoms),
- a **nitrogen-containing** organic **base**,
- a **phosphate** group.

'Organic' means that it contains carbon.

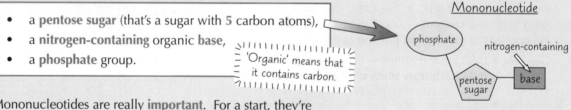

Mononucleotide

phosphate — nitrogen-containing — pentose sugar — base

2) Mononucleotides are really **important**. For a start, they're the **monomers** (see page 22) that make up **DNA** and **RNA**.

The Sugar in DNA is Called Deoxyribose

1) The **pentose sugar** in a **DNA mononucleotide** is called **deoxyribose**.

2) Each DNA mononucleotide has the **same sugar** and a **phosphate group**. The **base** on each mononucleotide can **vary** though.

3) There are **four** possible bases — adenine (**A**), thymine (**T**), cytosine (**C**) and guanine (**G**).

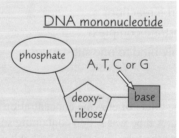

DNA mononucleotide

phosphate — A, T, C or G — deoxyribose — base

The Sugar in RNA is Called Ribose

1) **RNA** contains mononucleotides with a **ribose sugar** (not deoxyribose).

2) Like DNA, an RNA mononucleotide also has a **phosphate group** and one of **four** different **bases**.

3) In RNA though, **uracil** (**U**) replaces **thymine** as a base.

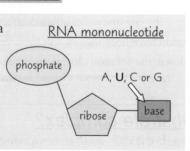

RNA mononucleotide

phosphate — A, U, C or G — ribose — base

Mary didn't care if it was ribose or deoxyribose, she just wanted her cuppa.

DNA and RNA Basics

Mononucleotides Join Together to Form Polynucleotides

1) A **polynucleotide** is a **polymer** of **mononucleotides**. Both DNA and RNA mononucleotides form polynucleotides.

2) The mononucleotides are joined through **condensation reactions** between the **phosphate** of one mononucleotide and the **sugar** group of another. As in all condensation reactions, **water** is a by-product (see page 22).

3) **DNA** is made of **two polynucleotide strands**, RNA has just **one strand**.

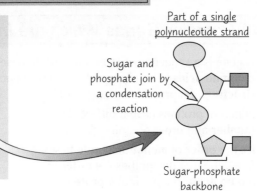

Part of a single polynucleotide strand

Sugar and phosphate join by a condensation reaction

Sugar-phosphate backbone

DNA is Made of Two Polynucleotide Chains in a Double-Helix Structure

1) **Two DNA** polynucleotide strands join together by **hydrogen bonding** between the bases.

2) Each base can only join with one particular partner — this is called **complementary base pairing** (or specific base pairing).

3) **Adenine** always pairs with **thymine (A - T)** and **cytosine** always pairs with **guanine (C - G)**. This means that there are always **equal amounts** of adenine and thymine in a DNA molecule and **equal amounts** of cytosine and guanine.

4) **Two** hydrogen bonds form between **A and T**, and **three** hydrogen bonds form between **C and G**.

5) Two **antiparallel** (running in opposite directions) polynucleotide strands **twist** to form the **DNA double-helix**.

6) DNA was first observed in the 1800s, but lots of scientists at the time **doubted** that it could carry the **genetic code** because it has a **relatively simple chemical composition**. Some argued that genetic information must be carried by **proteins** — which are much more **chemically varied**.

7) By 1953, experiments had shown that DNA was the carrier of the genetic code. This was also the year in which the **double-helix structure**, which helps DNA to carry out its function, was determined by **Watson** and **Crick**.

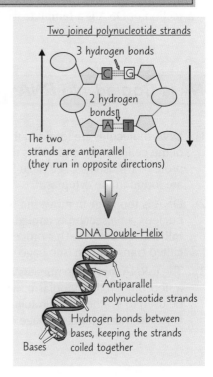

Two joined polynucleotide strands

3 hydrogen bonds

C · · · G

2 hydrogen bonds

A · · T

The two strands are antiparallel (they run in opposite directions)

DNA Double-Helix

Antiparallel polynucleotide strands

Bases

Hydrogen bonds between bases, keeping the strands coiled together

Practice Questions

Q1 Name the bases in RNA.

Q2 Describe the structure of DNA.

Exam Questions

Q1 The bar chart shows the percentage of the bases in a DNA sample that are adenine and cytosine. On the chart, draw bars to show the percentages of thymine and guanine in the sample. [2 marks]

Q2 a) Describe how mononucleotides are joined together in DNA. [2 marks]

b) Describe how two single polynucleotide strands are joined to make a DNA double helix. [3 marks]

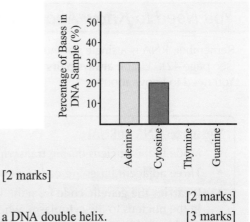

Give me a D, give me an N, give me an A! What do you get? — confused...

You need to learn the structures of DNA and RNA as well as the mononucleotides that make them up. Remember that RNA is made up of a single polynucleotide strand, whereas DNA is made up of two strands joined by hydrogen bonds.

The Genetic Code and Protein Synthesis

You need to know how DNA is used to carry information — and how that information gets turned into proteins. Luckily for you, it's all here over the next few pages...

DNA Contains **Genes** Which are **Instructions** for **Making Proteins**

1) A **gene** is a sequence of **mononucleotide bases** on a DNA molecule that codes for the sequence of **amino acids** in a **polypeptide**. The sequence of **amino acids** in a polypeptide forms the **primary structure** of a **protein** (see page 36).

2) Different proteins have a **different number** and **order** of amino acids.

3) It's the **order** of **mononucleotide bases** in a gene that determines the **order of amino acids** in a particular **protein**.

4) Each amino acid is coded for by a sequence of **three bases** (called a **triplet**) in a gene.

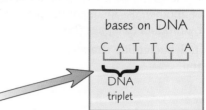

5) **Different sequences** of bases code for **different amino acids**. So the **sequence of bases** in a section of DNA is a **template** that's used to make **proteins** during **protein synthesis**.

DNA is **Copied** into **RNA** for **Protein Synthesis**

1) DNA molecules are found in the **nucleus** of the cell, but the organelles that make proteins (**ribosomes**, see page 59) are found in the **cytoplasm**.

2) DNA is **too large** to move out of the nucleus, so a section is **copied** into **mRNA** (see below). This process is called **transcription** (see page 46).

3) The mRNA **leaves** the nucleus and joins with a ribosome in the cytoplasm, where it can be used to synthesise a protein. This process is called **translation** (see page 47).

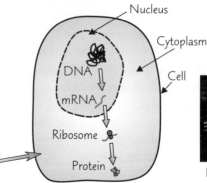

Rita Some knew how to synthesise some great tunes.

You Need to **Know** About **Two Types** of **RNA**

Remember, RNA is a **single** polynucleotide strand and it contains **uracil (U)** as a base instead of thymine (see page 42). Uracil **always pairs** with **adenine** during protein synthesis. RNA isn't all the same though. You need to know about:

Messenger RNA (mRNA)
- Made in the **nucleus** during **transcription**.
- **Three adjacent bases** are called a **codon**.
- It **carries the genetic code** from the DNA in the **nucleus** to the **cytoplasm**, where it's used to make a **protein** during **translation**.

Transfer RNA (tRNA)
- Found in the **cytoplasm**.
- It has an **amino acid binding site** at one end and a **sequence of three bases** at the other end called an **anticodon**.
- It **carries** the amino acids that are used to make **proteins** to the **ribosomes** during **translation**.

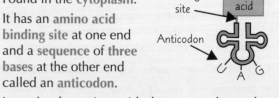

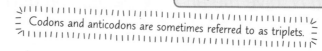
Codons and anticodons are sometimes referred to as triplets.

The Genetic Code and Protein Synthesis

The Genetic Code is Non-Overlapping and Degenerate

1) The genetic code is the **sequence of base triplets (codons)** in **DNA** or **mRNA**, which **codes** for **specific amino acids**.

2) In the genetic code, each base triplet is **read** in sequence, **separate** from the triplet **before** it and **after** it. Base triplets **don't share** their **bases** — the code is **non-overlapping**.

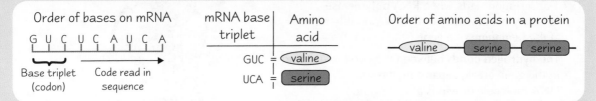

3) The genetic code is also **degenerate** — there are **more** possible combinations of **triplets** than there are amino acids (20 amino acids but 64 possible triplets). This means that some **amino acids** are coded for by **more than one** base triplet, e.g. tyrosine can be coded for by UAU or UAC.

4) Some triplets are used to tell the cell when to **start** and **stop** production of the protein — these are called **start** and **stop codons** (or start and stop signals). They're found at the **beginning** and **end** of the gene. E.g. UAG is a stop codon.

Practice Questions

Q1 What is a gene?

Q2 What is the function of mRNA?

Q3 Why is the genetic code described as degenerate?

Exam Questions

Q1 Which of the following is **not** a correct description of tRNA?

   A It has an amino acid binding site.

   B It contains the bases adenine, guanine, cytosine and uracil.

   C The process by which it is made is called transcription.

   D It carries amino acids to the ribosomes during translation.   [1 mark]

Q2 A piece of mRNA has the sequence: GUGUGUCGCGCA.

   a) How many amino acids does this sequence code for?   [1 mark]

   b) Using the table on the right, give the
       amino acid sequence it codes for.   [2 marks]

mRNA codon	amino acid
UGU	Cysteine
CGC	Arginine
GGG	Glycine
GUG	Valine
GCA	Alanine
UUG	Leucine
UUU	Phenylalanine

Q3 An artificial mRNA was synthesized to code for a particular protein. Part of the mRNA sequence was: UUGUGUGGGUUUGCAGCA. This produced the following sequence of amino acids: Leucine–Cysteine–Glycine–Phenylalanine–Alanine–Alanine. Use the table above to help you answer the following questions.

   a) Explain how the result suggests that the genetic code is based on triplets of mononucleotides in mRNA. [2 marks]

   b) Explain how the result suggests that the genetic code is non-overlapping.   [2 marks]

Genes contain instructions — wash at 40 °C...

You really need to get your head around how DNA and RNA work together to produce proteins, or the next two pages are going to be a teeeny weeny bit tricky. Don't say I didn't warn you. Turn over too quickly at your own peril...

Transcription and Translation

Time to find out how RNA works its magic to make proteins. It gets a bit complicated but bear with it.

First Stage of Protein Synthesis — Transcription

During transcription an **mRNA copy** of a gene
(a section of DNA) is made in the **nucleus**:

1) Transcription starts when **RNA polymerase**
(an **enzyme**) **attaches** to the **DNA** double-helix
at the **beginning** of a gene (start codon).

2) The **hydrogen bonds** between the two DNA strands
in the gene **break**, **separating** the strands, and the
DNA molecule **unwinds** at that point.

3) One of the strands is then used as a **template**
to make an **mRNA copy**.

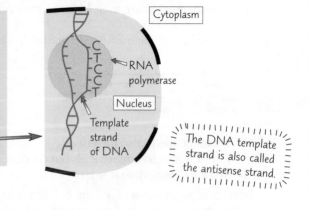

The DNA template strand is also called the antisense strand.

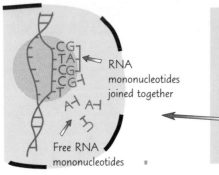

RNA mononucleotides joined together

Free RNA mononucleotides

4) The RNA polymerase **lines up** free **RNA mononucleotides**
alongside the template strand. **Complementary base pairing** means
that the mRNA strand ends up being a **complementary** copy of the
DNA template strand (except the base **T** is replaced by **U** in **RNA**).

5) Once the RNA mononucleotides have **paired up**
with their **specific bases** on the DNA strand
they're **joined together** by **RNA polymerase**,
forming an **mRNA molecule**.

DNA
triplet A T C

codon
on mRNA U A G

In eukaryotes, it's actually a complex of proteins including a DNA helicase that separates the strands. RNA polymerase just assembles the mRNA strand.

6) The RNA polymerase moves **along**
the DNA, separating the strands and
assembling the mRNA strand.

7) The **hydrogen bonds** between the unwound
strands of DNA **re-form** once the RNA
polymerase has passed by and the strands
wind back up into a double-helix.

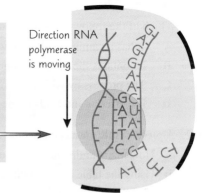

Direction RNA polymerase is moving

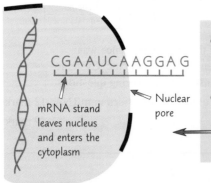

mRNA strand leaves nucleus and enters the cytoplasm

Nuclear pore

8) When RNA polymerase reaches a **stop codon**
(see previous page) it stops making mRNA
and **detaches** from the DNA.

9) The **mRNA** moves **out** of the **nucleus** through
a **nuclear pore** and attaches to a **ribosome** in
the cytoplasm, where the next stage of protein
synthesis takes place (see next page).

Transcription and Translation

Second Stage of Protein Synthesis — Translation

Translation occurs at the **ribosomes** in the **cytoplasm**. During **translation**, **amino acids** are **joined together** to make a **polypeptide chain** (protein), following the sequence of **codons** carried by the mRNA.

1) The **mRNA attaches** itself to a **ribosome** and **transfer RNA (tRNA)** molecules **carry amino acids** to the ribosome.

2) A tRNA molecule, with an **anticodon** that's **complementary** to the **start codon** on the ⟹ mRNA, attaches itself to the mRNA by **complementary base pairing**.

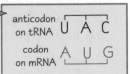

3) A second tRNA molecule attaches itself to the **next codon** on the mRNA in the **same way**.

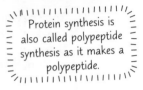

4) The two amino acids attached to the tRNA molecules are then **joined** together by a **peptide bond**. The first tRNA molecule **moves away**, leaving its amino acid behind.

5) The ribosome **moves** along to the **next codon**.

6) A third tRNA molecule binds to that codon on the mRNA. Its amino acid **binds** to the first two and the second tRNA molecule **moves away**.

Protein synthesis is also called polypeptide synthesis as it makes a polypeptide.

7) This process continues, producing a chain of linked amino acids (a **polypeptide chain**), until there's a **stop codon** on the mRNA molecule.

8) The polypeptide chain **moves away** from the ribosome and translation is complete.

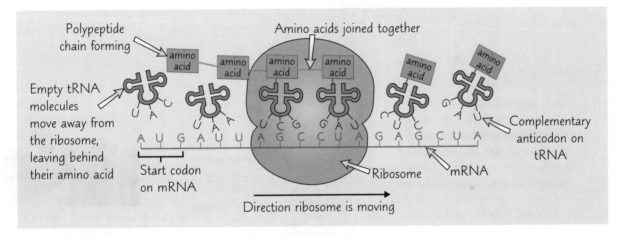

Practice Questions

Q1 What are the two stages of protein synthesis called?

Q2 Where does the first stage of protein synthesis take place?

Q3 When does RNA polymerase stop making mRNA?

Q4 Where does the second stage of protein synthesis take place?

Exam Questions

Q1 A DNA sequence is GCGAAGTCCATG.
   a) Give the complementary mRNA sequence. [1 mark]
   b) Give the sequence of the tRNA anticodons. [1 mark]

Q2 A drug that inhibits cell growth is found to be able to bind to DNA, preventing RNA polymerase from binding. Explain how this drug will affect protein synthesis. [2 marks]

Q3 A polypeptide chain (protein) from a eukaryotic cell is 10 amino acids long. Predict how long the mRNA for this protein would be in mononucleotides. Explain your answer. [2 marks]

I could do with a translation for this page...

So you start off with DNA, lots of cleverness happens and bingo... you've got a protein. Only problem is you need to know the cleverness bit in quite a lot of detail. So scribble it down, recite it to yourself, explain it to your best mate or do whatever else helps you remember the joys of protein synthesis. And then think how clever you are to know it all.

Replication of DNA

DNA has the amazing ability to replicate (copy) itself. These pages cover the facts behind the replication mechanism, as well as some of the history behind its discovery. This stuff is really clever. Honest.

DNA Replicates by **Semi-Conservative** Replication

DNA **copies** itself **before** cell division (see page 66) so that each **new** cell has the **full** amount of **DNA**. The method is called **semi-conservative replication** because **half** of the strands in **each new DNA molecule** are from the **original** DNA molecule. This means that there's **genetic continuity** between generations of cells (i.e. the cells produced by cell division inherit their genes from their parent cells).

1) The enzyme **DNA helicase** **breaks** the **hydrogen bonds** between bases on the two **polynucleotide** DNA strands. This makes the helix **unwind** to form two single strands.

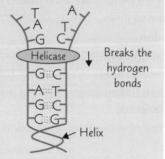

Breaks the hydrogen bonds

See p. 42-43 for more on DNA structure.

2) Each **original** single strand acts as a **template** for a new strand. **Complementary base pairing** means that **free-floating DNA nucleotides** are attracted to their complementary **exposed bases** on each original template strand — A with T and C with G.

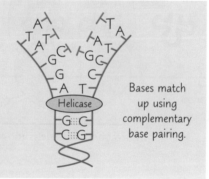

Bases match up using complementary base pairing.

Gerald doesn't need helicase to unwind. He just needs a beach full of seals.

3) **Condensation reactions** join the nucleotides of the new strands together — catalysed by the enzyme **DNA polymerase**. Hydrogen bonds **form** between the bases on the original and new strands.

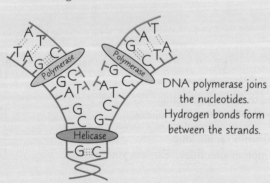

DNA polymerase joins the nucleotides. Hydrogen bonds form between the strands.

4) Each new DNA molecule contains **one strand** from the **original** DNA molecule and one **new strand**.

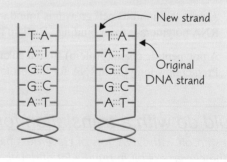

New strand

Original DNA strand

Replication of DNA

Meselson and Stahl *Provided* Evidence *for* Semi-Conservative Replication

1) Before **Meselson** and **Stahl's** experiment (see below), people were unsure whether DNA replication was **semi-conservative** or **conservative**. If the method was **conservative**, the original DNA strands would **stay together** and the new DNA molecules would contain **two new strands**.

2) Meselson and Stahl showed that DNA is replicated using the **semi-conservative method**. Their experiment used two **isotopes** of **nitrogen** (DNA contains nitrogen) — **heavy** nitrogen (^{15}N) and **light** nitrogen (^{14}N). Here's how it worked:

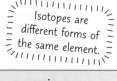
Isotopes are different forms of the same element.

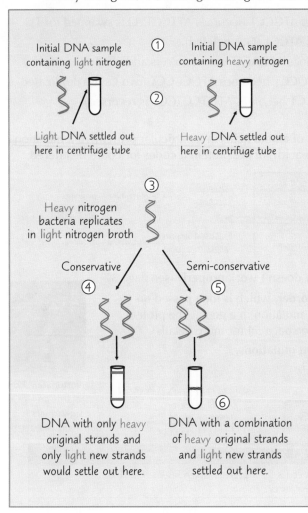

Initial DNA sample containing light nitrogen ①

Light DNA settled out here in centrifuge tube

②

Initial DNA sample containing heavy nitrogen

Heavy DNA settled out here in centrifuge tube

③

Heavy nitrogen bacteria replicates in light nitrogen broth

Conservative ④ Semi-conservative ⑤

⑥

DNA with only heavy original strands and only light new strands would settle out here.

DNA with a combination of heavy original strands and light new strands settled out here.

1) Two samples of bacteria were grown — one in a nutrient broth containing **light** nitrogen, and one in a broth with **heavy** nitrogen. As the **bacteria reproduced**, they **took up nitrogen** from the broth to help make nucleotides for new DNA. So the nitrogen gradually became part of the bacteria's DNA.

2) A **sample of DNA** was taken from each batch of bacteria, and spun in a **centrifuge**. The DNA from the **heavy** nitrogen bacteria settled **lower** down the **centrifuge tube** than the DNA from the **light** nitrogen bacteria — because it's **heavier**.

3) Then the bacteria grown in the **heavy** nitrogen broth were **taken out** and put in a broth containing only **light** nitrogen. The bacteria were left for **one round of DNA replication**, and then **another DNA sample** was taken out and spun in the centrifuge.

4) If replication was **conservative**, the original **heavy** DNA, which would still be together, would settle at the bottom and the new **light** DNA would settle at the top.

5) If replication was **semi-conservative**, the new bacterial DNA molecules would contain **one strand** of the **old** DNA containing **heavy** nitrogen and **one strand** of **new** DNA containing **light** nitrogen. So the DNA would settle out **between** where the **light** nitrogen DNA settled out and where the **heavy** nitrogen DNA settled out.

6) As it turned out, the DNA settled out in the **middle**, showing that the DNA molecules contained a **mixture** of **heavy** and **light** nitrogen. The bacterial DNA had **replicated semi-conservatively** in the **light** nitrogen.

Practice Questions

Q1 What is the role of DNA helicase in DNA replication?

Q2 What's the key difference between the conservative and semi-conservative theories of DNA replication?

Exam Question

Q1 a) Describe the process of semi-conservative DNA replication. [5 marks]

b) Describe Meselson and Stahl's experiment to prove the semi-conservative replication of DNA. [4 marks]

c) Explain how the experiment supports semi-conservative replication and refutes competing theories. [2 marks]

DNA DNA Replication Replication is is Semi-Conservative Semi-Conservative

Make sure you can recall the mechanism of DNA replication — you might be asked for it in your exam. You might also be asked to describe Meselson and Stahl's classic experiment, and also to explain how it provided support for the theory of semi-conservative replication of DNA. Don't turn over until you've got these things firmly wedged in your brain.

Genes and Inheritance

*Time to learn about genetic disorders — inherited disorders caused by abnormal genes or chromosomes.
But first you need to understand how these disorders arise and learn a load of genetic terms — will the fun ever stop...*

Some **Genetic Disorders** are **Caused** by **Mutations**

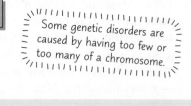
Some genetic disorders are caused by having too few or too many of a chromosome.

1) Mutations are **changes** to the **base sequence** of DNA.
2) They can be caused by **errors** during **DNA replication**.
3) The **type** of errors that can occur include:

> **Substitution** — one base is substituted with another, e.g. ATGCCT becomes ATTCCT (G is **swapped** for T).
> **Deletion** — one base is deleted, e.g. ATGCCT becomes ATCCT (G is **deleted**).
> **Insertion** — an extra base is added, e.g. ATGCCT becomes ATGACCT (an extra A is **added**).
> **Duplication** — one or more bases are repeated, e.g. ATGCCT becomes ATGCCCCT (two Cs are **duplicated**).
> **Inversion** — a sequence of bases is reversed, e.g. ATGCCT becomes ATGTCC (CCT is **reversed**).

4) The **order** of **DNA bases** in a gene determines the **order of amino acids** in a particular **protein**. If a mutation occurs in a gene, the **primary structure** (the sequence of amino acids) of the protein it codes for could be **altered**:

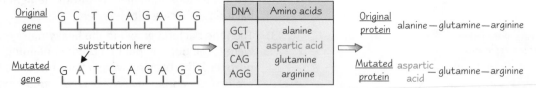

This could **change** the final **3D shape** of the protein so it **doesn't work properly** (see page 37).

5) If a mutation occurs in a **gene** it can cause a **genetic disorder**, which is then **passed on**.
E.g. **cystic fibrosis** (**CF**) is a genetic disorder caused by a mutation in a gene. The protein the gene codes for is important for **mucus production** (see page 54 for more details).

6) Some genetic disorders can be caused by lots of **different mutations**, e.g. over 1000 possible mutations are known to cause CF.

Unfortunately, liking leotards and '80s legwarmers is a dominant characteristic.

You **Need to Know** These **Genetic Terms**

There's more on genes on p. 44.

TERM	DESCRIPTION
Gene	A sequence of bases on a DNA molecule that codes for a protein, which results in a characteristic, e.g. the gene for eye colour.
Allele	A different version of a gene. Most plants and animals, including humans, have two copies of each gene, one from each parent. The two copies can be the same or they can be different. Different versions (alleles) have slightly different base sequences, which code for different versions of the same characteristic, e.g. brown eyes and blue eyes. They're represented using letters, e.g. the allele for brown eyes (B) and the allele for blue eyes (b).
Genotype	The alleles a person has, e.g. BB, Bb or bb for eye colour.
Phenotype	The characteristics displayed by an organism, e.g. brown eyes.
Dominant	An allele whose characteristic appears in the phenotype even when there's only one copy, e.g. the allele for brown eyes (B) is dominant — if a person's genotype is Bb or BB, they'll have brown eyes. Dominant alleles are shown by a capital letter.
Recessive	An allele whose characteristic only appears in the phenotype if two copies are present, e.g. the allele for blue eyes (b) is recessive — if a person's genotype is bb, they'll have blue eyes. Recessive alleles are shown by a lower case letter.
Incomplete Dominance	When the trait from a dominant allele isn't completely shown over the trait produced by the recessive allele, so both alleles influence the phenotype. Some flowers show incomplete dominance, e.g. snapdragons can have alleles for red flowers (RR), white flowers (rr) or pink flowers (Rr).
Homozygote	An organism that carries two copies of the same allele for a certain characteristic, e.g. BB or bb.
Heterozygote	An organism that carries two different alleles for a certain characteristic, e.g. Bb.
Carrier	If a recessive allele can cause disease, a carrier is someone who has one dominant and one recessive allele (heterozygous). They won't have the disease but they carry a copy of the allele for the disease.

Genes and Inheritance

Genetic Diagrams show the Possible Alleles of Offspring

Monohybrid inheritance is the inheritance of a **single characteristic** controlled by **different** alleles. **Genetic diagrams** can be used to predict the **genotypes** and **phenotypes** of the **offspring** produced if two parents are **crossed** (**bred**). You need to be able to **interpret** genetic diagrams for characteristics, so here's an example:

Plant Height

1) The **height** of garden pea plants is controlled by a **single** gene with **two alleles**.
2) The allele for **tall** plants (T) is **dominant** over the allele for **dwarf** plants (t).
3) The diagrams below show the predicted genotypes and phenotypes of the offspring if **two heterozygous** pea plants (**Tt**) are crossed, and if **two homozygous** pea plants (**TT** and **tt**) are crossed:

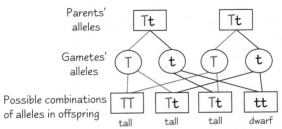

See page 68 for more on gametes.

Predicted genotypes and phenotypes:
- 2 in 4 (**50%**) **chance** of offspring having the **genotype Tt** (phenotype = **tall**).
- 1 in 4 (**25%**) chance of offspring having the **genotype TT** (phenotype = **tall**).
- 1 in 4 (**25%**) chance of offspring having the **genotype tt** (phenotype = **dwarf**).

The phenotypic ratio is just the ratio of different phenotypes in the offspring.

So there's a **75%** (3 in 4) chance of offspring being **tall**, and the **phenotypic ratio** of tall to dwarf plants is **3 : 1**.

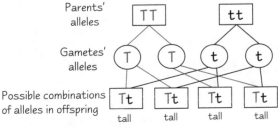

Predicted genotypes and phenotypes:
- 4 in 4 (**100%**) **chance** of offspring having the **genotype Tt** (phenotype = **tall**).
- 0 in 4 (**0%**) chance of offspring having the **genotype TT** (phenotype = **tall**).
- 0 in 4 (**0%**) chance of offspring having the **genotype tt** (phenotype = **dwarf**).

Practice Questions

Q1 What are mutations?

Q2 Explain the difference between a dominant and a recessive allele.

Q3 What is incomplete dominance?

Q4 What is monohybrid inheritance?

Exam Question

Q1 A garden pea plant is heterozygous for seed colour.
The allele for yellow colour (Y) is dominant over the allele for green colour (y).

a) Give the genotype and phenotype of the heterozygous plant. [2 marks]

b) Draw a genetic diagram to show the possible genotypes of the offspring produced if the heterozygous plant is crossed with a homozygous plant with green seeds. [3 marks]

c) Give the predicted ratio of green seeds to yellow seeds in the offspring from the genetic cross in part b). [1 mark]

What do you get if you cross a one-legged donkey with a one-eyed donkey?*

There's quite a lot to get to grips with on these two pages — that list of genetic terms just goes on and on and on. You won't get very far in this section without learning them first though, so just grin and bear it. Oh... and learn it of course.

* A winky wonky donkey.

The Chi-Squared Test

Just when you thought it was safe to turn the page... I stick in some maths. Surprise!

The **Chi-Squared Test** Can Be Used to **Check** the **Results** of **Genetic Crosses**

1) The **chi-squared** (χ^2) **test** is a **statistical test** that's used to see if the **results** of an experiment **support** a **theory**.
2) First, the theory is used to **predict** a **result** — this is called the **expected result**.
   Then, the experiment is carried out and the **actual result** is recorded — this is called the **observed result**.
3) To see if the results support the theory you have to make a **hypothesis** called the **null hypothesis**.
4) The null hypothesis is always that there's **no significant difference** between the observed and expected results (your experimental result will usually be a bit different from what you expect, but you need to know if the difference is just **due to chance**, or because your **theory is wrong**).
5) The χ^2 **test** is then carried out and the **outcome** either **supports** or **rejects** the **null hypothesis**.
6) You can use the χ^2 test in **genetics** to test theories about the **inheritance** of **characteristics**. For example:

> **Theory**: **Wing length** in fruit flies is controlled by a **single gene** with **two alleles (monohybrid inheritance)**. The **dominant** allele (N) gives **normal** wings, and the **recessive** allele (n) gives **vestigial** (little) wings.
>
> **Expected results**: With monohybrid inheritance, if you cross **two heterozygous** parents, you'd expect a **3 : 1 phenotypic ratio** of **normal : vestigial** wings in the offspring (see previous page).
>
> **Observed results**: The **experiment** (of crossing two heterozygous parents) is **carried out** on fruit flies and the **number of offspring** with normal and vestigial wings is **counted**.
>
> **Null hypothesis**: There's **no significant difference** between the observed and expected results. (If the χ^2 test shows the observed and expected results are **not significantly different** then we are **unable to reject** the null hypothesis — the data supports the **theory** that wing length is controlled by **monohybrid inheritance**.)

In this kind of statistical test, you can never prove that the null hypothesis is true — you can only 'fail to reject it'. This just means that the evidence doesn't give you a reason to think the null hypothesis is wrong.

First, **Work** Out the **Chi-Squared Value...**

Chi-squared (χ^2) is calculated using this formula: where **O** = **observed** result and **E** = **expected** result.

$$\chi^2 = \sum \frac{(O-E)^2}{E}$$

The best way to understand the χ^2 test is to work through an example — here's one for testing the **wing length** of **fruit flies** as explained above:

You don't need to learn the formula for chi-squared — it'll be given to you in the exam.

> **Heterozygous (Nn)** flies are **crossed** and **160 offspring** are produced.

① First, the **number of offspring** (out of a total of 160) **expected** for each phenotype is worked out. E for normal wings: 160 (total) ÷ 4 (ratio total) × 3 (predicted ratio for normal wings) = 120. E for vestigial wings: 160 ÷ 4 × 1 = 40.

Phenotype	Ratio	Expected Result (E)	Observed Result (O)
Normal wings	3	120	
Vestigial wings	1	40	

② Then the **actual number** of offspring **observed** with each phenotype (out of the 160 offspring) is **recorded**, e.g. 111 with normal wings.

Phenotype	Ratio	Expected Result (E)	Observed Result (O)
Normal wings	3	120	111
Vestigial wings	1	40	49

③ The results are used to work out χ^2, taking it **one step at a time**:

(a) First calculate **O – E** (subtract the **expected result** from the **observed result**) for each phenotype. E.g. for normal wings: 111 – 120 = –9.

(b) Then the resulting numbers are **squared**, e.g. $9^2 = 81$.

(c) These figures are divided by the **expected results**, e.g. 81 ÷ 120 = 0.675.

Phenotype	Ratio	Expected Result (E)	Observed Result (O)	O – E	$(O-E)^2$	$\frac{(O-E)^2}{E}$
Normal wings	3	120	111	–9	81	0.675
Vestigial wings	1	40	49	9	81	2.025
					$\sum\frac{(O-E)^2}{E} =$	2.7

Remember, you need to work it out for each phenotype first, then add all the numbers together.

(d) Finally, the numbers are **added** together to get χ^2, e.g. 0.675 + 2.025 = **2.7**.

The Chi-Squared Test

...Then *Compare* it to the *Critical Value*

1) To find out if there is a **significant difference** between your observed and expected results you need to **compare** your χ^2 **value** to a **critical value**.

2) The critical value is the value of χ^2 that corresponds to a 0.05 (**5%**) level of **probability** that the **difference** between the observed and expected results is **due to chance**.

3) If your χ^2 value is **larger** than or equal to the critical value then there **is a significant difference** between the observed and expected results (something **other than chance** is causing the difference) — and the **null hypothesis** can be **rejected**.

4) If your χ^2 value is **smaller** than the critical value then there **is no significant difference** between the observed and expected results — the null hypothesis **can't be rejected**. E.g. for the example on the previous page the χ^2 value is **2.7**, which is **smaller** than the critical value of **3.84** (see table below) — there's **no significant difference** between the observed and expected results. We've failed to reject the null hypothesis, so the **theory** that wing length in fruit flies is controlled by **monohybrid inheritance** is **supported**.

5) In the exam you might be **given** the **critical value** or asked to **work it out** from a **table**:

Using a χ^2 table:

If you're not given the critical value, you may have to find it yourself from a χ^2 **table** — this shows a range of **probabilities** that correspond to different **critical values** for different **degrees of freedom** (explained below). Biologists normally use a **probability** level of **0.05** (5%), so you only need to look in that column.

- First, the **degrees of freedom** for the experiment are worked out — this is the **number of classes** (number of phenotypes) **minus one**. E.g. 2 – 1 = 1.
- Next, the **critical value** corresponding to a **probability** of **0.05** at **one degree of freedom** is found in the table — here it's **3.84**.
- Then just **compare** your χ^2 value of **2.7** to this critical value, as explained above.

degrees of freedom	no. of classes	Critical values					
1	2	0.46	1.64	2.71	3.84	6.64	10.83
2	3	1.39	3.22	4.61	5.99	9.21	13.82
3	4	2.37	4.64	6.25	7.82	11.34	16.27
4	5	3.36	5.99	7.78	9.49	13.28	18.47
probability that result is due to chance only		0.50 (50%)	0.20 (20%)	0.10 (10%)	0.05 (5%)	0.01 (1%)	0.001 (0.1%)

Fisher, Statistical tables for Biological, Agricultural & Medical Research, 1st Ed. © 1930 p47. Reprinted by permission of Pearson Education Inc., New York, New York.

Practice Questions

Q1 What is a χ^2 test used for?

Q2 How do you tell if the difference between your observed and expected results is due to chance?

Exam Question

Q1 A scientist comes up with the following theory:

> 'Height in plants is controlled by a single gene with two alleles. The dominant allele gives tall plants. The recessive allele gives dwarf plants.'

The scientist predicts that if this theory is true, when two heterozygous plants are crossed, a 3 : 1 ratio of tall : dwarf plants will be produced. The scientist then comes up with a null hypothesis and carries out the cross. Of the 52 offspring produced, 9 were dwarf.

a) What should the scientist's null hypothesis be? [1 mark]

b) The formula for calculating chi-squared is: $\chi^2 = \Sigma \dfrac{(O - E)^2}{E}$

The critical value at one degree of freedom at a probability level of 0.05 is 3.84.
Use the chi-squared test to explain whether the results of the scientist's experiment support his theory. [4 marks]

The expected result of revising these pages — boredom...

...the observed result — boredom (except for the maths geeks among you). Don't worry if you're not brilliant at maths though, you don't have to be to do the chi-squared test — just make sure you know the steps above off by heart.

Cystic Fibrosis

As you enjoyed the genetic diagrams on p. 51 so much, here are some more, only this time they're slightly different.

Genetic Pedigree Diagrams Show How Traits Run in Families

Genetic pedigree diagrams show an **inherited trait** (characteristic) in a group of **related individuals**.
You need to be able to **interpret** genetic pedigree diagrams, so here are some examples for cystic fibrosis:

Cystic fibrosis (CF) is an inherited disorder that mainly affects the
respiratory, **digestive** and **reproductive systems** (see next page).
It's caused by a **recessive** allele (f), so a person will only have the disorder if they're
homozygous for the allele (ff) — they must inherit one recessive allele **from each
parent**. If a person is **heterozygous** (Ff), they **won't** have CF but they'll be a **carrier**.

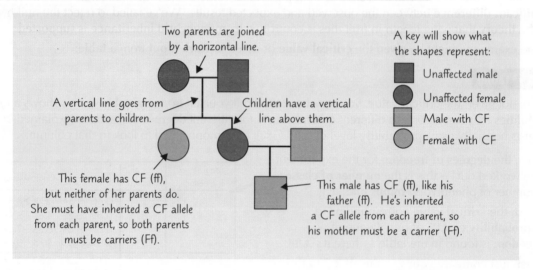

Two parents are joined by a horizontal line.

A vertical line goes from parents to children.

Children have a vertical line above them.

This female has CF (ff), but neither of her parents do. She must have inherited a CF allele from each parent, so both parents must be carriers (Ff).

This male has CF (ff), like his father (ff). He's inherited a CF allele from each parent, so his mother must be a carrier (Ff).

A key will show what the shapes represent:

■ Unaffected male
● Unaffected female
■ Male with CF
● Female with CF

Sometimes carriers are also shown on the key:

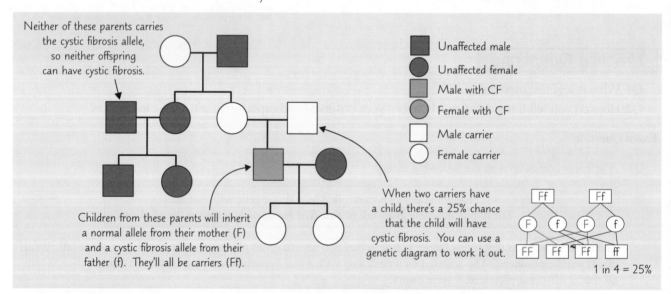

Neither of these parents carries the cystic fibrosis allele, so neither offspring can have cystic fibrosis.

■ Unaffected male
● Unaffected female
■ Male with CF
● Female with CF
□ Male carrier
○ Female carrier

Children from these parents will inherit a normal allele from their mother (F) and a cystic fibrosis allele from their father (f). They'll all be carriers (Ff).

When two carriers have a child, there's a 25% chance that the child will have cystic fibrosis. You can use a genetic diagram to work it out.

Ff   Ff
F f F f
FF Ff Ff ff

1 in 4 = 25%

Cystic Fibrosis Causes the Production of Thick Sticky Mucus

1) Cystic fibrosis is caused by a **mutation** in the **gene** that codes for the **CFTR** protein (**C**ystic **F**ibrosis **T**ransmembrane Conductance **R**egulator).

See page 31 for more on osmosis.

2) CFTR is a **channel protein** (see page 32). It transports **chloride ions** out of cells and into mucus — this causes water to move **into** the mucus by **osmosis**, which makes mucus **watery**.

3) **Mutant** CFTR protein is much **less efficient** at transporting chloride ions **out** of the cell, so **less water moves out by osmosis**. This makes the mucus of people with CF abnormally **thick** and **sticky**.

4) This thick and sticky mucus causes **problems** in the **respiratory**, **digestive** and **reproductive systems**.

Cystic Fibrosis

Cystic Fibrosis Affects the **Respiratory System**...

Everybody has **mucus** in their respiratory system — it helps **prevent lung infections** by trapping **microorganisms**. The mucus (with the microorganisms) is transported towards the throat by **cilia** (small **hair-like** structures that beat to move mucus along). In people with CF the mucus is abnormally **thick** and **sticky**, which causes some problems:

1) The cilia are **unable** to **move** the mucus towards the throat because it's so thick and sticky.
2) This means the **mucus builds up** in the **airways**.
3) Some airways can become completely **blocked** by the mucus — **gas exchange** can't take place in the area **below the blockage**.
4) This means that the **surface area** available for gas exchange is **reduced**, causing breathing difficulties.
5) People with CF are also more prone to **lung infections** as mucus containing microorganisms can't be removed.

See page 28 for more on gas exchange in the lungs.

People with CF can be given **antibiotics** to **kill** the **bacteria** trapped in mucus, and they can also have **physiotherapy** to help dislodge mucus and **improve gas exchange**.

...the **Digestive System**...

Everyone also has mucus in their digestive system. The abnormally thick mucus produced by people with CF can also cause **digestive problems** because:

1) The **tube** that connects the **pancreas** to the **small intestine** can become **blocked** with mucus — preventing **digestive enzymes** produced by the pancreas from **reaching** the small intestine. This reduces the ability of someone with CF to **digest food** and so **fewer nutrients** can be absorbed.
2) The mucus can cause **cysts** (**growths**) to form in the **pancreas**. These **inhibit the production** of **enzymes**, which also reduces the ability to digest food and absorb nutrients.
3) The mucus **lining the small intestine** is **abnormally thick** — this inhibits the **absorption** of nutrients.

...and the **Reproductive System**

Mucus is also secreted by the reproductive system — it helps to **prevent infections** and **transport sex cells** (sperm or eggs). The thick and sticky mucus of people with CF causes problems here because:

1) In some men with CF, the **tubes** connecting the **testicles** (where sperm are produced) to the **penis** are **absent** and can become **blocked** by the thick mucus in others. So, any **sperm** produced **can't reach the penis**.
2) In women, thickened **cervical mucus** can **prevent** the sperm from **reaching the egg**. The sperm has to travel through this mucus to reach the egg — thick mucus reduces the **motility** of the sperm, reducing its chances of **making it** to the egg.

Practice Questions

Q1 What is a genetic pedigree diagram?
Q2 Why do people with cystic fibrosis have abnormally thick and sticky mucus?

Exam Question

Q1 The genetic pedigree diagram above shows the inheritance of cystic fibrosis (CF) in one family.

a) Name one female who is homozygous for the CF allele and one individual who is a carrier. [2 marks]

b) If James and Martha have another child, what is the chance it will have CF? Show your working. [3 marks]

c)* Explain the effect of CF on the digestive system. [6 marks]

* You will be assessed on the quality of your written response in this question.

Pedigree Diagram — because your dog's worth it...

Pedigree diagrams aren't as scary as they look, just work through them slowly. And remember, with recessive disorders affected individuals are always homozygous, so any children they have will always have at least one recessive allele.

Genetic Screening

Most genetic disorders can only be treated, not cured, so it's important to be able to screen for these conditions.

There are **Three Main Uses** of Genetic Screening

Genetic screening involves analysing **DNA** to see if it contains **alleles** for genetic disorders. The **three** main uses are:

1. Identification *of Carriers*

1) **Carrier testing** is offered to individuals with a **family history** of genetic disorders.
2) It shows whether people **without** a disorder **carry an allele** that can cause a disorder (e.g. CF).
3) Couples can be tested **before having children** to determine the **chances** of any **future** children having the disorder, e.g. if both parents are **carriers** there's a **25%** chance their child will have the disorder.
4) Carrier testing allows people to make **informed decisions** about things like **whether to have children** and whether to carry out **prenatal testing** if the woman is pregnant (see below).
5) Carrier testing raises **social** and **ethical issues**:

- Finding out you're a carrier may cause **emotional stress** or affect your ability to **find a partner**.
- The tests **aren't** always 100% **accurate** — they could give a **false result**. This means decisions could be based on **incorrect information**.
- Other genetic **abnormalities** may be found, which could cause **further stress**.
- There are concerns that the **results** of genetic tests could be used by **employers** or **life insurance companies** — resulting in **genetic discrimination**.

2. *Preimplantation Genetic Diagnosis (PGD)*

1) **PGD** is carried out on **embryos** produced by *in vitro* **fertilisation (IVF)**.
2) It involves **screening** embryos for genetic disorders **before** they're implanted into the woman.
3) The **advantages** of PGD are that it **reduces** the chance of having a baby with a genetic disorder — only embryos **without** the genetic disorders tested for will be implanted. Also, because it's performed **before implantation**, it avoids the issue of **abortion** that could be raised by **prenatal testing** (see below).
4) PGD also raises **social** and **ethical issues**:

- It can be used to find out **other characteristics** (e.g. **gender, eye colour**) — leading to concerns that **in the future**, embryos may be selected for other characteristics (**designer babies**).
- **False results** could provide **incorrect information**.

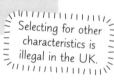

Selecting for other characteristics is illegal in the UK.

3. *Prenatal Testing*

1) Prenatal tests involve screening **unborn babies** (fetuses) for genetic disorders.
2) They're offered to pregnant women with a **family history** of genetic disease.
3) There are **two** types of test — **amniocentesis** and **chorionic villus sampling**.

Amniocentesis

1) This is usually carried out at **15-20 weeks** of pregnancy.
2) A sample of **amniotic fluid** (the fluid that surrounds the fetus) is obtained via the **abdomen** using a very fine **needle**.
3) This fluid contains fetal **cells**. The cells contain **DNA**, which can be **analysed**.
4) Amniocentesis has a **1% risk** of **miscarriage**.
5) Results aren't available until **2-3 weeks after** the sample is taken, although a **rapid test** (which only looks for a **few** of the **most common** disorders) can also be performed. The results of the rapid test are usually available in **3-4 days**.

Genetic Screening

Chorionic Villus Sampling (CVS)

1) CVS is usually performed at **11-14 weeks** of pregnancy.

2) Because it can take place **earlier** in a pregnancy than amniocentesis, an earlier **decision** to abort can be made, meaning that the procedure is less physically traumatic.

3) A sample of **cells** is taken from the **chorionic villi** (part of the fetus that connects it to its mother). The cells contain fetal **DNA**, which can be **analysed**.

4) This procedure is done via either the **abdomen** (using a fine **needle**) or the **vagina** (using a **catheter** — a thin flexible tube).

5) CVS has a **1-2% risk** of **miscarriage**, which is greater than with amniocentesis.

6) **Initial** results (which tell you whether any **obvious major issues** have been found) are available in a **few days**, but the results of more **in-depth** and **detailed** tests can take **two weeks** or **more**.

Testing Allows People to **Make Decisions**

1) Prenatal testing allows parents to make **informed decisions**. If the test is positive, the parents may decide to **have the child** or to have an **abortion**. The results can also help parents to **prepare for the future care** of the child — any **medical treatment** available could be started as soon as the child is born.

2) As with the other forms of testing, prenatal testing raises **social** and **ethical issues**:

- Prenatal tests slightly **increase** the risk of **miscarriage**.
- **False results** could provide **incorrect information**.
- Some people consider it **unethical** to **abort** a fetus because it has a genetic disorder.

Practice Questions

Q1 What is genetic screening?

Q2 Describe one ethical issue raised by prenatal testing.

Exam Questions

Q1 Which of the following is true about chorionic villus sampling (CVS)?
- **A** It has a lower risk of miscarriage and can be carried out earlier than amniocentesis.
- **B** It has a higher risk of miscarriage and is carried out later than amniocentesis.
- **C** It has a higher risk of miscarriage and can be carried out earlier than amniocentesis.
- **D** It has a lower risk of miscarriage and is carried out later than amniocentesis. [1 mark]

Q2 Duchenne muscular dystrophy is a genetic disorder caused by a recessive allele. It is caused by a mutated gene, which normally codes for a protein needed for healthy muscle tissue.

a) Explain why an individual with a family history of Duchenne muscular dystrophy may be offered carrier testing. [3 marks]

b) Preimplantation genetic diagnosis is available for Duchenne muscular dystrophy.

   i) Explain what preimplantation genetic diagnosis is. [1 mark]

   ii) Describe one benefit of preimplantation genetic diagnosis. [1 mark]

   iii) Describe two social or ethical issues raised by preimplantation genetic diagnosis. [2 marks]

Carrier testing — which bag has the strongest handles?

There's lots to learn when it comes to genetic screening. You need to understand the three main uses, the implications of each, and all the possible ethical issues. As with any ethics question in the exam, don't forget to cover both the advantages and the issues surrounding it (whatever your personal opinion). Chin up, kettle on, and back to it.

Eukaryotic Cells and Organelles

Ah, cells. Where would we be without them? There are two types of cell — prokaryotic and eukaryotic. This topic is about eukaryotic cells and their organelles (all the tiny bits and bobs that you can only see in detail with a fancy microscope)...

Organisms Can be **Prokaryotes** or **Eukaryotes**

All living organisms are made of **cells** and share some **common features**.

1) Prokaryotic organisms are **prokaryotic cells** (i.e. they're single-celled organisms) and eukaryotic organisms are made up of **eukaryotic cells**.

2) Both types of cells contain **organelles**. Organelles are **parts** of cells — each one has a **specific function**.

3) If you examine a cell through an **electron microscope** (see page 62) you can see its **organelles** and the **internal structure** of most of them — this is known as the **cell ultrastructure**.

1) Eukaryotic cells are **complex** and include all **animal** and **plant cells**.

2) Prokaryotic cells are **smaller** and **simpler**, e.g. bacteria. See page 61 for more.

Animal Cells are *Eukaryotic*

Eukaryotic cells are generally a **bit more complicated** than prokaryotic cells. You've probably been looking at **animal cell** diagrams for years, so hopefully you'll be familiar with some of the bits and pieces...

Animal Cell

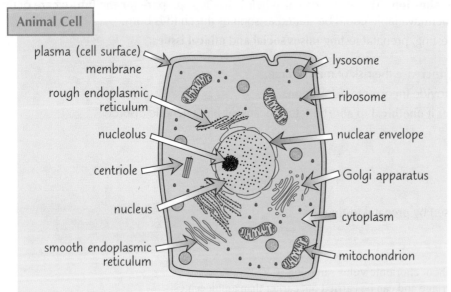

plasma (cell surface) membrane · rough endoplasmic reticulum · nucleolus · centriole · nucleus · smooth endoplasmic reticulum · lysosome · ribosome · nuclear envelope · Golgi apparatus · cytoplasm · mitochondrion

> Plant cells also contain these organelles, along with a few different organelles that aren't found in animal cells — see pages 90-91.

> You're expected to be able to recognise organelles from images taken through an electron microscope — so make sure you learn to recognise all the structures on pages 58-59.

Different Organelles Have *Different Functions*

This giant table contains a big list of organelles — you need to know the **structure** and **function** of them all. Sorry. Most organelles are surrounded by **membranes**, which sometimes causes confusion — don't make the mistake of thinking that a diagram of an organelle is a diagram of a whole cell. They're not cells — they're **parts of** cells.

ORGANELLE	DIAGRAM	DESCRIPTION	FUNCTION
Nucleus	nuclear envelope · nucleolus · nuclear pore · chromatin	A large organelle surrounded by a **nuclear envelope** (double membrane), which contains many **pores**. The nucleus contains **chromatin** (which is made from DNA and proteins) and a structure called the **nucleolus**.	The nucleus **controls the cell's activities** (by controlling the transcription of DNA — see page 46). DNA contains instructions to make proteins — see page 44. The **pores** allow substances (e.g. RNA) to move between the nucleus and the cytoplasm. The **nucleolus** makes **ribosomes** (see next page).

Eukaryotic Cells and Organelles

ORGANELLE	DIAGRAM	DESCRIPTION	FUNCTION
Lysosome		A **round organelle** surrounded by a **membrane**, with no clear internal structure.	Contains **digestive enzymes**. These are kept separate from the cytoplasm by the surrounding membrane, and can be used to **digest invading cells** or to **break down** worn out components of the cell.
Ribosome	small subunit / large subunit	A **very small organelle** that either **floats free** in the cytoplasm or is attached to the **rough endoplasmic reticulum**. It's made up of **proteins** and **RNA** (see page 42). It's **not** surrounded by a membrane.	The site where **proteins** are made.
Rough Endoplasmic Reticulum (RER)	ribosome / fluid	A system of membranes enclosing a fluid-filled space. The surface is **covered with ribosomes**.	**Folds** and **processes proteins** that have been made at the ribosomes.
Smooth Endoplasmic Reticulum (SER)		Similar to rough endoplasmic reticulum, but with no **ribosomes**.	**Synthesises** and **processes lipids**.
Golgi Apparatus	vesicle	A group of fluid-filled, membrane-bound, **flattened sacs**. Vesicles are often seen at the edges of the sacs.	It **processes** and **packages** new lipids and proteins. It also **makes lysosomes**.
Mitochondrion	outer membrane / inner membrane / crista / matrix	They're usually oval-shaped. They have a **double membrane** — the inner one is folded to form structures called **cristae**. Inside is the **matrix**, which contains enzymes involved in respiration.	The **site of aerobic respiration**, where **ATP** is produced. They're found in large numbers in cells that are very **active** and require a lot of **energy**.
Centriole	microtubule	Small, **hollow cylinders**, made of **microtubules** (tiny protein cylinders). Found in animal cells, but only some plant cells.	Involved with the **separation of chromosomes** during cell division (see page 66).

Eukaryotic Cells and Organelles

Organelles are Involved in Protein Production and Transport

1) Proteins are made at the **ribosomes**.

2) The ribosomes on the **rough endoplasmic reticulum (ER)** make proteins that are **excreted** or attached to the **cell membrane**. The free ribosomes in the **cytoplasm** make proteins that **stay in the cytoplasm**.

3) New proteins produced at the rough ER are **folded** and **processed** (e.g. sugar chains are added) in the rough ER.

4) Then they're **transported** from the ER to the **Golgi apparatus** in **vesicles**.

5) At the Golgi apparatus, the proteins may undergo **further processing** (e.g. sugar chains are trimmed or more are added).

6) The proteins enter more **vesicles** to be transported around the cell. E.g. **extracellular enzymes** (like digestive enzymes) move to the cell surface and are **secreted**.

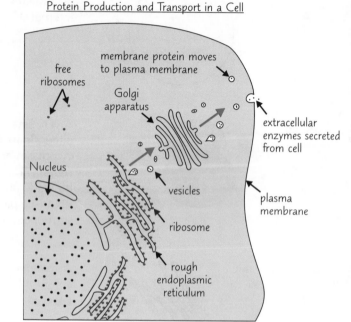

Protein Production and Transport in a Cell

Practice Questions

Q1 Describe the structure of a nucleus.

Q2 What is the function of lysosomes?

Q3 How does the structure of rough endoplasmic reticulum differ from that of smooth endoplasmic reticulum?

Q4 What is the function of the smooth endoplasmic reticulum?

Exam Questions

Q1 Which of the following describes an organelle that is involved in the separation of chromosomes?

    A A system of membranes enclosing a fluid-filled space. The surface is covered in ribosomes.

    B A small, hollow cylinder, made up of microtubules.

    C A small organelle consisting of two subunits. It is not surrounded by a membrane.

    D A round, membrane-bound organelle with no clear internal structure. [1 mark]

Q2 a) Identify these two organelles from their descriptions.

    i) An oval-shaped organelle surrounded by a double membrane. The inner membrane is folded and projects into the inner space, which is filled with a grainy material. [1 mark]

    ii) A collection of flattened membrane 'sacs' arranged roughly parallel to one another. Small, circular structures are seen at the edges of these 'sacs'. [1 mark]

    b) State the function of the two organelles that you have identified. [2 marks]

That's enough talk of fluid-filled sacs for my liking. Scientists eh...

'Organelle' is a very pretty-sounding name for all those blobs. Actually, under a microscope some of them are really quite fetching — well I think so anyway, but then my mate finds sheep fetching, so there's no accounting for taste. Anyway, you need to know the names of all the organelles and also what they look like.

Prokaryotic Cells

Now we're on to prokaryotic cells. They're much smaller than eukaryotic cells — and, luckily for both of us, so is the section on them in this book. Nevertheless, you need to know everything in it for your exams...

The Structure of **Prokaryotic** Cells is Different to **Eukaryotic** Cells

Remember, prokaryotic cells are **smaller** and **simpler** than eukaryotic cells (see page 58). **Bacteria** are examples of prokaryotic cells. You need to know the **structure** of a prokaryotic cell.

The **cytoplasm** of a prokaryotic cell has **no membrane-bound organelles** (unlike a eukaryotic cell). It has **ribosomes** — but they're **smaller** than those in a eukaryotic cell.

As with eukaryotic cells, the **plasma membrane** is mainly made of lipids and proteins (see p. 30). It controls the movement of substances into and out of the cell.

The **cell wall supports** the cell and prevents it from changing shape. It's made of a polymer called **murein**. Murein is a **glycoprotein** (a protein with a carbohydrate attached).

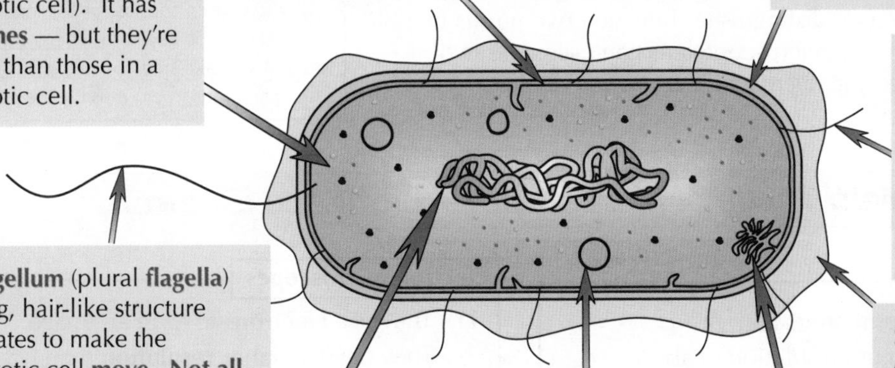

Some prokaryotes have short hair-like structures called **pili**. Pili help prokaryotes **stick** to other cells and can be used in the **transfer** of **genetic material** between cells.

The **flagellum** (plural **flagella**) is a long, hair-like structure that rotates to make the prokaryotic cell **move**. Not all prokaryotes have a flagellum. Some have **more than one**.

Some prokaryotes, e.g. bacteria, also have a **capsule** made up of secreted **slime**. It helps to **protect** bacteria from attack by cells of the immune system.

Unlike a eukaryotic cell, a prokaryotic cell **doesn't have** a nucleus. Instead, the **DNA** floats free in the cytoplasm. It's **circular DNA**, present as one long coiled-up strand. It's **not attached** to any **histone proteins** (see p. 77).

Plasmids are **small loops of DNA** that aren't part of the main circular DNA molecule. Plasmids contain genes for things like **antibiotic resistance**, and can be passed between prokaryotes. Plasmids are **not always** present in prokaryotic cells. **Some** prokaryotic cells have **several**.

Mesosomes are **inward folds** in the **plasma membrane**. Scientists are still debating what their **function** is. Some believe that they play a role in various **cellular processes** (e.g. respiration). However, others think that they're **not natural** features at all, and are just **artefacts** produced when the cells are being **prepared** for viewing with an **electron microscope**.

See pages 58-59 and 90-91 for more on organelles.

Practice Questions

Q1 What is a plasmid?
Q2 What is a flagellum?
Q3 What are pili?

Exam Questions

Q1 Which of the following structures can only be found in prokaryotic cells?
  A Cytoplasm **B** Plasma membrane **C** Pili **D** Ribosome [1 mark]

Q2 Describe two ways in which DNA can be stored in a prokaryotic cell. [2 marks]

Prokaryotes — in favour of a good take-away...

You need to know the structures in prokaryotic cells and how these differ from those in eukaryotic cells. Make sure you spend plenty of time memorising them (see page 58 for more on eukaryotic cells). You could even make a song...

Looking at Cells and Organelles

You can use microscopes to look at all the lovely organelles you've been learning about...

Magnification is Size, Resolution is Detail

We all know that microscopes produce a **magnified image** of a sample, but **resolution** is just as important...

1) MAGNIFICATION is how much **bigger** the image is than the specimen (the sample you're looking at). It's calculated using this formula:

$$\text{magnification} = \frac{\text{size of image}}{\text{size of real object}}$$

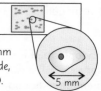

For example:
If you have a magnified image that's 5 mm wide and your specimen is 0.05 mm wide, the magnification is: 5 ÷ 0.05 = **× 100**.

2) RESOLUTION is how **detailed** the image is. More specifically, it's how well a microscope **distinguishes** between **two points** that are **close together**. If a microscope lens can't separate two objects, then increasing the magnification won't help.

> If you're given the size of the image and the size of the object in <u>different units</u> in the exam, make sure you <u>convert them</u> into the <u>same units</u> before using the formula.

There are Two Main Types of Microscope — Light and Electron

Light microscopes

1) They use **light** to form an image.
2) They have a maximum resolution of about **0.2 micrometres (μm)**. This means you can't use a light microscope to view organelles smaller than 0.2 μm. That includes **ribosomes**, the **endoplasmic reticulum** and **lysosomes**. You may be able to make out **mitochondria** — but not in perfect detail. You can also see the **nucleus**.
3) The maximum useful **magnification** of a light microscope is about × 1500.

Electron microscopes

1) They use **electrons** to form an image.
2) They have a **higher resolution** than light microscopes so give a **more detailed image** (and can be used to look at more organelles).
3) They have a maximum resolution of about **0.0002 micrometres (μm)**. (About 1000 times higher than light microscopes.)
4) The maximum useful **magnification** of an electron microscope is about **× 1 500 000**.

> A micrometre (μm) is three orders of magnitude smaller than a millimetre (1 μm = 0.001 mm). To convert from μm to mm, divide by 1000.

Electron Microscopes are either 'Scanning' or 'Transmission'

Transmission electron microscopes (TEMs)

1) TEMs use **electromagnets** to focus a **beam of electrons**, which is then transmitted **through** the specimen.
2) **Denser** parts of the specimen absorb **more electrons**, which makes them look **darker** on the image you end up with.
3) TEMs are good because they give **high resolution images**, so you see the **internal structure** of **organelles** like mitochondria.
4) But they can only be used on **thin specimens**.

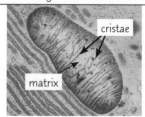

TEM image of a mitochondrion
cristae
matrix
K.R. PORTER/SCIENCE PHOTO LIBRARY

Scanning electron microscopes (SEMs)

1) SEMs **scan** a beam of electrons across the specimen. This **knocks off** electrons from the **specimen**, which are gathered in a **cathode ray tube** to form an **image**.
2) The images you end up with show the **surface** of the specimen and they can be **3D**.
3) SEMs are good because they can be used on **thick specimens**.
4) But they give **lower resolution images** than TEMs.

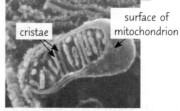

SEM image of a mitochondrion
cristae
surface of mitochondrion
PROFESSORS P. MOTTA & T. NAGURO/
SCIENCE PHOTO LIBRARY

Looking at Cells and Organelles

Here's How to Use an Eyepiece Graticule and Stage Micrometer...

1) Sometimes, you might want to know the **size** of your specimen. When you're using a light microscope, you can use an **eyepiece graticule** and **stage micrometer** to do this — they're a bit like **rulers**.

2) An **eyepiece graticule** is fitted onto the **eyepiece** (the bit that you look down). It's like a transparent ruler with **numbers**, but **no units**.

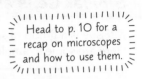
Head to p. 10 for a recap on microscopes and how to use them.

3) The **stage micrometer** is placed on the **stage** (the platform where you put your slide). It's a microscope slide with an **accurate scale** (it has units) and it's used to work out the **value** of the divisions on the **eyepiece graticule** at a **particular magnification**.

4) This means that when you take the stage micrometer away and replace it with the slide containing your specimen, you'll be able to **measure** the size of the specimen. Here's an **example**:

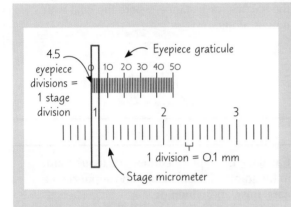

1) **Line up** the eyepiece graticule and the stage micrometer.
2) Each **division** on the stage micrometer is **0.1 mm** long.
3) At this magnification, **1 division** on the **stage micrometer** is the same as **4.5 divisions** on the **eyepiece graticule**.
4) To work out the size of **1 division** on the **eyepiece graticule**, you need to divide 0.1 by 4.5:
   1 division on eyepiece graticule = 0.1 ÷ 4.5 = **0.022 mm**
5) So if you look at an object under the microscope at this magnification and it's **20 eyepiece divisions** long, you know it measures:
   20 × 0.022 = **0.44 mm**

Remember: at a different magnification, 1 division on the stage micrometer will be equal to a different number of divisions on the eyepiece graticule — so the eyepiece graticule will need to be re-calibrated.

Practice Questions

Q1 What is the formula for calculating the magnification of an image?

Q2 How do you convert micrometers (μm) to millimetres (mm)?

Exam Questions

Q1 An insect is 0.5 mm long. In a book, a picture of the insect is 8 cm long.
Calculate the magnification of the image. [2 marks]

Q2 An image from a light microscope shows a human cheek cell at × 100 magnification.
The actual diameter of the cell is 59 μm. What is the diameter of the cell in the image? [2 marks]

Q3 The table shows the dimensions of some different organelles found in animal cells.

organelle	diameter / mm
lysosome	0.0001
mitochondrion	0.002
nucleus	0.005
ribosome	0.00002

a) Name those organelles in the table that would be visible using a good quality light microscope (max. resolution ≈ 0.2 μm)? [1 mark]

b) Which organelles would be visible using a transmission electron microscope (max. resolution ≈ 0.0002 μm)? [1 mark]

Q4 a) A microscope is set up with an eyepiece graticule and a stage micrometer. Each division on a stage micrometer is 10 μm long. At ×10 magnification, 1 division of the stage micrometer is equal to 6.5 divisions on the eyepiece graticule. Calculate the size of 1 division on the eyepiece graticule. Give your answer to the nearest 0.1 μm. [2 marks]

b) A specimen is viewed under this microscope at ×10 magnification. It is 14 eyepiece divisions long.
Use your answer to part a) to calculate the specimen's length. Give your answer to the nearest μm. [2 marks]

A light microscope is better than a heavy one — for your back anyway...

OK, there's quite a bit of info on these pages, but the whole magnification thing isn't all that bad once you've given it a go. Just make sure you can use the formula to work out magnification, the size of the image and the size of the real object. There's more maths to do when measuring the size of a specimen with a graticule. Good job you love maths.

Cell Organisation

Multicellular organisms are made up of lots of different cell types, which are organised to work together — cells that carry out the same job are organised into tissues (e.g. epithelium), different tissues are organised into organs (e.g. the lungs) and organs work together as organ systems (e.g. the respiratory system).

Similar Cells are Organised into Tissues

A **tissue** is a group of similar cells that are **specially adapted** to **work together** to carry out a particular function. Here are some examples:

1) <u>**Squamous epithelium**</u> is a **single layer** of **cells** lining a surface. It's found in many places, including the alveoli in the lungs.

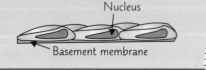

Epithelium is a tissue that forms a covering or a lining.

2) <u>**Ciliated epithelium**</u> is a layer of cells covered in **cilia** (tiny **hair-like** structures). It's found on surfaces where things need to be **moved** — in the trachea for instance, where the cilia waft mucus along.

3) <u>**Xylem tissue**</u> is a plant tissue with two jobs — it **transports water** around the plant, and it **supports** the plant. It contains **xylem vessel cells** and **parenchyma cells**.

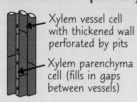

4) <u>**Cartilage**</u> is a type of **connective tissue** found in the **joints**. It also **shapes** and **supports** the **ears**, **nose** and **windpipe**.

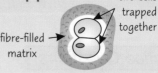

Tissues are Organised into Organs

An **organ** is a group of different tissues that **work together** to perform a particular function. Here are a couple of examples:

<u>The leaf</u> is an example of a plant organ. It's made up of the following **tissues:**
1) **Lower epidermis** — contains stomata (holes) to let air in and out for gas exchange.
2) **Spongy mesophyll** — full of spaces to let gases circulate.
3) **Palisade mesophyll** — most photosynthesis occurs here.
4) **Xylem** — carries water to the leaf.
5) **Phloem** — carries sugars away from the leaf.
6) **Upper epidermis** — covered in a waterproof waxy cuticle to reduce water loss.

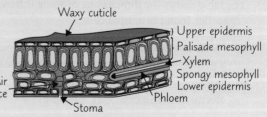

<u>The lungs</u> are an example of animal organs. They're made up of the following **tissues:**

1) **Squamous epithelium tissue** — surrounds the alveoli (where gas exchange occurs).
2) **Fibrous connective tissue** — helps to force air back out of the lungs when exhaling.
3) **Endothelium tissue** — makes up the wall of the capillaries, which surround the alveoli, and lines the larger blood vessels.

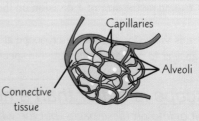

Cell Organisation

Different Organs *Make up an* Organ System

Organs work together to form **organ systems** — each system has a **particular function**.
Yup, you've guessed it, more examples:

1) The **respiratory system** is made up of all the organs, tissues and cells involved in **breathing**.
   The lungs, trachea, larynx, nose, mouth and diaphragm are all part of the respiratory system.

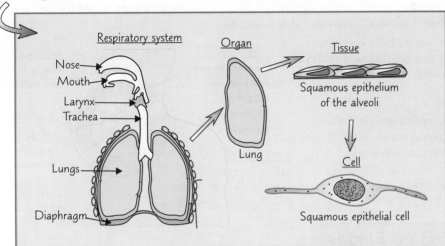

John and Fido —
working together as part
of an organ system.

2) The **circulatory system** is made up of the organs involved in **blood supply**.
   The heart, arteries, veins and capillaries are all parts of this system.

Practice Questions

Q1 Explain what is meant by the term tissue.

Q2 Name one organ found in plants and one organ found in animals.

Q3 Explain what is meant by the term organ system.

Exam Questions

Q1 The liver is made of hepatocyte cells, blood vessels (to provide nutrients and oxygen),
and connective tissue (that holds the liver together).
Is the liver best described as a tissue, organ or an organ system? Explain your answer.   [2 marks]

Q2 Which of the following statements about xylem tissue is correct?

   A Xylem tissue is made up of a group of specialised cells.

   B Xylem tissue is made up of a group of organs that work together.

   C Xylem tissue is made up of a group of tissues that perform a particular function.

   D Xylem tissue is made up of a group of organ systems.   [1 mark]

Q3 Squamous epithelium in the alveoli is made up of a single layer of flat cells.
Squamous epithelium tissue, fibrous connective tissue and endothelium tissue make up the lungs.
The lungs are part of the respiratory system.

Using the lungs as an example, describe how the cells of multicellular organisms
are organised in tissues, organs and organ systems.   [3 marks]

Soft and quilted — the best kind of tissues...

*So, similar cells group together to form tissues. Then, because they love being so helpful, tissues work together in
an organ to perform a particular function. But even organs are better together — along comes the organ system.
Mmmmmmmm it's always better when we're together... or something like that. You get the idea.*

The Cell Cycle and Mitosis

If it wasn't for cell division, we'd still only be one cell big. If it wasn't for pies, my favourite jeans would still fit.

Mitosis *is* Cell Division *that Produces* Genetically Identical Cells

There are two types of cell division in **eukaryotes** — **mitosis** and **meiosis** (see page 70 for more on meiosis).

1) In **mitosis** a **parent cell** divides to produce **two genetically identical daughter cells** (they contain an **exact copy** of the **DNA** of the parent cell).

2) Mitosis is needed for the **growth** of multicellular organisms (like us), for **repairing damaged tissues** and for **asexual reproduction** (reproduction from just one parent).

3) In multicellular organisms, not all cells keep their ability to divide. The ones that do, follow a **cell cycle**. Mitosis is part of the cell cycle:

> The cell cycle consists of a period of **cell growth** and **DNA replication** called **interphase**. Mitosis happens after that. Interphase (cell growth) is subdivided into three separate growth stages. These are called G_1, **S** and G_2.

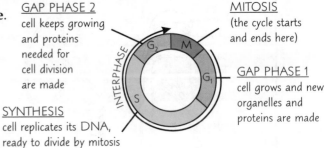

GAP PHASE 2
cell keeps growing and proteins needed for cell division are made

MITOSIS
(the cycle starts and ends here)

GAP PHASE 1
cell grows and new organelles and proteins are made

SYNTHESIS
cell replicates its DNA, ready to divide by mitosis

Mitosis *has* Four Division Stages

Mitosis is really one **continuous process**, but it's described as a series of **division stages** — prophase, metaphase, anaphase and telophase. **Interphase** comes **before** mitosis in the cell cycle.

Interphase — The cell carries out normal functions, but also prepares to divide. The cell's **DNA** is **unravelled** and **replicated**, to double its genetic content. The **organelles** are also **replicated** so it has spare ones, and its ATP content is increased (ATP provides the energy needed for cell division).

Cell
Chromosome
Cytoplasm
Nucleus
Centriole

Interphase

Unravelled DNA containing two copies of each chromosome

1) **Prophase** — The **chromosomes condense**, getting **shorter** and **fatter**. Tiny bundles of protein called **centrioles** start moving to opposite ends of the cell, forming a network of protein fibres across it called the **spindle**. The **nuclear envelope** (the membrane around the nucleus) **breaks down** and chromosomes lie free in the cytoplasm.

Centrioles move to opposite ends of the cell

Nuclear envelope starts to break down

Centromere

As mitosis begins, the chromosomes are made of two strands joined in the middle by a <u>centromere</u>. The separate strands are called <u>chromatids</u>. There are two strands because each chromosome has already made an <u>identical copy</u> of itself during <u>interphase</u>. When mitosis is over, the chromatids end up as one-strand chromosomes in the daughter cells.

One chromatid
Centromere
Sister chromatids

2) **Metaphase** — The chromosomes (each with two chromatids) **line up** along the middle of the cell and become **attached** to the **spindle** by their **centromere**.

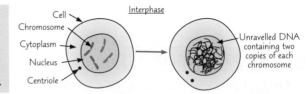

Spindle fibres

Centromeres on spindle equator

3) **Anaphase** — The **centromeres divide, separating** each pair of sister **chromatids**. The **spindles contract**, pulling chromatids to **opposite poles** (ends) of the spindle, centromere first. This makes the chromatids appear **v-shaped**.

Sister chromatids moving to opposite poles of the spindle

4) **Telophase** — The chromatids reach the **opposite poles** on the spindle. They **uncoil** and become **long** and **thin** again. They're now called **chromosomes** again. A **nuclear envelope** forms around each group of chromosomes, so there are now **two nuclei**. The **cytoplasm divides** (cytokinesis) and there are now **two daughter cells** that are **genetically identical** to the original cell and to each other. Mitosis is finished and each daughter cell starts the **interphase** part of the cell cycle to get ready for the next round of mitosis.

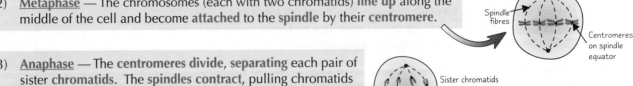

Centriole

Cytoplasm beginning to divide

The Cell Cycle and Mitosis

Root Tips Can be Stained and Squashed to Observe Mitosis

You need to know how to **prepare** and **stain** a **root tip** in order to observe the **stages of mitosis**. Make sure you're wearing **safety goggles** and a **lab coat** before you start. You should also wear **gloves** when using **stains**.

1) **Cut 1 cm** from the **tip** from a **growing root** (e.g. of an onion). It needs to be the **tip** because that's where **growth** occurs (and so that's where **mitosis** takes place). *If you're using ethano-orcein to stain the cells, the tips will also need to be fixed in ethanoic acid.*

> *Remind yourself how to prepare a slide on p. 10.*

2) **Prepare** a boiling tube containing **1 M hydrochloric acid** and put it in a **water bath** at **60 °C**.

3) **Transfer** the **root tip** into the **boiling tube** and incubate for about **5 minutes**.

4) Use a pipette to **rinse** the **root tip** well with **cold water**. Leave the tip to **dry** on a **paper towel**.

5) Place the root tip on a **microscope slide** and cut **2 mm** from the **very tip** of it. Get **rid** of the **rest**.

6) Use a **mounted needle** to **break** the tip **open** and **spread** the cells out thinly.

> *Take care when you're using sharp equipment.*

7) **Add** a small drop of **stain** and leave it for a few minutes. The stain will make the **chromosomes easier** to **see** under a microscope. There are loads of different stains, all with crazy names (**toluidine blue O, ethano-orcein, Feulgen stain**...) *If you're using the Feulgen stain, you'll need an extra rinse.*

8) **Place** a **cover slip** over the cells and **push** down firmly to **squash** the tissue. This will make the tissue **thinner** and allow **light** to pass through it. **Don't smear** the cover slip sideways (or you'll damage the chromosomes).

9) Now you can look at all the stages of mitosis under a **light microscope** (see page 10). You should see something that looks like the photograph on the right.

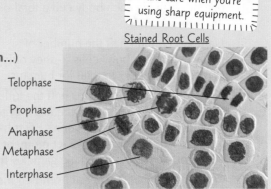

Stained Root Cells

Telophase
Prophase
Anaphase
Metaphase
Interphase

HERVE CONGE, ISM/SCIENCE PHOTO LIBRARY

The Mitotic Index is the Proportion of Cells Undergoing Mitosis

You can **calculate** the **mitotic index** of your cells using this **formula**:

$$\text{mitotic index} = \frac{\text{number of cells with visible chromosomes}}{\text{total number of cells observed}}$$

This lets you work out how quickly the **tissue** is growing. A **plant root tip** is constantly **growing**, so you'd expect a **high mitotic index** (i.e. **lots** of cells in **mitosis**).

Practice Questions

Q1 Give the main functions of mitosis.

Q2 List the four stages of mitosis.

Q3 Why do you need to squash the tissue when preparing a slide of plant root tip cells?

Exam Questions

Q1 The diagrams show cells at different stages of mitosis.

a) For each of the cells A, B and C, name the stage of mitosis. [3 marks]

b) Name the structures labelled X, Y and Z in cell A. [3 marks]

Cell A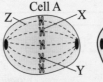
Cell B
Cell C

Q2 A sample of cells was prepared to observe mitosis. In total, 42 cells were observed. 32 of those had visible chromosomes. Calculate the mitotic index (the proportion of cells undergoing mitosis) for this sample. Give your answer to 2 decimal places. [2 marks]

Doctor, I'm getting short and fat — don't worry, it's just a phase...

Quite a lot to learn on these pages — but it's all important stuff, so no slacking. Mitosis is vital — it's how cells multiply and how organisms like us grow. Don't forget — the best way to learn is to get drawing those diagrams.

Gametes and Fertilisation

Ahh, now on to some really exciting stuff — gametes (sex cells to you and me) and fertilisation. I won't tell you any more because it's all explained on these pages. You have to read it though — don't just giggle at the rude diagram...

DNA is Passed to New Offspring by Gametes

1) **Gametes** are the male and female **sex cells** found in all organisms that reproduce **sexually**.

2) They join together at **fertilisation** to form a **zygote**, which divides and develops into a **new organism**.

3) In animals, the male gametes are **sperm** and the female gametes are **egg cells** (ova).

4) Normal body cells contain the **full number** of chromosomes. Humans have **two sets** of **23 chromosomes** — one set from the **male** parent and one from the **female** parent — giving each body cell a total of **46 chromosomes**.

5) **Gametes** contain **half** the number of chromosomes as body cells — they only contain **one set** (23 in total for humans).

6) Since each gamete contains **half** the full number of chromosomes, **fertilisation** creates a **zygote** with the **full** number of chromosomes. Fertilisation is the term used to describe the **exact moment** when the **nuclei** of the male and female gametes **fuse**.

7) **Combining** genetic material from **two individuals** makes offspring that are **genetically unique**.

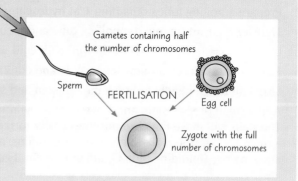

Gametes containing half the number of chromosomes

Sperm   FERTILISATION   Egg cell

Zygote with the full number of chromosomes

NB: you can't fertilise farmland with sperm.

Mammalian Gametes are Specialised for Their Function

Egg cells and sperm cells have all the **same organelles** as other **eukaryotic cells** (see pages 58-59), including a **nucleus** (which contains their genetic material) and a **cell membrane** (also known as a **plasma membrane**). But the structures of egg cells and sperm cells are also **specialised** for their **function** — bringing the **female** and **male DNA together** at **fertilisation** to form a **zygote**.

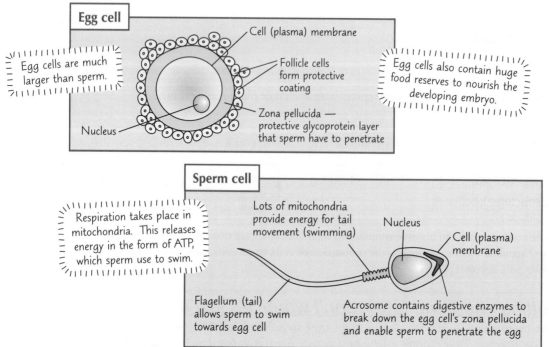

Egg cell

Egg cells are much larger than sperm.

Cell (plasma) membrane

Follicle cells form protective coating

Egg cells also contain huge food reserves to nourish the developing embryo.

Zona pellucida — protective glycoprotein layer that sperm have to penetrate

Nucleus

Sperm cell

Respiration takes place in mitochondria. This releases energy in the form of ATP, which sperm use to swim.

Lots of mitochondria provide energy for tail movement (swimming)

Nucleus

Cell (plasma) membrane

Flagellum (tail) allows sperm to swim towards egg cell

Acrosome contains digestive enzymes to break down the egg cell's zona pellucida and enable sperm to penetrate the egg

Gametes and Fertilisation

In Mammals Fertilisation Occurs in the Oviduct

1) In mammals, **sperm** are deposited high up in the female **vagina** close to the entrance of the **cervix**.

2) Once there, they have to make their way up through the **cervix** and **uterus**, and into one of the **oviducts**. The diagram on the right shows the **human** female reproductive system.

3) Once the sperm are in the oviduct, **fertilisation** may occur. Here's how it works:

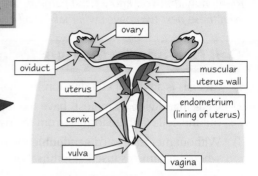

1) The **sperm swim** towards the **egg cell** in the oviduct.

2) Once **one** sperm makes contact with the **zona pellucida** of the egg cell (see previous page), the **acrosome reaction** occurs — this is where **digestive enzymes** are released from the acrosome of the sperm.

3) These enzymes **digest** the zona pellucida, so that the sperm can move through it to the cell membrane of the egg cell.

The Acrosome Reaction

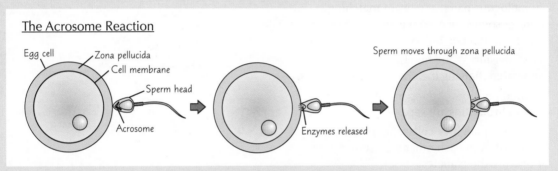

4) The sperm head **fuses** with the **cell membrane** of the egg cell. This triggers the **cortical reaction** — the egg cell releases the contents of vesicles called **cortical granules** into the space between the cell membrane and the zona pellucida.

5) The chemicals from the cortical granules make the zona pellucida **thicken**, which makes it **impenetrable** to other sperm. This makes sure that **only one** sperm fertilises the egg cell.

6) Only the **sperm nucleus** enters the egg cell — its **tail** is **discarded**.

7) The nucleus of the sperm **fuses** with the nucleus of the egg cell — this is **fertilisation**.

A **zygote** is now formed, which has the full number of chromosomes.
It immediately begins to divide by **mitosis** (see page 66) to develop into a fully formed organism.

Practice Questions

Q1 What is a gamete?

Q2 What is the zona pellucida?

Q3 Describe what happens in the acrosome reaction.

Exam Questions

Q1 Explain how sperm are specialised for their function. [3 marks]

Q2 Describe the process of fertilisation in mammals, following the acrosome reaction. [4 marks]

Reproduction isn't as exciting as some people would have you believe...

You don't need to learn the diagram of the female reproductive system — it's just there to give words like 'oviduct' and 'uterus' some sort of meaning when you're trying to learn what goes where. See, never say that I don't try my very best to help you. Now help yourself and get this stuff learnt — you'll be glad you put the effort in come exam time.

Meiosis and Inheritance

Right, now that you know what gametes are, I just know you're desperate to find out how they're formed. Luckily for you, these next two pages will make it all crystal clear (as long as you're wide awake with your learning head on first).

Cell Division by Meiosis Produces Gametes

1) **Meiosis** is a type of cell division that happens in the **reproductive organs** to produce **gametes**.

2) Cells that divide by meiosis have the **full number** of chromosomes to start with, but the cells that are formed from meiosis have **half the number**.

3) Without meiosis, you'd get **double** the number of chromosomes when the gametes **fused** at fertilisation. Not good.

You don't need to learn the stages of meiosis, just understand that it produces genetically different gametes.

Here's a brief overview of meiosis:

1) The DNA **replicates** so there are **two** identical copies of **each** chromosome, called **chromatids**.

2) The DNA condenses to form double-armed chromosomes, made from **two sister chromatids**.

3) The chromosomes arrange themselves into **homologous pairs** — pairs of **matching** chromosomes (one from each set of 23 — e.g. both number 1s).

4) **First division** — the homologous **pairs** are **separated**, **halving** the chromosome number.

5) **Second division** — the pairs of sister **chromatids** are separated.

6) **Four new daughter cells** that are **genetically different** from each other are produced. These are the **gametes**.

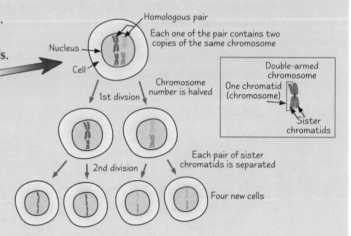

Meiosis Produces Cells that are Genetically Different

Genetic variation is the **differences** that exist between **individuals' genetic material**. The reason that meiosis is so important is that it **creates** genetic variation — it makes gametes that are **genetically different** (non-identical). It does this in two ways:

1) Crossing over of chromatids

1) Before the first division of meiosis, **homologous pairs** of chromosomes come together and **pair up**.

2) Two of the **chromatids** in each homologous pair **twist around** each other.

3) The twisted bits **break off** their original chromatid and **rejoin** onto the other chromatid, **recombining** their genetic material.

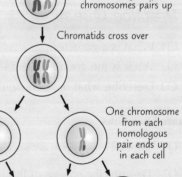

Each homologous pair of chromosomes pairs up

Chromatids cross over

1st division

2nd division

One chromosome from each homologous pair ends up in each cell

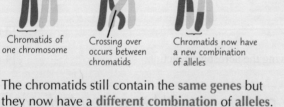

Chromatids of one chromosome

Crossing over occurs between chromatids

Chromatids now have a new combination of alleles

4) The chromatids still contain the **same genes** but they now have a **different combination** of alleles.

5) This means that each of the **four new cells** formed from meiosis contains chromatids with **different alleles**.

Each cell has a different chromatid and therefore a different set of alleles, which increases genetic variation.

Meiosis and Inheritance

2) Independent assortment of chromosomes

1) The four daughter cells formed from meiosis have completely **different combinations** of **chromosomes**.

2) All your cells have a **combination** of chromosomes from your parents, half from your mum (**maternal**) and half from your dad (**paternal**).

3) When the gametes are produced, different **combinations** of those maternal and paternal **chromosomes** go into each cell.

4) This is called **independent assortment** (separation) of the chromosomes.

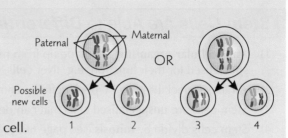

Some *Genes* are *Linked*

1) The **position** of a gene on a chromosome is called a **locus** (plural: **loci**). Independent assortment means that **genes** with loci on **different chromosomes** end up **randomly distributed** in the **gametes**.

2) But genes with loci on the **same chromosome** are said to be **linked** — because the genes are on the same chromosome, they'll stay together during **independent assortment** and their alleles will be **passed on to the offspring together**. The only reason this won't happen is if **crossing over** splits them up first.

A chromosome

Genes A, B and C are all linked.

Genes A and B are more closely linked than genes A and C.

3) The **closer together** the loci of two genes on a chromosome, the **more closely** they are said to be **linked**. This is because **crossing over** is **less likely** to split them up.

Some *Characteristics* are *Sex-linked*

1) A **characteristic** is said to be **sex-linked** when the **locus** of the **allele** that codes for it is on a **sex chromosome**.

2) In mammals, **females** have **two X** chromosomes (XX) and **males** have **one X** and **one Y** chromosome (XY).

3) The **Y chromosome** is **smaller** than the X chromosome and carries **fewer genes**. So most genes on the sex chromosomes are **only carried** on the X chromosome (called **X-linked** genes).

4) As **males** only have **one X chromosome**, they often only have **one allele** for sex-linked genes. So because they **only** have one copy, they **express** the **characteristic** of this allele even if it's **recessive**. This makes males **more likely** than females to show **recessive phenotypes** for genes that are sex-linked.

Look back at page 50 if you need a reminder of genetic terms such as 'recessive phenotype'.

5) Genetic disorders caused by **faulty alleles** on sex chromosomes include **colour blindness** and **haemophilia**. The faulty alleles for both of these disorders are carried on the X chromosome — they're called **X-linked disorders**.

Practice Questions

Q1 What name is given to the process that produces gametes?

Q2 What word is used to describe a gene's position on a chromosome?

Q3 What is a sex-linked characteristic?

Exam Questions

Q1 The genes for eye colour and wing length in fruit flies are linked.
    a) What does it mean when two genes are linked? [1 mark]
    b) Explain how the loci of the genes affects the likelihood that they will stay linked following meiosis. [2 marks]

Q2 a) Explain what crossing over is and how it leads to genetic variation. [3 marks]
    b) Explain how independent assortment leads to genetic variation. [2 marks]

Some genes are linked... so are some sausages...

These pages are tricky, so use the diagrams to help you. The key thing to understand about meiosis is that it produces four genetically different daughter cells and that the genetic variation in the daughter cells occurs because of crossing over and independent assortment. Then there's just the linkage business to get your head around and you're sorted.

Cell Differentiation and Gene Expression

If I had to choose a favourite type of cell, I'd choose a stem cell and here's why...

Stem Cells are Able to Differentiate into Specialised Cells

1) **Multicellular organisms** are made up from many **different cell types** that are **specialised** for their function, e.g. liver cells, muscle cells, white blood cells.

2) **All** these specialised cell types originally came from **stem cells**.

3) Stem cells are **unspecialised** cells that can develop into **other types** of cell.

4) Stem cells divide by **mitosis** (see page 66) to become **new** cells, which then become **specialised**.

5) The **process** by which a cell becomes specialised is called **differentiation**.

6) All multicellular organisms have some form of stem cell.

7) In humans, some stem cells are found in the **embryo** (where they become all the **specialised cells** needed to form a **fetus**).

8) The ability of stem cells to differentiate into specialised cells is called **potency** and there are **two types** you need to know about:

> 1) **Totipotency** — the ability to produce **all cell types**, including all the **specialised cells** in an organism and **extraembryonic cells** (cells of the placenta and umbilical cord).
>
> 2) **Pluripotency** — the ability of a stem cell to produce all the **specialised cells** in an organism (but **not** extraembryonic cells, because the genes for these cell types have become inactivated — see below).

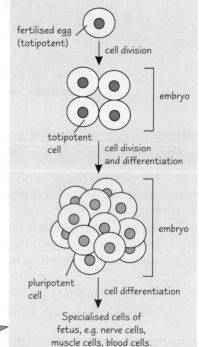

fertilised egg
(totipotent)

cell division

embryo

totipotent cell

cell division and differentiation

embryo

pluripotent cell

cell differentiation

Specialised cells of fetus, e.g. nerve cells, muscle cells, blood cells.

9) **Totipotent** stem cells are **only** present in mammals in the **first few cell divisions** of an **embryo**. After this point the **embryonic stem cells** become **pluripotent**. They can still specialise into **any** cell in the body, but **lose** the **ability** to become the cells that make up the **placenta** and **umbilical cord**.

10) Stem cells are also found in **some adult tissues** (where they become **specialised** cells that need to be **replaced**, e.g. stem cells in the intestines constantly replace intestinal epithelial cells). Adult stem cells are much **less flexible** than embryonic stem cells though — they can only develop into **some** cell types.

11) **Plants** also have **stem cells**. They're found in areas where the plant is **growing**, e.g. in **roots** and **shoots**.

Stem Cells Become Specialised Through Differential Gene Expression

A cell's **genome** is its **entire set of DNA**, including all the **genes** it contains. However, a cell **doesn't express** (make proteins from) **all the genes** in its genome. Stem cells become **specialised** because **different genes** in their DNA **become active** and get **expressed**:

> 1) **Stem cells** all contain the **same genes**, but not all of them are **expressed** because not all of them are **active**.
>
> 2) Under the **right conditions**, some **genes** are **activated** and others are **inactivated**.
>
> 3) **mRNA** is only **transcribed** from the **active genes**.
>
> 4) The mRNA from the active genes is then **translated** into **proteins**.
>
> 5) These proteins **modify** the cell — they determine the **cell structure** and **control cell processes** (including the activation of **more** genes, which produces more proteins).
>
> 6) **Changes** to the cell produced by these proteins cause the cell to become **specialised** (**differentiate**). These changes are **difficult** to **reverse**, so once a cell has specialised it **stays** specialised.

Transcription is when DNA is copied into mRNA. Translation is when proteins are produced using the code in mRNA. See pages 46-47 for more.

All of the girls expressed different jeans.

Example	**Red blood cells** contain lots of **haemoglobin** and have **no nucleus** (to make room for more haemoglobin). They are produced from a type of **stem cell** in the **bone marrow**. The stem cell produces a new cell in which the genes for **haemoglobin production** are **activated**. Other genes, such as those involved in **removing the nucleus**, are **activated** too. Many other genes are activated or inactivated, resulting in a specialised red blood cell.

Cell Differentiation and Gene Expression

Transcription Factors Can Control the Expression of Genes

1) **Gene expression** can be **controlled** by **altering** the rate of **transcription** of genes.
   E.g. **increased** transcription produces **more mRNA**, which can be used to make **more protein**.

2) This is controlled by **transcription factors** — proteins that **bind** to **DNA** and **activate** or **deactivate** genes by **increasing** or **decreasing** the **rate** of **transcription**.

3) Factors that **increase** the rate of transcription are called **activators** and those that **decrease** the rate are called **repressors**. Activators often work by helping **RNA polymerase bind** to the **DNA** and **begin** transcription. **Repressors** often work by **preventing** RNA polymerase from **binding** and so **stopping** transcription.

4) In **eukaryotes**, such as **animals** and **plants**, transcription factors bind to **specific DNA sites** near the **start** of their **target genes** — the genes they **control** the **expression** of. In **prokaryotes**, control of gene expression often involves transcription factors binding to **operons**.

5) An **operon** is a **section** of **DNA** that contains a cluster of **structural genes**, that are **transcribed together**, as well as **control elements** and sometimes a **regulatory gene**:

   - The **structural genes** code for **useful proteins**, such as **enzymes**.
   - The **control elements** include a **promoter** (a DNA sequence located **before** the structural genes that **RNA polymerase** binds to) and an **operator** (a DNA sequence that **transcription factors** bind to).
   - The **regulatory gene** codes for an **activator** or **repressor**.

6) You need to know about the **lac operon** in **E. coli**:

   1) *E. coli* is a bacterium that **respires glucose**, but it can use **lactose** if glucose isn't available.
   2) The genes that produce the **enzymes** needed to **respire lactose** are found on an operon called the *lac* operon.
   3) The *lac* operon has **three structural genes** — *lacZ*, *lacY* and *lacA*, which produce proteins that help the bacteria digest lactose (including β-**galactosidase** and **lactose permease**).

Lactose NOT present

The **regulatory** gene (*lacI*) produces the *lac* **repressor**, which is a **transcription factor** that **binds** to the **operator** site when there's **no lactose** present. This **blocks transcription** because RNA polymerase can't bind to the promoter.

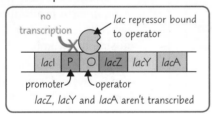

lacZ, lacY and lacA aren't transcribed

Lactose present

When **lactose is present**, it **binds** to the **repressor**, **changing** the repressor's **shape** so that it can **no longer bind** to the operator site.

RNA polymerase can now **begin** transcription of the structural genes.

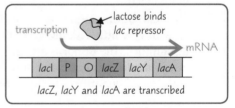

lacZ, lacY and lacA are transcribed

The lac operon controls a cell process in E. coli.

Practice Questions

Q1 What is the name of the process by which a stem cell becomes specialised?

Q2 What do the structural genes on the *lac* operon do?

Exam Question

Q1 During the development of an embryo, stem cells specialise to become all the different types of cell that make up the body. During very early development, stem cells are totipotent, but they soon become pluripotent.

   a) Explain the difference between totipotent stem cells and pluripotent stem cells. [3 marks]

   b)* Describe how differential gene expression results in the production of specialised cells from stem cells. [6 marks]

* You will be assessed on the quality of your written response in this question.

And you thought differentiation was just boring maths stuff...

Stem cells are pretty amazing when you think about it — they can differentiate to become any cell in the whole body. Totipotent stem cells are the coolest cells though — they can divide and differentiate into a whole organism.

Stem Cells in Medicine

These pages are about how stem cells can be used in medicine to replace damaged cells. It's got me thinking... perhaps I could grow another brain from some of my stem cells — then I'd be twice as clever.

Stem Cells Could be Used to Treat Some Diseases

1) **Stem cells** can develop into **any** specialised cell type, so scientists think they could be used to **replace damaged tissues** in a **range** of **diseases**.

2) Some stem cell therapies **already exist**. For example, the treatment for **leukaemia** (a cancer of the bone marrow) kills all the **stem cells** in the bone marrow, so **bone marrow transplants** can be given to patients to **replace** them.

3) Scientists are **researching** the use of stem cells as a **treatment** for lots of conditions, including:

   - **Spinal cord injuries** — stem cells could be used to repair damaged **nerve tissue**.

   - **Heart disease and damage caused by heart attacks** — stem cells could be used to replace damaged heart tissue.

4) People who make **decisions** about the **use** of stem cells in medicine and research have to consider the **potential benefits** of stem cell therapies:

   - They could **save** many **lives** — e.g. many people waiting for organ transplants **die** before a **donor organ** becomes available. Stem cells could be used to **grow organs** for those people awaiting transplants.

   - They could **improve** the **quality of life** for many people — e.g. stem cells could be used to replace damaged cells in the eyes of people who are **blind**.

Human Stem Cells Can Come from Adult Tissue or Embryos

1) In order to **use stem cells** in medicine and research, scientists have to get them from somewhere.

2) There are **two** potential **sources** of human stem cells:

1 Adult stem cells

1) These are obtained from the **body tissues** of an **adult**. For example, adult stem cells are found in **bone marrow**.

2) They can be obtained in a relatively **simple operation** — with very **little risk** involved, but quite a lot of **discomfort**. The **donor** is anaesthetised, a **needle** is **inserted** into the centre of a **bone** (usually the hip) and a **small quantity** of bone marrow is **removed**.

3) Adult stem cells **aren't** as **flexible** as embryonic stem cells — they can only develop into a **limited** range of cells.

4) However, if a **patient** needs a stem cell transplant and their **own** adult stem cells can be used (from elsewhere in their body) there's **less risk of rejection**.

2 Embryonic stem cells

1) These are obtained from **early embryos**.

2) Embryos are created in a **laboratory** using *in vitro* fertilisation (IVF) — egg cells are **fertilised** by sperm **outside the womb**.

3) Once the embryos are approximately **4 to 5 days old**, **stem cells** are **removed** from them and the rest of the embryo is **destroyed**.

4) Embryonic stem cells can develop into **all types** of specialised cells.

Rejection of transplants occurs quite often and is caused by the patient's immune system recognising the cells as foreign and attacking them.

3) Obtaining stem cells from **embryos** created by IVF raises **ethical issues** because the procedure results in the **destruction** of an embryo that's **viable** (could become a fetus if placed in a womb).

4) Many people believe that at the moment of **fertilisation** a **genetically unique individual** is formed that has the **right** to **life** — so they believe that it's **wrong** to **destroy** embryos.

5) Some people have **fewer objections** to stem cells being **obtained** from **egg cells** that **haven't** been fertilised by sperm, but have been **artificially activated** to start dividing. This is because the cells **couldn't survive** past a few days and **wouldn't** produce a fetus if placed in a womb.

6) Some people think that **scientists** should **only use** adult stem cells because their production **doesn't** destroy an embryo. But adult stem cells **can't** develop into all the specialised cell types that embryonic stem cells can.

7) The decision-makers in **society** have to take into account **everyone's views** when making decisions about **important scientific work** like stem cell research and its use in medicine.

Stem Cells in Medicine

Society Makes Decisions About the Use of Stem Cells in Medicine

1) Embryonic stem cells could be really **useful** in **medicine**, but **research** into their use raises many **ethical issues** (see previous page).

2) **Society** has to consider all the arguments **for** and **against** stem cell research before allowing it to go ahead.

3) To help society make these decisions, **regulatory authorities** have been established to consider the **benefits** and **ethical issues** surrounding embryonic stem cell research.

4) The work of regulatory authorities includes:

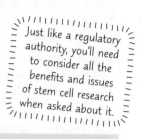

Just like a regulatory authority, you'll need to consider all the benefits and issues of stem cell research when asked about it.

   1) Looking at proposals of **research** and deciding if they should be **allowed**, taking the **ethical issues** surrounding the work **into account** — this ensures that any research involving embryos is carried out for a **good reason**. This also makes sure research isn't unnecessarily **repeated** by different groups.

   2) **Licensing** and **monitoring centres** involved in embryonic stem cell research — this ensures that only **fully trained staff** carry out the research. These staff will understand the **implications** of the research and **won't** waste precious resources, such as embryos. This also helps to **avoid unregulated research**.

   3) Producing **guidelines** and **codes of practice** — this ensures all scientists are working in a **similar manner** (if scientists don't use similar methods their results can't be compared). It also ensures that the scientists are using an **acceptable source** of stem cells and that the **methods** they use to **extract** the cells are **controlled**. This includes regulating the **maximum age** of an **embryo** that can be used as a source of stem cells.

   4) **Monitoring developments** in scientific research and advances — this ensures that any changes in the field are **regulated appropriately** and that all the **guidelines** are **up to date** with the latest in scientific understanding.

   5) Providing **information** and **advice** to governments and professionals — this helps to **promote** the science involved in embryo research, and it helps **society** to **understand** what's involved and why it's important.

Practice Questions

Q1 Describe how stem cells could be used to treat a range of diseases.

Q2 Name two potential sources of human stem cells.

Q3 Give three ways in which regulatory authorities help society to consider the benefits and ethical issues of embryonic stem cell research.

Exam Question

Q1 Stem cell research is permitted in the UK, but it is regulated by a number of authorities.

   a) Give one potential benefit of using stem cells in medicine. [1 mark]

   b) Embryonic stem cells can be used for research.

      i) Explain one benefit of using embryonic stem cells for research rather than adult stem cells. [2 marks]

      ii) State two reasons why some people are opposed to using stem cells from embryos. [2 marks]

Stem cells — I think they prove that we all evolved from plants...

Stem cells have the potential to cure or relieve the symptoms of some diseases, but as you've seen, there are some issues surrounding embryonic stem cells. Scientists are working towards producing stem cells that are as flexible as embryonic stem cells (i.e. can become any cell type) but that have come from other sources (e.g. skin or bone marrow).

Variation

Ever wondered why no two people are exactly alike? No, well nor have I, actually, but it's time to start thinking about it. Variation is the differences that exist between individuals — it's partly due to genes and partly due to differences in the environment.

Variation in **Phenotype** can be **Continuous** or **Discontinuous**

> *Phenotype is the characteristics displayed by an organism.*

Continuous variation

This is when the individuals in a population vary **within a range** — there are **no distinct categories**. For example:

Height — you could be any height within a range.

Mass — you could be any mass within a range.

Skin colour — any shade from very dark to very pale.

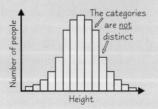

The categories are <u>not</u> distinct

Number of people / Height

Discontinuous variation

This is when there are two or more **distinct categories** — each individual falls into **only one** of these categories.
For example:

Blood group — you can be group A, group B, group AB or group O, but nothing else.

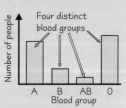

Four distinct blood groups

Number of people / A B AB O / Blood group

Variation in **Phenotype** is Influenced by **Variation** in Genotype (Genes)...

1) Individuals of the same species have **different genotypes** (different combinations of alleles).

2) This **variation** in **genotype** results in **variation** in **phenotype** — the **characteristics** displayed by an organism. For example, in humans there are six different combinations of blood group alleles, which can produce one of four different blood groups.

3) Some characteristics are controlled by only **one gene** — they're called **monogenic**. They tend to show **discontinuous variation**, e.g. blood group.

4) Most characteristics are controlled by a **number of genes** at **different loci** — they're said to be **polygenic**. They usually show **continuous variation**, e.g. height.

Different alleles for the **same gene** are found in the **same position** on **chromosomes**. This position is called the **locus**.

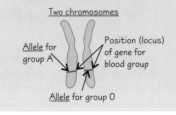

Two chromosomes

Allele for group A

Position (locus) of gene for blood group

Allele for group O

...and the **Environment**

1) Some characteristics are **only influenced** by **genotype**, e.g. blood group.

2) **Most** characteristics are influenced by **both** genotype and the environment, e.g. weight.

3) Here are a few examples of how the **environment interacts** with an organism's **genotype** to produce its **phenotype**:

1) <u>Height</u> is **polygenic** and affected by **environmental factors**, especially **nutrition**. E.g. **tall parents** usually have **tall children**, but if the children are **undernourished** they **won't** grow to their **maximum height** (because **protein** is required for **growth**).

2) <u>Monoamine Oxidase A</u> (MAOA) is an **enzyme** that breaks down **monoamines** (a type of **chemical**) in **humans**. **Low levels** of MAOA have been linked to **mental health problems**. MAOA production is controlled by a **single gene** (it's **monogenic**), but taking **anti-depressants** or **smoking tobacco** can **reduce** the amount produced.

3) <u>Cancer</u> is the **uncontrolled division of cells** that leads to lumps of cells (**tumours**) forming. The **risk of developing** some cancers is affected by **genes**, but **environmental factors** such as **diet** can also **influence** the risk.

4) <u>Animal hair colour</u> is **polygenic**, but the environment also plays a part in **some** animals. E.g. some **arctic animals** have **dark hair** in **summer** but **white hair** in **winter**. **Environmental factors** like decreasing temperature **trigger** this change but it **couldn't** happen if the animal **didn't** have the **genes** for it.

Variation

Changes in the Environment Can Cause Changes in Gene Expression

1) In **eukaryotes**, **epigenetic control** can determine **whether** certain genes are expressed, **altering** the **phenotype**.

2) Epigenetic control **doesn't** alter the **base sequence** of DNA. It works by **attaching** or **removing** chemical groups **to** or **from** the DNA. This alters how **easy** it is for the **enzymes** and other proteins needed for **transcription** to **interact** with and **transcribe** genes.

3) **Epigenetic changes** to gene expression play a **role** in lots of normal **cellular processes**. They can also occur in **response** to **changes** in the **environment** — e.g. pollution and availability of food.

Increased Methylation of DNA Represses a Gene

1) One method of **epigenetic control** is **methylation** of DNA — this is when a **methyl group** is **attached** to the **DNA** coding for a **gene**.

2) The group always attaches at a **CpG site**, which is where a **cytosine** and **guanine** base are **next to** each other in the DNA.

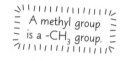
A methyl group is a -CH$_3$ group.

3) **Increased** methylation **changes** the **DNA structure**, so that the **proteins** and **enzymes** needed for transcription **can't bind to** the gene — so the gene is **not expressed** (i.e. it's **repressed** or **inactivated**).

Modification of Histones Also Affects Gene Expression

Histones are **proteins** that DNA **wraps around** to form **chromatin**, which makes up **chromosomes**. Chromatin can be **highly** condensed or **less** condensed. How **condensed** it is affects the **accessibility** of the **DNA** and whether or not the **proteins** and **enzymes** needed for transcription can **bind** to it.

Epigenetic modifications to histones include the **addition** or **removal** of **acetyl** groups:

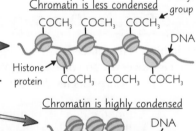
Chromatin is less condensed
Acetyl group
COCH$_3$ COCH$_3$ COCH$_3$
DNA
Histone protein
COCH$_3$ COCH$_3$ COCH$_3$

Chromatin is highly condensed
DNA
Histone protein

1) When histones are **acetylated**, the chromatin is **less condensed**. This means that the proteins involved in transcription can bind to the DNA, allowing genes to be **transcribed** (i.e. the genes are **activated**).

2) When **acetyl groups** are **removed** from the histones, the chromatin becomes **highly condensed** and genes in the DNA **can't be transcribed** because the transcription proteins **can't** bind to them — the genes are **repressed**.

Epigenetic Changes Can be Passed On After Cell Division

1) When a cell **divides** and **replicates**, **epigenetic changes** to its gene expression may be **passed on** to the resulting **daughter cells**. For example, **methyl groups** are usually **removed** from DNA during the production of gametes, but some **escape the removal process** and end up in the sperm or egg cells.

2) If epigenetic changes get passed on, it means that certain **genes** that are **activated** or **deactivated** in the **original cell** will also be **activated** or **deactivated** in the **daughter cells**.

3) If an epigenetic change occurred in **response** to a **change** in the **environment**, this means that the **daughter cells** will be **equipped** to deal with the **changed environment** in the same way as the **original cell** was.

Practice Questions

Q1 Give one example of continuous and one example of discontinuous variation.

Exam Question

Q1 Some cancers can be caused by epigenetic modifications to histones associated with genes related to cell division.
   a) What are histones? [1 mark]
   b) Describe how histone modifications can affect the transcription of the genes that the histones are associated with. [2 marks]

Histones are great, but hisrhythm is way off...

Remember that variation can be continuous or discontinuous and can be affected by both genetic and environmental factors. Epigenetic changes can also affect gene expression and can even be passed on. Whoever would've thought...

Biodiversity and Endemism

Bet you've noticed how there are loads of different living things in the world — well that's biodiversity in a nutshell. What's even more nutty is that scientists quite like to measure it. There's no accounting for taste...

Biodiversity is the Variety of Organisms

1) Biodiversity is the **variety** of **living organisms** in an **area**. It includes:

   - **Species diversity** — the number of **different species** and the **abundance** of each species in an **area**. For example, a wood could contain many different species of plants, insects, birds and mammals.

   - **Genetic diversity** — the variation of **alleles within a species** (or a population of a species). For example, human blood type is determined by a gene with three different alleles.

   > A population is a group of organisms of the same species living in a particular area.

2) **Endemism** is when a species is **unique** to a **single place** (isn't naturally found anywhere else in the world) — e.g. the **giant tortoise** is **endemic** to the Galapagos Islands — it can only be found there.

3) **Natural selection**, leading to **adaptation** and **evolution** (see pages 81-82), has **increased biodiversity** on Earth over time. But **human activities**, such as farming and deforestation, are **reducing species diversity** — causing **biodiversity** to fall as a result.

4) **Conservation** is needed to **help maintain** biodiversity (see pages 88-89). It is also really important for endemic species because they're particularly **vulnerable to extinction**. They're only found in one place, so if their habitat is threatened they can't usually migrate and their **numbers** will **decline**.

Mr Tiddles was endemic to blue silk sheets — he could only be found there.

The Species Diversity in a Habitat can be Measured

A **habitat** is the **place** where an organism **lives**, e.g. a rocky shore or a field. It's important to be able to **measure species diversity** so you can **compare different habitats**, or study how a habitat has **changed over time**. You can measure species diversity in different ways:

1) Count the number of **different species** in an area. The number of different species in the area is called the **species richness**. The **higher** the number of species, the **greater** the species richness. But species richness gives **no indication** of the **abundance** of each species.

2) Count the number of **different species** <u>and</u> the number of **individuals in each species**. Then use an **index of diversity** (worked out with a fancy equation — see page 80) to **calculate** the species diversity.

When measuring species diversity, it's usually **too time-consuming** to count every individual organism in a habitat. Instead, a **sample** of the population is taken. **Estimates** about the whole habitat are based on the sample. Here's what sampling involves:

1) Choose an area to **sample** — a small area within the habitat being studied.

2) To avoid **bias** in your results, the sample should be **random**. For example, if you were investigating the species of plants in a field you could pick random sample sites by dividing the field into a **grid** and using a **random number generator** to select coordinates.

3) **Count** the number of individuals of **each species** in the sample area. How you do this depends on **what** you're counting, for example:

   - For plants you'd use a **quadrat** (a frame which you place on the ground).
   - For flying insects you'd use a **sweepnet** (a net on a pole).
   - For ground insects you'd use a **pitfall trap** (a small pit that insects can't get out of).
   - For aquatic animals you'd use a **net**.

4) **Repeat** the process — take as many samples as possible. This gives a better indication of the **whole habitat**.

5) Use the results to **estimate** the **total number of individuals** or the **total number of different species** (the species richness) in the habitat being studied.

6) When sampling **different habitats** and comparing them, always use the **same sampling technique**.

Biodiversity and Endemism

The *Genetic Diversity* within a *Species* can also be *Measured*

You can measure diversity **within a species** by looking at **genetic diversity**.

1) Diversity within a species is the variety shown by individuals of that species (or within a population of that species).
2) Individuals of the same species vary because they have different alleles (different versions of the same gene, see page 50).
3) Genetic diversity is the variety of alleles in the gene pool of a species (or population).
4) The gene pool is the complete set of alleles in a species (or population).
5) The greater the variety of alleles, the greater the genetic diversity. For example, animals have different alleles for blood group. In humans there are three alleles for blood group, but gorillas have only one, so humans show greater genetic diversity for blood group than gorillas.
6) You can investigate the changes in the genetic diversity of a population over time, or how two populations of the same species show different diversity.

To measure the genetic diversity of a species you can look at **two things**:

1 Phenotype

1) Phenotype describes the **observable characteristics** of an **organism**.
2) **Different alleles** code for slightly **different versions** of the same characteristics.
3) By looking at the different phenotypes in a population of a species, you can get an idea of the **diversity of alleles** in that population.
4) The **larger the number** of different phenotypes, the **greater** the genetic diversity.
5) For example, humans have **different eye colours** due to **different alleles**. Humans in northern Europe show a **variety** of blue, grey, green or brown eyes. Outside this area, eye colour shows **little variety** — they're **usually brown**. There's **greater genetic diversity** in eye colour in northern Europe.

2 Genotype

1) Samples of an organism's DNA can be taken and the sequence of **base pairs analysed**.
2) The **order of bases** in different alleles is **slightly different**, e.g. the allele for brown hair will have a slightly different order of bases than the allele for blonde hair.
3) By sequencing the DNA of individuals of the same species, you can look at **similarities** and **differences** in the alleles within a species.
4) You can measure the **number of different alleles** a species has for one characteristic to see how **genetically diverse** the species is. The **larger the number** of different alleles, the **greater** the genetic diversity.
5) You can also look at the **heterozygosity index** (see below).

The *Heterozygosity Index* Measures *Genetic Diversity*

You can measure **genetic diversity within** a species using the **heterozygosity index**. Heterozygotes have **two different alleles** at a particular **locus** (the position of a gene on a chromosome). A **higher proportion** of heterozygotes in a population means that the population has **greater genetic diversity**. The **heterozygosity index** (H) can be **calculated** using the following **formula**:

$$H = \frac{\text{number of heterozygotes}}{\text{number of individuals in the population}}$$

EXAMPLE

The fruit fly has **many different alleles** which code for eye colour. In a particular **population** of **456** fruit flies, **276** were found to be **heterozygous** at the locus for eye colour.

Calculate the **heterozygosity index** for the flies at the locus for eye colour.

$$H = \frac{\text{number of heterozygotes}}{\text{number of individuals in the population}} = \frac{276}{456} = \textbf{0.61}$$

You can find an **average** value for H at many loci — this can be used to estimate genetic diversity in the **whole genome** of the population.

Biodiversity and Endemism

Biodiversity Can be Measured Using an Index of Diversity

1) As you might remember from page 78, an **index of diversity** is a way of **measuring** species diversity. It's calculated using an equation that takes **both** the **number** of species (species richness) and the **abundance** of each species (population sizes) into account.

2) You can **calculate** an index of diversity (D) using this formula: ⟹

$$D = \frac{N(N-1)}{\sum n(n-1)}$$

Where...
N = **Total number** of organisms of **all** species
n = **Total number** of organisms of **one** species
Σ = '**Sum of**' (i.e. added together)

The **higher** the **number**, the **more diverse** the area is. If all the individuals are of the **same species** (i.e. no biodiversity) the **index is 1**.

3) By calculating the **index of diversity**, you can **compare** the **species diversity** in **different habitats**. Here's an example:

There are 3 different species of flower in this field — a red species, a white and a blue.

There are 11 organisms altogether, so N = 11.

There are 3 of the red species, 5 of the white and 3 of the blue.

So the species diversity index of this field is:

$$D = \frac{11\,(11-1)}{3\,(3-1)+5\,(5-1)+3\,(3-1)} = \frac{110}{6+20+6} = \mathbf{3.44}$$

When calculating the bottom half of the equation you need to work out the n(n–1) bit for each different species then add them all together.

In another field there are the same 3 species of flower and 11 organisms altogether, but in this field there are 9 of the red species, 1 of the white and 1 of the blue.

The species diversity index of this field is:

$$D = \frac{11\,(11-1)}{9\,(9-1)+1\,(1-1)+1\,(1-1)} = \frac{110}{72+0+0} = \mathbf{1.53}$$

Although both fields have the **same number** of **species**, the second field has **lower species diversity** compared to the **first field** because the **abundance** of the white and blue species in this field is **lower**.

Practice Questions

Q1 What is endemism?

Q2 What is species richness?

Q3 What does the heterozygosity index (H) measure?

Site 1 — No Field Margins		Site 2 — Enhanced Field Margins	
Bombus lucorum	15	*Bombus lucorum*	35
Bombus lapidarius	12	*Bombus lapidarius*	25
Bombus pascuorum	24	*Bombus pascuorum*	34
		Bombus ruderatus	12
		Bombus terrestris	26

Exam Question

Q1 A study was conducted to investigate the impact of introducing enhanced field margins on the diversity of bumblebees. Enhanced field margins are thick bands of land around the edges of fields that are not farmed, but instead are planted with plants that are good for wildlife. Scientists studied two wheat fields, one where the farmer sowed crops right to the edge of the field and another where the farmer created enhanced field margins. The scientists counted the number of bees of different species at each site. Their results are shown in the table above.

a) What two things does an index of diversity take into account when measuring biodiversity? [2 marks]

b) The index of diversity (D) for site 1 was found to be 2.85.
Use the data in the table and the formula on the right
to calculate the index of diversity for site 2. $D = \dfrac{N(N-1)}{\sum n(n-1)}$ [3 marks]

c) What conclusions can be drawn from the findings of this study? [2 marks]

Species richness — goldfish and money spiders top the list...

I know endemism sounds like some sort of disease, but it's not so bad. Knowing these terms is important for your exams — so write out the definitions for biodiversity, endemism, etc. a few times. As for the formulae for the heterozygosity index and the index of diversity — be prepared to use them and to say what the numbers they churn out actually mean.

Adaptation and Evolution

Every species has a role in the environment where it lives. All the variation between organisms means that some organisms are better adapted to their role than others, which can lead to evolution by natural selection...

A *Niche* is the *Role* of a *Species Within Its Habitat*

> Remember, a habitat is where an organism lives.

1) The **niche** a species occupies within its habitat includes:

- Its **interactions** with **other living organisms** — e.g. the organisms it eats, and those it's eaten by.
- Its **interactions** with the **non-living environment** — e.g. the oxygen an organism breathes in, and the carbon dioxide it breathes out.

2) Every species has its own **unique niche** — a niche can only be occupied by **one species**.

3) It may **look like** two species are filling the **same niche** (e.g. they're both eaten by the same species), but there'll be **slight differences** (e.g. variations in what they eat).

4) If **two species try** to occupy the **same niche**, they will **compete** with each other. One species will be **more successful** than the other, until **only one** of the species is **left**.

5) Here are a couple of examples of niches:

<table><tr><td>

Common Pipistrelle Bat

This bat lives throughout Britain on **farmland**, **open woodland**, **hedgerows** and **urban areas**. It feeds by **flying** and catching **insects** using **echolocation** (**high-pitched sounds**) at a **frequency** of around **45 kHz**.

</td><td>

Soprano Pipistrelle Bat

This bat lives in Britain in **woodland** areas, close to **lakes** or **rivers**. It feeds by **flying** and catching **insects** using **echolocation**, at a **frequency** of **55 kHz**.

</td></tr></table>

It may **look like** both species are filling the **same niche** (e.g. they **both eat insects**), but there are **slight differences** (e.g. they use **different frequencies** for their echolocation).

Organisms Can be *Adapted* to their *Niche* in *Three Ways*

1) Adaptations are features that **increase** an organism's chance of **survival** and **reproduction**.

2) They can be **behavioural**, **physiological** or **anatomical**:

Behavioural adaptations

Ways an organism **acts** that increase its chance of survival. For example:

- **Possums** sometimes '**play dead**' — if they're being threatened by a **predator** they play dead to **escape attack**. This **increases** their chance of **survival**.
- **Scorpions dance** before **mating** — this makes sure they attract a mate of the **same species**, increasing the likelihood of **successful mating**.

Bob and Sue were well adapted to hiding in candyfloss shops.

Physiological adaptations

Processes inside an organism's body that increase its chance of survival. For example:

- **Brown bears hibernate** — they **lower their rate of metabolism** (all the chemical reactions taking place in their body) over **winter**. This **conserves energy**, so they don't need to look for **food** in the months when it's scarce — **increasing** their chance of **survival**.
- **Some bacteria** produce **antibiotics** — these **kill** other species of bacteria in the area. This means there's **less competition**, so they're **more likely** to **survive**.

Anatomical (structural) adaptations

Structural features of an organism's body that increase its chance of survival. For example:

- **Otters** have a **streamlined shape** — making it easier to **glide** through the **water**. This makes it easier for them to **catch prey** and **escape predators**, increasing their chance of **survival**.
- **Whales** have a **thick layer** of **blubber** (fat) — this helps to keep them **warm** in the cold sea. This increases their chance of survival in places where their **food** is found.

Adaptation and Evolution

Adaptations *Become* More Common *by* Evolution

Useful adaptations become more common in populations of species because of **evolution** by **natural selection**:

1) **Mutations** (see page 50) can introduce **new alleles** into a population, so individuals within a population show **variation** in their **phenotypes** (characteristics). Some of these alleles determine **characteristics** that can make the individual **more likely** to **survive**.

2) **Selection pressures** such as **predation**, **disease** and **competition** create a **struggle for survival**.

3) Individuals **without** the advantageous alleles **don't survive**. This means there are **fewer individuals** and **less competition** for **resources**.

A selection pressure is anything that affects an organism's chance of survival and reproduction.

4) Individuals with **better adaptations** (characteristics that give a selective advantage, e.g. being able to run away from predators faster) are **more likely** to **survive**, **reproduce** and **pass on** their advantageous alleles to their **offspring**.

5) Over time, the **number** of individuals with the advantageous alleles **increases**.

6) Over generations this leads to **evolution** as the frequency of the advantageous alleles in the population increase and the favourable adaptations become **more common**.

Natural selection is one process by which evolution occurs.

Charles Darwin came up with the original theory of evolution by natural selection. Over time the theory has become **increasingly accepted** as more **evidence** has been found to support it, and no evidence has been shown to disprove it. Evidence increases scientists' **confidence** in a theory — the more evidence there is, the more chance of something becoming an **accepted scientific explanation** (see page 2).

Here's an example to show you how natural selection leads to evolution:

> ### Peppered Moths
>
> 1) Peppered moths show **variation** in **colour** — there are **light** ones (with alleles for light colour) and **dark** ones (with alleles for dark colour, which arose from **mutations**).
>
> 2) Before the 1800s, there were **more light moths** than dark moths.
>
> 3) During the 1800s, **pollution** had **blackened** many of the trees.
>
> 4) Dark coloured moths were now **better adapted** to this environment — the alleles for dark colour made them better **camouflaged** from predators.
>
> *That colour is marvellous on you, really darling.*
>
> 5) The light coloured moths were **more susceptible** to **predation** (the selection pressure) as they **stood out** against the **blackened** tree bark, meaning that they were **less likely** to survive. This meant the dark moths had **less competition** for resources (such as food).
>
> 6) So the dark moths were more likely to **survive**, reproduce and **pass on** the **alleles** for their dark colouring to their offspring.
>
> 7) Over time, the **frequency** of the **alleles** for **dark colour** in the population **increased** and the **dark moths** became **more common**.

Speciation *is the Development of a* New Species

1) A **species** is defined as a group of **similar organisms** that can **reproduce** to give **fertile offspring**.

2) **Speciation** is the development of a **new species**.

3) It occurs when **populations** of the **same species** become **reproductively isolated** — the **changes** in the alleles and phenotypes of the populations **prevent** them from **successfully breeding together**. These changes include:

- **Seasonal changes** — individuals from the same population develop different **flowering** or **mating** seasons, or become **sexually active** at **different times** of the year.
- **Mechanical changes** — changes in **genitalia** prevent successful mating.
- **Behavioural changes** — a group of individuals develop **courtship rituals** that **aren't attractive** to the main population.

4) A population could become **reproductively isolated** due to **geographical isolation** (see next page) or **random mutations** that introduce **new alleles** to the population, resulting in the changes mentioned above.

Janice's courtship ritual was still successful in attracting mates.

Adaptation and Evolution

Geographical Isolation can lead to Speciation

1) Geographical isolation happens when a **physical barrier divides** a population of a species — **floods**, **volcanic eruptions** and **earthquakes** can all cause barriers that isolate some individuals from the main population.

2) **Conditions** on either side of the barrier will be slightly **different**. For example, there might be a **different climate** on each side.

3) Because the environment is different on each side, **different characteristics** will become **more common** due to **natural selection** (because there are **different selection pressures**):

> • Because different **characteristics** will be **advantageous** on each side, the **allele frequencies** will change in each population, e.g. if one allele is more advantageous on one side of the barrier, the frequency of that allele on that side will **increase**.
>
> • **Mutations** will take place **independently** in each population, also changing the **allele frequencies**.
>
> • The changes in allele frequencies will lead to changes in **phenotype frequencies**, e.g. the advantageous characteristics (**phenotypes**) will become more common on that side.

Remember, an organism's phenotype is the characteristics that it displays.

4) Eventually, the different populations will have become **genetically distinct**. Individuals from the different populations will have changed so much that they won't be able to breed with one another to produce **fertile** offspring — they'll have become **reproductively isolated**.

5) The two groups will have become separate **species**.

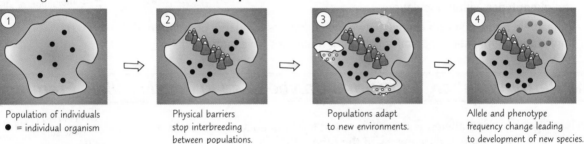

Population of individuals
● = individual organism

Physical barriers stop interbreeding between populations.

Populations adapt to new environments.

Allele and phenotype frequency change leading to development of new species.

Practice Questions

Q1 What is meant by the term niche?

Q2 What is meant by the term adaptation?

Q3 Describe the differences between behavioural, physiological and anatomical adaptations.

Exam Questions

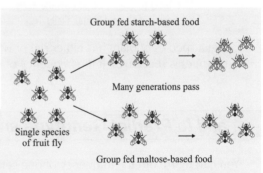

Group fed starch-based food

Many generations pass

Single species of fruit fly

Group fed maltose-based food

Q1 The diagram shows an experiment conducted with fruit flies. One population was split in two and each population was fed a different food. After many generations the two populations were placed together and it was observed that they were unable to breed together.

   a) What evidence shows that the formation of a new species occurred? [1 mark]

   b) Explain why the experiment resulted in the formation of a new species. [3 marks]

Q2 Tawny owls show variation in colour. There are light grey owls and darker brown owls. Before the 1970s there were more grey owls than brown owls in Finland. Since then, climate change has been causing a decrease in the amount of snowfall in Finland. During this period, the darker brown owls have become more common.

Explain how natural selection has led to the brown owls becoming more common. [5 marks]

I've evolved to revise for hours and still not remember things...

Basically, natural selection leads to adaptation and evolution — if an organism has alleles that make it better adapted, it's more likely to survive, reproduce and pass on those advantageous alleles, increasing their frequency in the population. If a population gets split up for any reason, the organisms might even evolve into separate species. Niche... I mean nice.

The Hardy-Weinberg Principle

Natural selection affects the frequency of alleles in a population — so by calculating the allele frequencies for a population, you can see whether the population is changing. That's where those fellows Hardy and Weinberg come in...

Evolution is a Change in Allele Frequency

1) How **often** an **allele occurs** in a population is called the **allele frequency**. It's usually given as a **percentage** of the total population, e.g. 35%, or a **number**, e.g. 0.35.

2) The **frequency** of an **allele** in a population **changes** over time — this is **evolution** (see p. 82).

3) **New alleles** are usually generated by **mutations** in **genes** (see page 50).

4) The **allele frequencies** of a population can be **calculated** using the **Hardy-Weinberg equations** (see below) and used to see if the population is **changing** over time (see next page).

> *Remember, a population is a group of organisms of the same species living in a particular area.*

The Hardy-Weinberg Principle Predicts Allele Frequencies Won't Change

1) The **Hardy-Weinberg principle** predicts that the **frequencies** of **alleles** in a population **won't change** from **one generation** to the **next**.

2) But this prediction is **only true** under **certain conditions** — it has to be a **large population** where there's **no immigration, emigration, mutations** or **natural selection**. There also needs to be **random mating** — all possible genotypes can breed with all others.

3) The **Hardy-Weinberg equations** (see below) are based on this principle. They can be used to **estimate the frequency** of particular **alleles**, **genotypes** and **phenotypes** within populations.

4) If the allele frequencies **do change** between generations in a large population then immigration, emigration, natural selection or mutations have happened.

> *Remember, the genotype of an organism is the combination of alleles it has (page 50).*

The Hardy-Weinberg Equations Can be Used to Predict Allele Frequency...

When a gene has two alleles, you can **figure out** the frequency of one of the alleles of the gene if you **know the frequency of the other allele**, using this equation:

> *Make sure you learn this equation — you might not get given it in the exams.*

$$p + q = 1$$

Where: **p** = the **frequency** of the **dominant** allele
q = the **frequency** of the **recessive** allele

The <u>total frequency</u> of <u>all possible alleles</u> for a characteristic in a certain population is <u>1.0</u>. So the frequencies of the <u>individual alleles</u> (e.g. the dominant one and the recessive one) must <u>add up to 1.0</u>.

E.g. a species of plant has either **red** or **white** flowers. Allele **R** (red) is **dominant** and allele **r** (white) is **recessive**. If the frequency of **R** is **0.4**, then the frequency of **r** is: 1 – 0.4 = **0.6**.

... and to Predict Genotype and Phenotype Frequency

You can **figure out** the frequency of one genotype if you **know the frequencies of the others**, using this equation:

$$p^2 + 2pq + q^2 = 1$$

Where: p^2 = the **frequency** of the **homozygous dominant genotype**
$2pq$ = the **frequency** of the **heterozygous genotype**
q^2 = the **frequency** of the **homozygous recessive genotype**

The <u>total frequency</u> of <u>all possible genotypes</u> for one characteristic in a certain population is <u>1.0</u>. So the frequencies of the <u>individual genotypes</u> must <u>add up to 1.0</u>.

E.g. if there are **two alleles** for **flower colour** (R and r), there are **three possible genotypes** — **RR, Rr** and **rr**. If the frequency of genotype **RR** (p^2) is **0.34** and the frequency of genotype **Rr** ($2pq$) is **0.27**, the frequency of genotype **rr** (q^2) must be: 1 – 0.34 – 0.27 = **0.39**.

Genotype frequencies can then be used to work out **phenotype frequencies** (the frequencies of observable traits).

E.g. the frequency of **red flowers** is equal to the genotype frequencies of **RR** and **Rr** added together (0.34 + 0.27 = **0.61**) and the frequency of **white flowers** is equal to the genotype frequency of **rr** (**0.39**).

The Hardy-Weinberg Principle

Sometimes You Need to Use **Both Hardy-Weinberg Equations**

EXAMPLE

The **frequency** of **cystic fibrosis** (genotype **ff**) in the UK is currently approximately **1 birth in every 2500**. From this information you can estimate the **percentage** of people in the UK that are cystic fibrosis **carriers** (**Ff**). To do this you need to find the **frequency** of **heterozygous genotype Ff**, i.e. **2pq**, using **both** equations:

$$p + q = 1$$

$$p^2 + 2pq + q^2 = 1$$

First calculate q:
Frequency of cystic fibrosis (homozygous recessive, ff) is 1 in 2500
$ff = q^2 = 1 \div 2500 = 0.0004$
So, $q = \sqrt{0.0004} = 0.02$

Next calculate p:
Using $p + q = 1$, $p = 1 - q$
$p = 1 - 0.02 = 0.98$

Then calculate 2pq:
$2pq = 2 \times 0.98 \times 0.02 = 0.039$

The **frequency** of **genotype Ff** is **0.039**, so the **percentage** of the UK population that are **carriers** is **3.9%**.

Allele Frequencies Show if a **Population** is **Changing** Over **Time**

EXAMPLE

If the **frequency** of **cystic fibrosis** is measured **50 years later** it might be found to be **1 birth in 3500**. From this information you can estimate the **frequency** of the **recessive allele** (f) in the population, i.e. **q**. ⟹

The frequency of the recessive allele is now **0.017**, compared to **0.02** currently (see above).

To calculate q:
Frequency of cystic fibrosis (homozygous recessive, ff) is 1 in 3500
$ff = q^2 = 1 \div 3500 = 0.00029$
So, $q = \sqrt{0.00029} = 0.017$

As the frequency of the allele has **changed** between generations the **Hardy-Weinberg principle doesn't apply** so there must have been some **factors** affecting **allele frequency**, e.g. **immigration**, **emigration**, **mutations** or **natural selection**.

Practice Questions

Q1 What is the relationship between allele frequency in a population and evolution?

Q2 What conditions are needed for the Hardy-Weinberg principle to apply?

Q3 Which term represents the frequency of the heterozygous genotype in the Hardy-Weinberg equation $p^2 + 2pq + q^2$?

Exam Questions

Q1 A breed of dog has either a black or brown coat. Allele B (black) is dominant and allele b (brown) is recessive. The frequency of the recessive allele is 0.23. The Hardy-Weinberg equation is $p^2 + 2pq + q^2 = 1$.
Find the frequency of the heterozygous (Bb) genotype. [1 mark]

Q2 Cleft chins are controlled by a single gene with two alleles. The allele coding for a cleft chin (T) is dominant over the allele coding for a non-cleft chin (t). In a particular population the frequency of the homozygous dominant genotype for cleft chin is 0.14. The Hardy-Weinberg equation is $p^2 + 2pq + q^2 = 1$.
a) What is the frequency of the recessive allele in the population? [1 mark]
b) What is the frequency of the homozygous recessive genotype in the population? [1 mark]
c) What percentage of the population have a cleft chin? [1 mark]

This stuff's surely not that bad — Hardly worth Weining about...

Not many of you will be thrilled with the maths content on these pages, but don't worry. Make sure you know what to use each Hardy-Weinberg equation for and what the different terms mean, so you can plug the numbers you're given into the right places. Don't forget to take a calculator into the exam with you either, or you'll be really, really sad.

Classification

All species need names. This is where classification comes in — it's about naming and organising species into groups.

Classification is All About Grouping Together Similar Organisms

Taxonomy is the science of classification. It involves **naming** organisms and **organising them** into **groups** based on their **similarities** and **differences**. This makes it **easier** for scientists to **identify** them and to **study** them.

1) There are **eight** levels of groups (called taxonomic groups) used in classification.

2) **Similar organisms** are first sorted into one of three **very large** groups called **domains**, e.g. animals, plants and fung are in the Eukaryota domain. Then they're sorted into **kingdoms**, e.g. all animals are in the animal kingdom.

3) **Similar** organisms from that kingdom are then grouped into a **phylum**. **Similar** organisms from each phylum are then grouped into a **class**, and **so on** down the eight levels of the hierarchy.

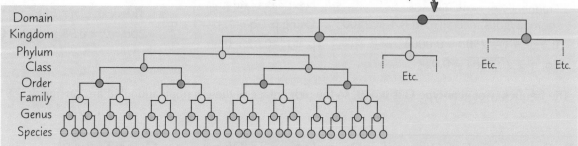

4) As you move **down** the hierarchy, there are **more groups** at each level but **fewer organisms** in each group.

5) The hierarchy **ends** with **species** — the groups that contain only **one type** of organism (e.g. humans, dogs, *E. coli*).

6) Species in the **same genus** can be **very similar**, with similar **phenotypes** and **genotypes**, but they're **separate** species because they **can't breed together** to produce **fertile offspring** (see p. 82). This is the **species concept**.

> All species are given a **unique scientific name** in **Latin** to **distinguish** them from similar organisms. In this **binomial** (**two-word**) system, the **first** word is the **genus** name and the **second** word is the **species** name — e.g. humans are *Homo sapiens*. Giving organisms a scientific name enables scientists to **communicate** about organisms in a standard way that **minimises confusion** — all scientists, in all countries, will call a species by the **same name**.

7) The classification of organisms is based on their **phenotypes**, **genotypes** and how **related** they are.

- Early classification systems **only** used **observable phenotypes** to place organisms into groups, e.g. whether they lay eggs or can fly. But scientists don't always agree on the **relative importance** of different features and groups based **solely** on **physical features** may not show how **related** organisms are. For example, **sharks** and **whales look** quite similar and they both **live** in the sea. But they're **not** actually **closely related**. Whales are **mammals** and sharks are **cartilaginous fish** — two completely **different classes**.

- **New technologies** that have enabled organisms' **genotypes** to be determined have resulted in **new discoveries** being made and the **relationships** between organisms being **clarified**. For example, skunks **were** classified in the family **Mustelidae** (e.g. weasels and badgers) until their **DNA sequence** was found to be significantly different to other members of that family. So they were reclassified into the family **Mephitidae**.

Organisms Can be Placed into One of Five Kingdoms

See pages 58-61 for more on prokaryotes and eukaryotes. Remember — eukaryotic cells have DNA contained within a nucleus.

All organisms can be placed into one of **five kingdoms** based on their **general features**:

KINGDOM	EXAMPLES	FEATURES
Prokaryotae (Monera)	bacteria	prokaryotes, unicellular (single-celled), no nucleus, less than 5 μm
Protoctista	algae, protozoa	eukaryotic cells, usually live in water, single-celled or simple multicellular organisms
Fungi	moulds, yeasts, mushrooms	eukaryotic, chitin cell wall, saprotrophic (absorb substances from dead or decaying organisms)
Plantae	mosses, ferns, flowering plants	eukaryotic, multicellular, cell walls made of cellulose, can photosynthesise, contain chlorophyll, autotrophic (produce their own food)
Animalia	nematodes (roundworms), molluscs, insects, fish, reptiles, birds, mammals	eukaryotic, multicellular, no cell walls, heterotrophic (consume plants and animals)

Classification

New Scientific Data Can Lead to New Taxonomic Groupings

1) **New data** about a species can influence the way it is **classified** (see previous page).

2) New data has to be **evaluated** by other scientists though (to check that experiments or studies were **designed properly** and that the conclusions are **fair**). Scientists can share their new discoveries in **meetings** and **scientific journals**. If scientists generally agree with the new data, it can lead to an **organism** being **reclassified** or lead to changes in the **classification system structure**.

3) This shows the **tentative nature** of scientific knowledge — it's always changing based on new data (see page 2).

EXAMPLE — Three Domains vs Five Kingdoms

1) A new, **three domain** classification system has been proposed based on **new data**.

2) The new data came from **molecular phylogeny**:

- **Phylogeny** is the study of the **evolutionary history** of groups of **organisms**.
- Phylogeny tells us **which species are related** to which and how **closely related** they are.
- **Molecular phylogeny** looks at molecules (**DNA** and **proteins**) to see how **closely related** organisms are, e.g. **more closely related** organisms have **more similar molecules**.

3) This new system classifies organisms in a **different way**:

1) In the **older**, **five kingdom** system of classification, all organisms are placed into **one** of five kingdoms.

2) In the **new**, **three domain** system all organisms are placed into one of three **domains** — **large superkingdoms** that are **above** the kingdoms in the **taxonomic hierarchy** (see previous page).

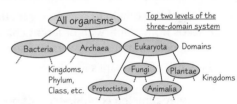

3) Organisms that were in the kingdom **Prokaryotae** (unicellular organisms **without a nucleus**) are separated into two domains — the **Archaea** and **Bacteria**. Organisms from the **other four** kingdoms (organisms with cells that **contain a nucleus**) are placed in the third domain — **Eukaryota**.

4) The **Prokaryotae** were **reclassified** into **two domains** because **molecular phylogeny** suggested that archaea and bacteria are **more distantly related** than originally thought.

Practice Questions

Q1 What is taxonomy?
Q2 Why should new data relating to the DNA sequence of a species be evaluated before that species is reclassified?
Q3 What is molecular phylogeny?
Q4 Name the three domains in the three domains classification system.

Exam Question

Q1 The brown trout is a species of fish and is part of the Salmonidae family. Its Latin name is *Salmo trutta*.

a) Complete the table below for the classification of the brown trout. [2 marks]

Domain		Phylum				Genus	Species
Eukaryota	Animalia	Chordata	Actinopterygii	Salmoniformes			

b) The brook trout is another member of the Salmonidae family. Rarely, a brook trout and a brown trout are able to mate to produce offspring known as tiger trout. Tiger trout are unable to reproduce. Explain how you know that a brook trout and a brown trout are different species. [1 mark]

Phylum — I thought that was the snot you get with a cold...

So classification systems can change if any new data rears its ugly mug... Just imagine thinking you were a prokaryote, then waking up one morning and discovering you'd been reclassified as an archaeon — it's enough to give anyone issues. But don't forget that any new data has to be evaluated by other scientists before it's accepted, to check it's OK.

Conservation of Biodiversity

Places like zoos and seedbanks help preserve biodiversity through conservation — they help species that are endangered get out of the woods, or back into the woods, depending on how you look at it...

Zoos and Seedbanks Help Conserve Endangered Species

1) The **extinction** of a **species**, or the loss of **genetic diversity** within a species, causes a **reduction** in **global biodiversity**.

2) Some species have **already become extinct** (e.g. the dodo) and there are lots of **endangered species** — species that are at **risk of extinction** because of a **low population** or a **threatened habitat**.

3) **Conservation** involves the **protection** and **management** of endangered species.

4) **Zoos** and **seedbanks** help to conserve endangered species and conserve genetic diversity.

> Remember, biodiversity is the variety of organisms in an area (see p. 78).

Seedbanks Store Seeds from Plants That are Endangered

1) A **seedbank** is a **store** of lots of **seeds** from lots of **different species** of **plant**.

2) They help to conserve biodiversity by storing the seeds of **endangered** plants.

3) If the plants become extinct in the wild the stored seeds can be used to **grow new plants**.

4) Seedbanks also help to conserve **genetic diversity**. For some species they store a **range** of seeds from plants with **different characteristics** (and so **different alleles**), e.g. seeds from tall sunflowers and seeds from short sunflowers.

5) The **work** of seedbanks involves:

Polly had enough seeds in the bank for a fancy new perch.

- Creating the **cool, dry conditions** needed for storage. This means seeds can be stored for **a long time**.
- **Testing** seeds for **viability** (the **ability** to grow into a plant). Seeds are **planted**, **grown** and **new seeds** are harvested to put back into storage.

6) There are **advantages** and **disadvantages** to using seedbanks:

Advantages

1) It's **cheaper** to store seeds than to store **fully grown plants**.

2) **Larger numbers** of seeds **can be stored** than grown plants because they need **less space**.

3) **Less labour** is required to look after seeds than plants.

4) Seeds can be **stored anywhere**, as long as it's cool and dry. Plants would need the **conditions** from their **original habitat**.

5) Seeds are **less likely** to be damaged by **disease**, **natural disaster** or **vandalism** than plants.

Disadvantages

1) Testing the seeds for **viability** can be **expensive** and **time-consuming**.

2) It would be **too expensive** to store **all types** of seed and **regularly** test them all for viability.

3) It may be **difficult to collect** seeds from some plants as they may grow in **remote locations**.

Zoos have Captive Breeding Programmes to Help Endangered Species

1) Captive breeding programmes involve breeding animals in **controlled environments**.

2) Species that are **endangered**, or already **extinct in the wild**, can be **bred together** in zoos to help **increase their numbers**, e.g. pandas are bred in captivity because their numbers are **critically low** in the wild.

3) There are some problems with captive breeding programmes though.

1) Animals can have **problems breeding** outside their **natural habitat**, which can be hard to **recreate** in a zoo. For example, pandas do not reproduce as successfully in captivity as they do in the wild.

2) Many people think it's **cruel** to keep animals in captivity, even if it's done to prevent them becoming extinct.

Conservation of Biodiversity

Organisms from *Zoos* and *Seedbanks* can be *Reintroduced* to the *Wild*

1) The **reintroduction** of plants grown from seedbanks or animals bred in zoos can **increase** their **numbers in the wild**, helping to **conserve** their numbers or bring them **back** from the **brink of extinction**.

2) This could also help **organisms** that rely on these plants or animals for **food**, or as part of their **habitat**.

3) The reintroduction of plants and animals also contributes to **restoring habitats** that have been **lost**, e.g. rainforests that have been cut down.

4) Reintroducing organisms to the wild can cause problems though:

> 1) Reintroduced organisms could bring **new diseases** to habitats, **harming** other organisms **living there**.
> 2) Reintroduced animals may not **behave as they would** if they'd been **raised in the wild**. E.g. they may have problems **finding food** or **communicating** with wild members of their species.

Example

The Californian condor was **nearly extinct** in the wild (only 22 birds were left). Thanks to **captive breeding programmes** there are now around 300, half of which have been **reintroduced** to the wild.

Seedbanks and Zoos Contribute to Scientific Research

Seedbanks

1) Scientists can study how plant species can be successfully grown from seeds. This is useful for reintroducing them to the wild.

2) Seedbanks can be used to grow endangered plants for use in medical research, as new crops or for new materials. This means we don't have to remove endangered plants from the wild.

3) A disadvantage is that only studying plants from seeds in a seedbank limits the data to small, interbred populations. So the information gained may not be representative of wild plants.

Zoos

1) Research in zoos **increases knowledge** about the **behaviour, physiology** and **nutritional needs** of animals. This can **contribute** to conservation efforts in the wild.

2) Zoos can carry out research that's **not possible** for some species **in the wild**, e.g. **nutritional** or **reproductive studies**.

3) A **disadvantage** is that animals **in captivity** may **act differently** to those in the wild.

Zoos and Seedbanks Help to Educate People about Conserving Biodiversity

Educating people about endangered species and reduced biodiversity helps to **raise public awareness** and **interest** in conserving biodiversity:

1) Zoos let people get **close** to organisms, **increasing** their **enthusiasm** for conservation work.

2) Seedbanks contribute to education by **providing training** and setting up **local seedbanks** all round the world. For example, the **Millennium Seed Bank Project** aims to conserve seeds in their **original country**.

Practice Questions

Q1 What is conservation?
Q2 Suggest two advantages of storing seeds in a seedbank, rather than storing grown plants.

Exam Question

Q1 The sand lizard is a threatened species in the UK. Captive breeding and reintroduction programmes are being used to increase their numbers in the wild. Give four problems that could be involved with the captive breeding and reintroduction of sand lizards to the wild. [4 marks]

The bank of seeds — high interest rates and 0% on branch transfers...

Zoos do a bit more than you thought — in fact they're just a front for all the covert operations to support conservation. Well, they're not that covert — there's a page here all about them actually. Sigh, I do try and make life more exciting...

Plant Cell Structure

Plants aren't everybody's cup of tea, but they should be — without them we'd be stuck. We get loads of useful stuff from plants, but before we delve into that there are a few important bits and pieces you need to know...

Plant Cells Have Different Organelles from Animal Cells

For more on animal organelles see p. 58-59.

You know all about the organelles in animal cells — well plant cells are a little bit different. Plant cells contain most of the organelles that animal cells do, **plus a few extras** that **animal cells don't have**:

ORGANELLE	DIAGRAM	DESCRIPTION	FUNCTION
Cell wall	cell wall, cell membrane, cytoplasm	A rigid structure that surrounds **plant cells**. It's made mainly of the carbohydrate **cellulose**.	**Supports** plant cells.
Middle lamella	middle lamella, cell A, cell B, cell wall	The **outermost layer** of the cell.	This layer acts as an **adhesive**, sticking adjacent plant cells together. It gives the plant **stability**.
Plasmodesmata	plasmodesma (plural = plasmodesmata), cell A, cell B, cell wall	**Channels** in the cell walls that **link** adjacent cells together.	Allow **transport** of **substances** and **communication** between cells.
Pits	pits, cell A, cell B, cell wall	Regions of the cell wall where the wall is **very thin**. They're arranged in **pairs** — the pit in one cell is lined up with the pit in the adjacent cell.	Allow **transport** of **substances** between cells.
Chloroplast	stroma, two membranes, granum (plural = grana), lamella (plural = lamellae)	A small, **flattened** structure. It's surrounded by a **double membrane**, and also has membranes inside called **thylakoid membranes**. These membranes are stacked up in some parts of the chloroplast to form **grana**. Grana are linked together by lamellae — thin, flat pieces of thylakoid membrane.	The **site** where **photosynthesis** takes place. Some parts of photosynthesis happen in the **grana**, and other parts happen in the **stroma** (a thick fluid found in chloroplasts).

Plant Cell Structure

ORGANELLE	DIAGRAM	DESCRIPTION	FUNCTION
Amyloplast	starch grain / membrane	A small organelle enclosed by a **membrane**. They contain **starch granules**.	**Storage** of **starch grains**. They also convert starch back to glucose for release when the plant requires it.
Vacuole and Tonoplast	vacuole / plant cell / tonoplast	The vacuole is a **compartment** surrounded by a **membrane** called the **tonoplast**.	The vacuole contains the **cell sap**, which is made up of water, enzymes, minerals and waste products. Vacuoles keep the cells **turgid** — this stops plants wilting. They're also involved in the **breakdown** and **isolation** of unwanted chemicals in the cell. The tonoplast controls what **enters** and **leaves** the vacuole.

You need to be able to recognise the different organelles in images taken with electron microscopes.

Practice Questions

Q1 What is the function of the middle lamella?

Q2 Which two organelles allow transport of substances between plant cells?

Q3 Describe the structure of pits in a plant cell.

Q4 Name the membrane that surrounds the vacuole.

Exam Questions

Q1 The image on the right shows a plant organelle as seen under a transmission electron microscope. Which of the following describes its function?

A It keeps the cell turgid and is involved in the breakdown and isolation of unwanted chemicals in the cell.

B It transports substances between cells.

C It is the site where photosynthesis takes place.

D It stores starch grains and converts starch back to glucose for release when the plant requires it. [1 mark]

Biophoto Associates/SCIENCE PHOTO LIBRARY

Q2 The image on the right shows a plant organelle as seen under a transmission electron microscope.

a) Identify the organelle. [1 mark]

b) State the function of the organelle. [1 mark]

Biophoto Associates/SCIENCE PHOTO LIBRARY

Esmerelda... the cells! the cells!

I know this table of organelles looks pretty daunting, but I'm afraid you've got to learn it — scribble down one diagram at a time and write out its description and function 'til you know it like the back of your hand. Then think back to the table of animal organelles on pages 58-59 and make you sure you can compare the two. So many organelles...

Plant Stems

Two whole pages on plant stems... just what I always dreamed of...

Different Parts of **Plant Stems** have **Different Functions**

Plant stems are made up of loads of different things — the only bits you need to worry about are **xylem vessels**, **sclerenchyma fibres** and **phloem tissue**.

Xylem vessels

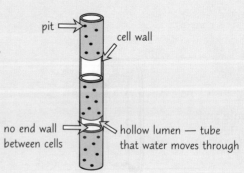

1) The function of xylem vessels is to transport water and mineral ions up the plant, and provide support.

2) They're very long, tube-like structures formed from dead cells, joined end to end. The tubes are found together in bundles.

3) The cells are longer than they are wide, they have a hollow lumen (they contain no cytoplasm) and have no end walls.

4) This makes an uninterrupted tube, allowing water and mineral ions to pass up through the middle easily.

5) Their walls are thickened with the woody substance lignin (see page 94), which helps to support the plant.

6) Water and mineral ions move into and out of the vessels through pits in the walls where there's no lignin.

Sclerenchyma fibres

1) The function of sclerenchyma fibres is to provide **support** — they are not involved in transport.

2) Like xylem vessels, they're also made of bundles of **dead cells** that run vertically up the stem.

3) The cells are **longer** than they are **wide**, and have a **hollow lumen** but, unlike xylem vessels, they do have **end walls**.

4) Their cell walls are also **thickened** with **lignin**, but they don't contain pits. They have more **cellulose** (see page 94) than other plant cells.

Phloem tissue

1) The function of phloem tissue is to **transport organic solutes** (mainly sugars like sucrose) from where they're made in the plant to where they're needed. This is known as **translocation**.

2) Like xylem, phloem is formed from cells arranged in **tubes**. But unlike xylem, it's purely a **transport tissue** — it **isn't** used for support as well.

3) Phloem tissue contains different types of cells including **sieve tube elements** and **companion cells**.

4) **Sieve tube elements** are **living cells** and are joined **end to end** to form **sieve tubes**.

5) The 'sieve' parts are the **end walls**, which have lots of **holes** in them to allow **solutes** to pass through.

6) Unusually for living cells, sieve tube elements have **no nucleus**, a **very thin** layer of **cytoplasm** and **few organelles**. The cytoplasm of adjacent cells is **connected** through the holes in the sieve plates.

7) The **lack** of a **nucleus** and **other organelles** in sieve tube elements means that they **can't survive** on their own. So there's a **companion cell** for **every** sieve tube element.

8) Companion cells carry out the living functions for **both** themselves and their sieve cells. For example, they provide the **energy** for the **active transport** of solutes.

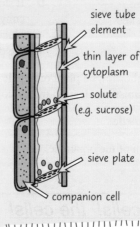

Take a look at page 32 for more on active transport.

Plant Stems

Xylem and Phloem are Found in Vascular Bundles

1) Xylem vessels, phloem tissue and sclerenchyma fibres are found throughout the plant, but you only need to know about their **position** in the **stem**.

2) In the stem, **xylem vessels** group together with **phloem tissue** to form **vascular bundles**. **Sclerenchyma fibres** are usually **associated** with the vascular bundles.

3) The position of the xylem, phloem and sclerenchyma fibres in the stem are shown in the **cross-sections** below:

This is a **transverse cross-section**. Transverse means the sections cut through each structure at a **right angle** to its **length**.

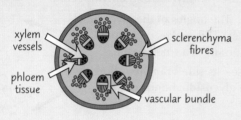

This is a **longitudinal** cross-section. **Longitudinal** cross-sections are taken **along the length** of a structure.

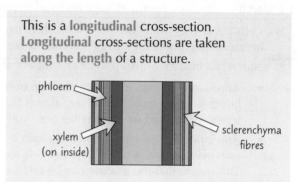

You May Need to Dissect Plant Stems

You can **look at** part of a **plant stem** under a **light microscope** and **identify** xylem vessels, sieve cells (phloem tissue) and sclerenchyma fibres. You might be given a **pre-prepared slide** to look at or you could **dissect the stem** and **prepare a section of tissue** yourself. If you're dissecting the plant stem yourself, you can use this method:

1) Use a scalpel (or razor blade) to cut a **cross-section** of the stem (transverse or longitudinal). Cut the sections as **thinly** as possible — thin sections are better for viewing under a microscope.

   Be careful when using sharp equipment — make sure you're cutting away from yourself and that any blades are free from rust.

2) Use **tweezers** to gently place the cut sections in **water** until you come to use them. This stops them from **drying out**.

3) Transfer each section to a dish containing a **stain**, e.g. **toluidine blue O (TBO)**, and leave for one minute. TBO stains **lignin blue-green**, so will let you see the positions of the xylem vessels and sclerenchyma fibres. The phloem cells and the rest of the tissue should appear **pinkish purple**.

4) **Rinse off** the sections in water and **mount** each one onto a **slide** (see page 10).

5) Place your prepared slide under a **microscope** and adjust the microscope until you get a **clear image** of your sample. Make a **labelled drawing** that shows the positions of the xylem vessels, phloem sieve tubes and sclerenchyma fibres.

There's more about how to use microscopes on page 10.

Practice Questions

Q1 What is the name of the substance that thickens the walls of xylem vessels?

Q2 What is the function of companion cells?

Exam Question

Q1 The image on the right shows a cross-section of a plant stem as seen under a light microscope.

   a) Identify the structures labelled X and Y. [2 marks]

   b) Describe the functions of structures X and Y. [2 marks]

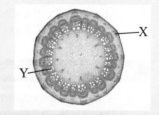

DR KEITH WHEELER/SCIENCE PHOTO LIBRARY

Sieve tube — WLTM like-minded cell for long-term companionship...

Sieve tube elements sound a bit feeble to me — not being able to survive on their own, and all that. Anyway, some of the structures and functions of the cell types covered here are quite similar, so it's important you learn them properly. You don't want to mix up your sieve tube elements with your sclerenchyma fibres in the exam — you'd never forgive yourself...

Starch, Cellulose and Plant Fibres

I know these pages don't have the most stimulating title, but they're actually pretty interesting... honest...

The **Structures** of Starch and **Cellulose** Determine Their **Functions**

You might remember some stuff about the structure of **starch** from Topic 1.
Well you need to know about it for Topic 4 as well — but now you've got to **compare** it to **cellulose**, another polysaccharide. Cellulose is made of similar stuff, but has a **different function**.

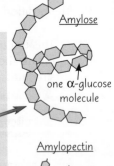

Amylose

one α-glucose molecule

Amylopectin

(1) Starch — the main **energy storage material** in **plants**

1) Cells get **energy** from glucose. Plants **store** excess glucose as **starch** (when a plant **needs more glucose** for energy it **breaks down** starch to release the glucose).

2) Starch is a mixture of **two** polysaccharides of **alpha-glucose** — **amylose** and **amylopectin**:

- **Amylose** — a long, **unbranched chain** of α–glucose. The angles of the glycosidic bonds give it a **coiled structure**, almost like a cylinder. This makes it **compact**, so it's really **good for storage** because you can **fit more in** to a small space.

- **Amylopectin** — a long, **branched chain** of α–glucose. Its **side branches** allow the **enzymes** that break down the molecule to get at the **glycosidic bonds easily**. This means that the glucose can be **released quickly**.

3) Starch is **insoluble** in water, so it doesn't cause water to enter cells by **osmosis** (which would make them swell). This makes it good for **storage**.

one cellulose molecule

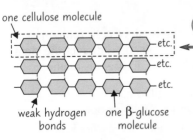

weak hydrogen bonds   one β-glucose molecule

(2) Cellulose — the major component of **cell walls** in **plants**

1) Cellulose is made of **long, unbranched** chains of **β-glucose**, joined by **1-4 glycosidic bonds**.

2) The glycosidic bonds are **straight**, so the cellulose chains are straight.

3) Between **50 and 80** cellulose chains are **linked together** by a large number of **hydrogen bonds** to form **strong threads** called **microfibrils**. The strong threads mean cellulose provides **structural support** for cells (e.g. they strengthen plant cell walls).

See page 22 for more on glycosidic bonds.

Plant Fibres are **Useful** to **Humans** Because They're **Strong**

1) Plant fibres are made up of **long tubes** of **plant cells**, e.g. sclerenchyma fibres and xylem vessels are made of tubes of dead cells (see page 92).

2) They're **strong**, which makes them useful for loads of things, e.g. **ropes** or **fabrics** like hemp.

3) They're strong for a **number of reasons**, but you only need to know **two**:

The arrangement of cellulose microfibrils in the cell wall

1) The cell wall contains **cellulose microfibrils** in a **net-like arrangement**.

2) The strength of the microfibrils and their arrangement in the cell wall gives plant fibres **strength**.

cell membrane   secondary cell wall   normal cell wall

layer of cellulose microfibrils in cell wall

The secondary thickening of cell walls

1) When some structural plant cells (like sclerenchyma and xylem) have finished growing, they produce a **secondary cell wall** between the normal cell wall and the cell membrane.

2) The secondary cell wall is **thicker** than the normal cell wall and usually has **more** of a woody substance called **lignin**.

3) The growth of a secondary cell wall is called **secondary thickening**.

4) Secondary thickening makes plant fibres even **stronger**.

Starch, Cellulose and Plant Fibres

You Can Measure the **Tensile Strength** of *Plant Fibres*

The **tensile strength** of a fibre is the **maximum load** it can take before it **breaks**.
Knowing the tensile strength of plant fibres can be really important, especially if they're
going to be used for things like ropes (e.g. a rock climber would want to know the rope
they're using is going to hold their weight).
Here's how you'd find out the tensile strength of a plant fibre:

I don't know Dave, we usually use weights to test tensile strength...

1) Attach the fibre to a **clamp stand** and **hang** a **weight** from the other end.

2) Keep **adding weights**, one at a time, until the **fibre breaks**.

3) Record the **mass needed** to break the fibre —
the **higher** the mass, the **higher** the tensile strength.

4) **Repeat** the experiment with different samples of the
same fibre and calculate the **mean** of the results.
This reduces the effect of **random error** and so
increases the **precision** of the results (see page 198).

5) The fibres being tested should always be the **same length**.

6) Throughout the experiment all **other variables**,
like temperature and humidity, must be kept **constant**.

7) You also need to take **safety measures** when doing this experiment, e.g. wear goggles to protect your eyes,
and leave the area where the weights will fall clear so they don't squish your toes.

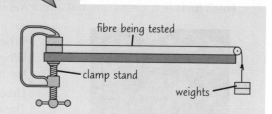

fibre being tested

clamp stand

weights

Practice Questions

Q1 Name the two polysaccharides that starch is made up from.

Q2 Compare the structure and function of starch and cellulose.

Q3 What is meant by tensile strength?

Exam Questions

Q1 The physical properties of plant fibres can make them useful to humans.

a) Describe the arrangement of cellulose microfibrils in a plant cell wall,
and explain how this relates to the properties of plant fibres.
[2 marks]

b) Describe secondary thickening of plant cell walls,
and explain how this relates to the properties of plant fibres.
[2 marks]

Q2 A group of students investigated the tensile
strength of four different plant fibres.
Their results are displayed in the table
on the right.

	fibre A	fibre B	fibre C	fibre D
mean mass which caused fibre to break / kg	3.5	220.0	52.7	17.2

a) Describe a method they could have used to obtain these results.
[3 marks]

b) Give two variables they should have kept constant in their investigation.
[2 marks]

c) Based on the results, which fibre would be most suitable to make a climbing rope?
Explain your answer.
[1 mark]

The world's strongest plant — live from the Bahamas...

*Well at least there are a few pretty pictures on these pages to look at. Anyway, it's not so bad — basically plant fibres
are really strong and there are lots of reasons, but you just need to know about how the cell walls are strong, which
makes the plant fibres super strong. They're strong to the finish, 'cos they eats their spinach...*

Sustainability and Plant Minerals

As you saw on page 94, you can use plants to make ropes and fabrics. But there are plenty of other things you can make from plants, like plastics, fuel and castles of mashed potatoes. Making things from plants is also sustainable, which is nice...

Sustainable Practices Don't Deplete Resources

1) Sustainability is all about **using resources** in a way that meets the **needs** of the **present generation** without messing it up for **future generations** (i.e. not using something up so there's none left).

2) To **make products sustainably** you have to use **renewable resources**.

3) Renewable resources are resources that can be **used indefinitely** without **running out**, e.g. **plants** are a renewable resource because harvested plants can be **regrown** (so there'll be plenty for future generations). **Fossil fuels** (e.g. petrol) are **not** a renewable resource — once you've used it all there's no more.

If only Amy's sweets were a renewable resource...

4) An example of a **sustainable practice** is replacing trees after logging. Whenever a tree is cut down, a **new one** is planted in its place. When the tree is fully grown the process can **begin again** — the environment isn't **significantly damaged** in the long term.

5) **Unsustainable practices** can't continue indefinitely. The **resources** would eventually **run out**.

6) An example of an unsustainable practice is the use of **fossil fuels** to make oil-based plastics like polythene.

Using Plant Fibres and Starch can Contribute to Sustainability

Plant fibres

1) **Ropes** and **fabrics** can be made of **plastic**, which is made from **oil**. They can also be made from **plant fibres** (see page 94).

2) Making products from plant fibres is **more sustainable** than making them from oil — **less fossil fuel** is **used up**, and crops can be **regrown** to **maintain the supply** for future generations.

One disadvantage of making ropes from plant fibres is that they're generally not as strong as ropes made of plastic.

3) Products made from plant fibres are **biodegradable** — they can be broken down by **microbes**, unlike most oil-based plastics (which can't be broken down and remain in the environment for many years).

4) Plants are **easier to grow** and **process** (to extract the fibres) than extracting and processing oil. This makes them **cheaper** and it's easier to do in developing countries (as less technology and expertise is needed).

Starch

1) Starch is found in **all plants** — crops such as **potatoes** and **corn** are particularly rich in starch.

2) **Plastics** are usually made from **oil**, but some can be made from **plant-based** materials, like **starch**. These plastics are called **bioplastics**.

3) Making plastics from starch is **more sustainable** than making them from oil because less fossil fuel is used up and the **crops** from which the starch came from can be **regrown**.

4) **Vehicle fuel** is also usually made from **oil**, but you can make fuel from **starch**. E.g. **bioethanol** is a fuel that can be made from starch.

5) Making fuel from starch is **more sustainable** than making it from oil because, you guessed it, **less fossil fuel** is used up and the **crops** from which the starch came from can be **regrown**.

The potatoes were getting worried about all this talk of using more starch — you could see it in their eyes.

Sustainability and Plant Minerals

Plants *Need Water* and *Inorganic Ions*

Plants need **water** and **inorganic ions** (**minerals**) for a number of different functions. They're absorbed through the **roots** and travel through the plant in the xylem. If there isn't enough water or inorganic ions in the soil, the plant will show **deficiency symptoms**, like stunted growth. You need to know why plants need water and these three minerals:

- **Water** is needed for **photosynthesis**, to **transport minerals**, to maintain **structural rigidity** (water exerts pressure in cell vacuoles — see page 91) and to **regulate temperature** (water evaporating from leaves helps cool plants down).
- **Magnesium ions** are needed for the production of **chlorophyll** — the **pigment** needed for **photosynthesis**.
- **Nitrate ions** are needed for the production of **DNA**, **proteins** (including enzymes) and **chlorophyll**. They're required for **plant growth**, **fruit production** and **seed production**.
- **Calcium ions** are important components in plant **cell walls**. They're required for **plant growth**.

You Can *Investigate Plant Mineral Deficiencies* in the *Lab*

Here's how to **investigate mineral deficiency** in a plant using calcium ions as an example (you could do the same experiment with any of the minerals mentioned above):

1) Make up three **nutrient broths** containing all the essential minerals, but vary the concentration of **calcium ions**. Make up one broth with a **high** concentration, one with a **medium** concentration and one with a **low** concentration of calcium ions.

2) Split 9 test tubes into **three groups** and fill the tubes of each group with one of the three broths.

3) Take 9 seedlings of the **same plant**, e.g. germinated mung beans (they should be the **same age**). For each seedling, measure its **mass** using a balance and record it. Then put it gently into the top of one of the test tubes so that the **root is suspended** in the nutrient broth. You will have to **support** the seedling to stop it from falling into the test tube, e.g. by putting cotton wool inside the opening of the tube.

Don't forget to label each of your tubes with the preparation of nutrient broth it contains and the starting mass of the seedling.

4) **Cover the outside** of each test tube in aluminium foil so that **no light** can get to the nutrient broth and cause other organisms, such as algae, to grow.

5) Place all the tubes near a **light source**, e.g. on a windowsill, and leave them for the same amount of time, e.g. **2 weeks**. You may have to **top up** the nutrient broth in each tube during this time to ensure the roots stay suspended in the liquid.

6) Carefully **remove** each plant from its test tube and **blot it dry**. Measure and record the **new mass** of each plant, then calculate the **mean change in mass** of the plants for each nutrient broth. It's good to note down any **visual differences** between the groups too.

7) During the experiment it's important to keep all other **variables the same**, e.g. the amount of light the plants receive.

You could use a similar method to investigate the effect on **plant growth** when plants are **completely deficient** in one mineral — instead of varying the concentration of one mineral in each broth, you would use broths containing **all the nutrients** apart from **the nutrient you were testing**. In this experiment you would also need two **control broths** — one **containing all** the nutrients and one **lacking all** the nutrients.

Practice Questions

Q1 What does it mean if a product is made sustainably?

Q2 Give two advantages of using plant fibres rather than oil-based plastics to make rope.

Q3 Name two products, other than rope, that can be made from plants.

Exam Question

Q1 A student wants to investigate both the effects of magnesium ion deficiency and nitrate ion deficiency on plant growth. Describe four different broths she would need to prepare for her investigation to produce valid results. [2 marks]

Potatoes, good for plastics and fuel — we'll be eating them next...

Renewable resources are great — they'll never run out (like my bad jokes — plenty more where they came from...). There's another experiment to learn here, but look at it like this — it could get you some easy marks in the exams.

Drugs from Plants and Drug Testing

A lot of drugs come from plants. Nowadays it's seen as a good idea to test drugs before we use them.
But back in the olden days drug testing tended to be a bit hit and miss...

Some Plants Have **Antimicrobial Properties**

Some plants have **antimicrobial properties** — they **kill** or **inhibit the growth** of microorganisms, which is why they're useful components of drugs. Here's how to investigate the antimicrobial properties of plants using **aseptic techniques**:

1) Start by preparing an **agar plate** of **bacteria** — you're likely to use bacteria that have been grown in **broth** (a mixture of distilled water, bacterial culture and nutrients). Use a **sterile pipette** to transfer the bacteria from the broth to the **agar plate** (a Petri dish containing agar jelly). **Spread the bacteria** over the plate using a **sterile plastic spreader**. Cover the plate with a **lid** until you're ready to start.

2) Once this is done, you can prepare **extracts** from the plants you want to test. To do this you need to **dry** and **grind** each plant, then soak them in **ethanol** (this will extract the antimicrobial substances, as they're soluble in ethanol). **Filter off** the **liquid bit** (the ethanol containing the dissolved plant extract).

3) Use **sterile forceps** to dip **equally-sized** discs of **sterile absorbent paper** in the plant extracts. Each disc should be left in the extract for the same amount of **time**, so they all absorb the same **volume** of liquid.

4) You also need to do a **control disc** soaked only in ethanol (to make sure it isn't the ethanol or the paper that's inhibiting bacterial growth).

5) Place the paper discs on the agar plate — make sure they're spaced out. Lightly tape the **lid on**, **invert**, and **incubate** the plate at about **25 °C** — this temperature is high enough for the bacteria to grow well, but low enough to prevent the growth of unwanted **human pathogens** (disease-causing microbes that could make you ill). Incubate for **24-48 hours** to allow the bacteria to **grow**, forming a 'lawn'.

6) Where the bacteria **can't grow** there'll be a **clear patch** in the lawn of bacteria. This is called a **clear zone**.

7) The size of a **clear zone** tells you how well the antimicrobial plant extract is working. The **larger** the zone, the **more effective** the plant extract is. You can measure the size of the clear zone by measuring the **diameter** or by working out the **area** using the formula: area = πr^2 ('r' stands for radius).

You should <u>repeat</u> the experiment at least <u>twice</u> more and take the <u>mean</u> of your results.

Agar plate with 'lawn' of bacteria

Plant extract 1 — lots of antimicrobial activity

Control disc — no antimicrobial activity

paper disc soaked in plant extract

Plant extract 2 — little antimicrobial activity

Make sure you keep all other variables (e.g. agar composition, temperature, etc.) constant.

Make Sure the **Conditions** are Right for **Bacterial Growth**

To test antimicrobial properties, the **conditions** need to be right for bacteria to **survive and reproduce**. For example:

1) Bacteria need a source of **nutrients** so they can respire and grow.

2) If they rely on aerobic respiration, they'll need a supply of **oxygen** too.

3) The **temperature** and **pH** of the environment are also important — if either of these factors is too high or too low it can affect **enzyme activity**, meaning metabolic processes (e.g. respiration) can't take place normally.

Always Use **Aseptic Techniques** to **Prevent Contamination** of Microbial Cultures

Aseptic techniques are used to **prevent contamination** of cultures by **unwanted** microorganisms. This is important because contamination can affect the **growth** of the microorganism that you're **working** with. It's also important to avoid contamination with **human pathogens**. When carrying out the investigation above, you need to use the following **aseptic techniques**:

- **Close windows** and **doors** to prevent draughts disturbing the air.
- Regularly **disinfect** work surfaces to minimise contamination. Don't put any utensils on the work surface. Contaminated utensils should be placed in a beaker of disinfectant.
- Use **sterile equipment** and **discard safely** after use. E.g. glassware can be sterilised before and after use in an autoclave (which steams equipment at high pressure). **Pre-sterilised** plastic instruments are used once then discarded.
- When **transferring bacteria** to the agar plate, work **near** a **Bunsen flame. Hot air rises**, so any microbes in the air should be drawn away from your plate.
- Briefly **flame** the neck of the glass **container of broth** just after it's **opened** and just before it's **closed** — this causes air to move out of the container, preventing **unwanted** organisms from **falling in**.

Ethanol is highly flammable so keep the plant extract and ethanol away from lit Bunsen burners. The bacteria should be transferred to the plates before the plant extract is prepared for this reason.

Drugs from Plants and Drug Testing

Testing Drugs Used to be Trial and Error

Before **new drugs** become available to the general public they need to be **tested** — to make sure they **work** and don't have any horrible **side effects**. In the past, drug testing was a lot **less scientific** than modern clinical trials (see below) and a bit more dangerous for the participants...

Example — William Withering's digitalis soup

1) **William Withering** was a scientist in the 1700s. He discovered that an extract of **foxgloves** could be used to treat **dropsy** (swelling brought about by heart failure). This extract contained the drug **digitalis**.

2) Withering made a **chance observation** — a patient suffering from dropsy made a good recovery after being treated with a **traditional remedy** containing foxgloves. Withering knew foxgloves were **poisonous**, so he started testing **different versions** of the remedy with **different concentrations** of digitalis — this became known as his **digitalis soup**.

3) **Too much** digitalis **poisoned** his patients, while **too little** had **no effect**.

4) It was through this crude method of **trial and error** that he discovered the right amount to give to a patient.

Modern Drug Testing is More Rigorous

Nowadays **drug testing protocols** are much more **controlled**. Before a drug is tried on any live subjects, computers are used to **model** the **potential effects**. Tests are also carried out on **human tissues** in a **lab**, then they're tested on **live animals** before **clinical trials** are carried out on **humans**. During clinical trials new drugs undergo **three phases of testing**. This involves three different stages, with more people at each stage:

Phase 1 — This involves testing a new drug on a **small group** of **healthy individuals**. It's done to find out things like **safe dosage**, if there are any **side effects**, and how the body **reacts** to the drug.

Phase 2 — If a drug passes Phase 1 it will then be tested on a **larger group of people** (this time **patients**) to see **how well** the drug actually **works**.

Phase 3 — During this phase the drug is **compared** to **existing treatments**. It involves testing the drug on **hundreds**, or even **thousands**, of patients. Using a large sample size makes the results of the test more **reliable**. Patients are randomly split into two groups — one group receives the **new treatment** and the other group receives the **existing treatment**. This allows scientists to tell if the new drug is **any better** than existing drugs.

Drugs that pass all three phases are considered for clinical use.

Using **placebos** and a **double blind study design** make the results of clinical trials **more valid**.

Placebos

In Phase 2 clinical trials the patients are split into **two groups**. One group is given the drug and the other is given a **placebo** — an **inactive substance** that looks exactly like the drug but doesn't actually do anything. Patients often show a **placebo effect** — where they show some improvement because they **believe** that they're receiving treatment. Giving half the patients a placebo allows researchers to see if the **drug actually works** (if it improves patients more than the placebo does).

Double blind study design

Phase 2 and 3 clinical trials are usually **double blind** — **neither** the **patients** nor the **doctors** know who's been given the new drug and who's been given the placebo (or old drug). This **reduces bias** in the results because the **attitudes** of the patients and doctors **can't affect the results**. E.g. if a doctor knows someone has received the real drug, they may think they've improved more than they actually have — but if they don't know this can't happen.

Practice Questions

Q1 Describe how modern drug testing differs from historic drug testing.

Exam Question

Q1* It has been suggested that an extract of a plant has stronger antimicrobial properties against bacterial species X than mouthwash Y.
Devise an investigation that would give valid results to show whether this suggestion is true. [6 marks]

* You will be assessed on the quality of your written response in this question.

Digitalis soup — like Alphabetti Spaghetti with numbers...

Drug testing these days is really quite complicated, what with all this three phase testing and placebos. Though if you ask me, anything that's double blind just sounds like a recipe for disaster. Anyway, you've got to know this stuff...

Factors Affecting Abundance and Distribution

You need to get to grips with what affects where organisms hang out and how many there are in an area.
(Warning: contains upsetting information about cute bunny-wunnys being eaten.)

You Need to **Learn Some Definitions** to get you **Started**

Ecosystem	— All the **organisms living** in a **particular area** and all the **non-living** (**abiotic**) factors.
Habitat	— The **place** where an organism **lives**, e.g. a rocky shore or a field.
Population	— All the organisms of **one species** in a **habitat**.
Population size	— The **number of individuals** of **one species** in a **particular area**.
Community	— All of the organisms of **different species** that live in the **same habitat** and **interact** with each other.
Abiotic factors	— The **non-living** features of the ecosystem, e.g. **temperature** and **availability of water**.
Biotic factors	— The **living** features of the ecosystem, e.g. the presence of **predators** or **food**.
Abundance	— The **number of individuals** of **one species** in a **particular area**. (It's the **same** as **population size**.)
Distribution	— **Where** a species is within a **particular area**.

The undead can find it hard to identify themselves as a living or a non-living feature of an ecosystem.

Population Size (Abundance) Varies Because of Abiotic Factors...

1) The **population size** of any species **varies** because of **abiotic** factors, e.g. the amount of **light**, **water** or **space** available, the **temperature** of their surroundings or the **chemical composition** of their surroundings.

2) When abiotic conditions are **ideal** for a species, organisms can **grow fast** and **reproduce successfully**.

> For example, when the temperature of a mammal's surroundings is the ideal temperature for **metabolic reactions** to take place, they don't have to **use up** as much energy **maintaining** their **body temperature**. This means more energy can be used for **growth** and **reproduction**, so their population size will **increase**.

3) When abiotic conditions **aren't ideal** for a species, organisms **can't** grow as **fast** or reproduce as **successfully**.

> For example, when the temperature of a mammal's surroundings is significantly **lower** or **higher** than their **optimum** body temperature, they have to **use** a lot of **energy** to maintain the right **body temperature**. This means less energy will be available for **growth** and **reproduction**, so their population size will **decrease**.

Abiotic and biotic factors are sometimes called abiotic and biotic conditions.

...and Because of Biotic Factors

(1) Interspecific Competition — Competition Between Different Species

1) Interspecific competition is when organisms of **different species compete** with each other for the **same resources**, e.g. **red** and **grey** squirrels compete for the same **food sources** and **habitats** in the **UK**.

2) Interspecific competition between two species can mean that the **resources available** to **both** populations are **reduced**, e.g. if they share the **same** source of food, there will be **less** available to both of them. This means both populations will be **limited** by a lower amount of food. They'll have less **energy** for **growth** and **reproduction**, so the population sizes will be **lower** for both species. E.g. in areas where both **red** and **grey** squirrels live, both populations are **smaller** than they would be if there was **only one** species there.

Plants compete for things like minerals, light and water.

Factors Affecting Abundance and Distribution

2) Intraspecific Competition — Competition Within a Species

Intraspecific competition is when organisms of the **same species compete** with each other for the **same resources**.

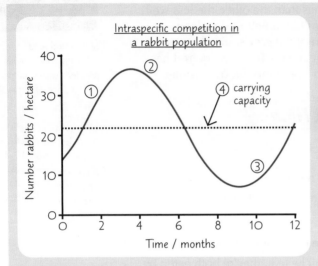

Intraspecific competition in a rabbit population

1) The **population** of a species (e.g. rabbits) **increases** when resources are **plentiful**. As the population increases, there'll be **more** organisms competing for the **same amount** of space and **food**.

2) Eventually, resources such as food and space become **limiting** — there **isn't enough** for all the organisms. The population then begins to **decline**.

3) A **smaller** population then means that there's **less competition** for space and food, which is **better** for **growth** and **reproduction** — so the population starts to **grow** again.

4) The **maximum stable population size** of a species that an ecosystem can **support** is called the **carrying capacity**.

3) Predation — Predator and Prey Population Sizes are Linked

Predation is where an organism (the predator) kills and eats another organism (the prey), e.g. lions kill and eat (**predate** on) buffalo. The **population sizes** of predators and prey are **interlinked** — as the population of one **changes**, it **causes** the other population to **change**:

1) As the **prey** population **increases**, there's **more food** for predators, so the **predator** population **grows**. E.g. in the graph on the right the **lynx** population **grows** after the **snowshoe hare** population has **increased** because there's **more food** available.

2) As the **predator** population **increases**, **more prey** is **eaten** so the **prey** population then begins to **fall**. E.g. **greater numbers** of lynx eat lots of snowshoe hares, so their population **falls**.

3) This means there's **less food** for the predators, so their population **decreases**, and so on. E.g. **reduced** snowshoe hare numbers means there's **less food** for the lynx, so their population **falls**.

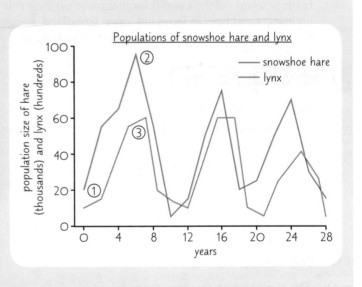

Populations of snowshoe hare and lynx

Predator-prey relationships are usually more **complicated** than this though because there are **other factors** involved, like availability of **food** for the **prey**. E.g. it's thought that the population of snowshoe hare initially begins to **decline** because there's **too many** of them for the amount of **food available**. This is then **accelerated** by predation from the lynx.

Distribution Varies Because of Abiotic Factors...

Organisms can **only exist** where the **abiotic** factors they can **survive in** exist. For example:

*   Some **plants** only grow on **south-facing slopes** in the northern hemisphere because that's where **solar input** (light intensity) is **greatest**.
*   Some plants **don't** grow near to the **shoreline** because the **soil** is **too saline** (salty).
*   **Large trees can't** grow in **polar regions** because the **temperature** is too low.

TOPIC 5A — ECOSYSTEMS AND PHOTOSYNTHESIS

Factors Affecting Abundance and Distribution

...and *Because* of *Biotic Factors*

Interspecific competition can affect the **distribution** of species. If **two** species are competing but one is **better adapted** to its surroundings than the other, the less well adapted species is likely to be **out-competed** — it **won't** be able to **exist** alongside the better adapted species. E.g. since the introduction of the **grey squirrel** to the UK, the native **red squirrel** has **disappeared** from large areas. The grey squirrel has a better chance of **survival** because it's **larger** and can store **more fat** over winter.

Never mind what the doctors said, Nutkin knew his weight problem would increase his chance of survival.

Every Species Occupies a *Different Niche*

1) A **niche** is the **role** of a species within its habitat. It includes:

   • Its **biotic** interactions — e.g. the organisms it **eats**, and those it's **eaten by**.
   • Its **abiotic** interactions — e.g. the **oxygen** an organism breathes in, and the **carbon dioxide** it breathes out.

> Don't get confused between habitat (where a species lives) and niche (what it does in its habitat).

2) Every species has its own **unique niche** — a niche can only be occupied by **one species**.

3) It may **look** like **two species** are filling the **same niche** (e.g. they're both eaten by the same species), but there'll be **slight differences** (e.g. variations in what they eat).

4) The **abundance** of different species can be **explained** by the niche concept — two species occupying **similar** niches will **compete** (e.g. for a **food source**), so **fewer individuals** of **both** species will be able to survive in the area. For example, common and soprano pipistrelle bats feed on the **same insects**. This means the **amount of food** available to both species is **reduced**, so there will be **fewer individuals** of **both** species in the same area.

5) The **distribution** of different species can also be **explained** by the niche concept — organisms can only **exist** in habitats where all the **conditions** that make up their **role exist**. For example, the soprano pipistrelle bat feeds on **insects** and lives in **farmland**, **open woodland**, **hedgerows** and **urban areas** — it **couldn't exist** in a **desert** because there are **different insects** and **no woodland**.

Practice Questions

Q1 Define the term abundance.
Q2 Give one example of how an abiotic factor can affect the abundance of organisms.
Q3 What is interspecific competition?
Q4 Give one example of interspecific competition.
Q5 Define intraspecific competition.
Q6 Give two examples of how abiotic factors can affect the distribution of organisms.

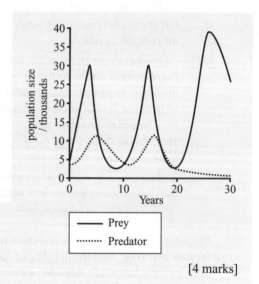

Exam Questions

Q1 The graph on the right shows the population size of a predator species and a prey species over a period of 30 years.

Analyse the data to explain how the population sizes of the predator and prey species vary over the first 10 years.

[4 marks]

Q2 Two species of lizard (X and Y) live in the same area. Both feed on the same insects and are eaten by the same predator species. Species X feeds mainly during the morning and species Y feeds mainly during the afternoon.

a) Explain the term 'niche'. [2 marks]

b) Explain how having a similar niche affects the abundance of each lizard species in the area. [2 marks]

Predator-prey relationships — they don't usually last very long...

You'd think they could have come up with names a little more different than inter- and intraspecific competition. I always remember it as int-er means diff-er-ent species. The factors that affect abundance and distribution are divided up nicely here into abiotic and biotic factors — just like predators nicely divide up their prey into bitesize chunks.

Investigating Populations and Abiotic Factors

Here are some techniques you can use while freezing to death in the rain in a field in the middle of nowhere.

You need to be able to *Investigate Populations* of *Organisms*

Investigating **populations** of organisms involves looking at the **abundance** and **distribution** of **species** in a particular **area**.

1) **Abundance** — the **number of individuals** of **one species** in a **particular area** (i.e. the **population size**). The abundance of many organisms can be estimated by simply counting the **number** of individuals in samples taken. **Percentage cover** can also be used to measure the abundance of **plants** and other **immobile organisms** — this is **how much** of the area you're investigating is **covered** by a species.

2) **Distribution** — this is **where** a particular species is within the **area you're investigating**.

Using Sampling can Speed Up Your Investigation

In most cases it'd be **too time-consuming** to count every individual organism in a habitat. Instead, a **sample** of the population is taken. **Estimates** about the whole habitat are based on the sample. Here's what sampling involves:

1) **Choose** an **area** to **sample** — a small area within the habitat being studied.

2) **Count** the number of individuals of **each species**. How you do this depends on **what** you're counting.

3) **Repeat** the process — take as many samples as possible. This gives a better indication of the **whole habitat**.

4) Use the results to **estimate** the total number of individuals or the total number of different species in the habitat being studied.

5) When sampling **different habitats** and comparing them, always use the **same sampling technique**.

Sampling can be Random or Non-Random

1) To avoid **bias** in your results, the **sample** should be **random**. For example, if you were looking at plant species in a field, you could pick random sample sites by dividing the field into a **grid** using **measuring tapes** and using a **random number generator** to select **coordinates**.

2) However, sometimes it's **necessary** to take a **non-random sample**. Non-random samples can be used in habitats where there's **a lot** of **variety** in the **abiotic features** and/or **distribution** of species in the habitat and you want to make sure **all** the **different** areas or species are **sampled**.

3) **Systematic sampling** is a type of non-random sampling. This is when samples are taken at **fixed intervals**, often along a **line**. For example, **quadrats** (see below) could be placed along a line (called a **transect**, see next page) in a habitat where the **abiotic factors** change **gradually** from one end of the sample area to the other. An example could be the coast where abiotic factors, such as soil salinity, change gradually as you get **further away** from the sea. A habitat that changes like this is said to have an **environmental gradient**.

Frame Quadrats can be used to Investigate Immobile Populations

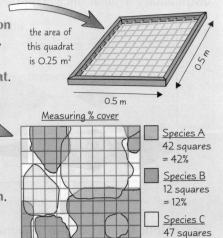

the area of this quadrat is 0.25 m²

0.5 m
0.5 m

1) A **frame quadrat** is a **square** frame, usually divided into a **grid** of 100 smaller squares by strings attached across the frame. They're **placed on the ground** within the area you're investigating. In **random sampling**, this can be done by selecting **random coordinates** (see above).

2) The **number of individuals** of each species is recorded in **each quadrat**.

3) The **percentage cover** of a **plant species** can also be measured by counting how much of the quadrat is **covered** by the plant species — you count a square if it's **more than half-covered**. Percentage cover is a **quick** way to investigate populations because you **don't** have to **count** all the **individual** plants.

4) Frame quadrats are useful for **quickly** investigating areas with species that **fit** within a **small quadrat** — most frame quadrats are **1 m by 1 m**.

5) Areas with **larger plants** and **trees** need **very large** quadrats. Large quadrats **aren't** always in a frame — they can be marked out with a **tape measure**.

Measuring % cover

Species A
42 squares
= 42%

Species B
12 squares
= 12%

Species C
47 squares
= 47%

Investigating Populations and Abiotic Factors

Point Quadrats *can also be used to* Investigate Plant Populations

1) A **point quadrat** is a **horizontal bar** on **two legs** with a series of holes at set intervals along its length.

2) Point quadrats are **placed on the ground** at **random points** within the area you're investigating.

3) **Pins** are dropped through the holes in the frame and **every plant** that each pin **touches** is **recorded**. If a pin touches several **overlapping** plants, **all** of them are recorded.

4) The **number of individuals** of each species is recorded in **each quadrat**.

5) The **percentage cover** of a species can also be measured by calculating the **number of pins** that touch a **given species**, as a **percentage** of the **total number** of pins dropped.

6) Point quadrats are especially useful in areas where there's lots of **dense vegetation** close to the ground.

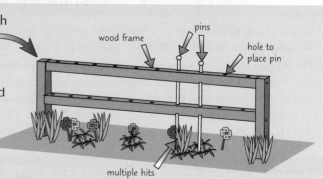

Transects *are used to* Investigate *the* Distribution *of* Plant Populations

You can use **lines** called **transects** to help find out how plants are **distributed across** an area, e.g. how species **change** from a hedge towards the middle of a field. There are **three** types of transect:

Transects can be used in any ecosystem, not just fields. For example, along a beach.

1) **Line transects** — a **tape measure** is placed **along** the transect and the species that **touch** the tape measure are **recorded**.

2) **Belt transects** — data is collected along the transect using **frame quadrats** placed **next to** each other.

3) **Interrupted transects** — instead of investigating the **whole transect** of either a line or a belt, you can take **measurements** at **intervals**. E.g. by placing **point quadrats** at **right angles** to the direction of the transect at **set intervals** along its length, such as **every 2 m**.

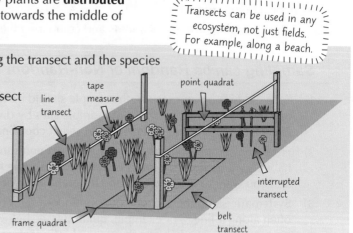

Abundance *and* Distribution *can be* Shown *on a* Kite Diagram

The results of **investigations** into the **abundance** and **distribution** of organisms can be plotted on a **kite diagram** — this allows you to **map** the distribution and abundance of organisms in an area. The **kite diagram** below shows the **distribution** and **abundance** of organisms along a **transect** in **coastal sand dunes**:

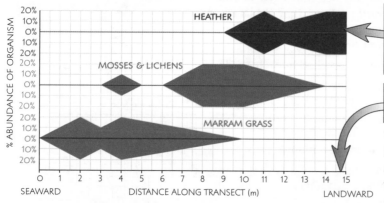

The **abundance** of each organism is shown by the **thickness** of the **kite shape**. The abundance is plotted above and below a central line to make the shape **symmetrical**.

The *x*-axis shows the **distance** along the transect line.

You can see that **marram grass** was **distributed between 0 and 10 m** along the transect. At **2 m** along the transect the **abundance** of marram grass was **20%** (i.e. it covered 20% of the quadrat). At **7 m** the abundance of marram grass was **10%**.

Some **abiotic factors** can also be plotted on a kite diagram — for example, the type of land surface along the transect, (sand, soil, rock, etc.). This information may help you to **determine** how **abiotic factors** affect the **distribution** and **abundance** of the organisms you are investigating.

TOPIC 5A — ECOSYSTEMS AND PHOTOSYNTHESIS

Investigating Populations and Abiotic Factors

You *can* also *Measure* Different *Abiotic Factors* Within a Habitat

The **abundance** and **distribution** of organisms is **affected** by **abiotic** factors. You need to know how to **measure** some of them. **Not all** habitats have the **same** abiotic factors, so you only need to measure the factors that are **appropriate** to the **habitat** that you're **investigating**. Here are some examples:

1) Climate — the weather conditions of a region over a long period of time:

   - **Temperature** is measured using a **thermometer**.
   - **Rainfall** is measured using a **rain gauge** — a **funnel** attached to a **measuring cylinder**. The rain **falls into** the funnel and **runs down** into the measuring cylinder. The **volume** of water collected over a **period of time** can be measured.
   - **Humidity** (the amount of **water vapour** in the air) is measured using an electronic **hygrometer**.

2) Oxygen availability — this only needs to be measured in aquatic habitats. The amount of oxygen dissolved in the water is measured using an electronic device called an oxygen sensor.

3) Solar input (light intensity) is measured using an electronic device called a light sensor.

4) Edaphic factors (soil conditions):

   - **pH** is measured using **indicator liquid** — a **sample** of the soil is **mixed** with **water** and an indicator liquid that **changes colour** depending on the pH. The colour is matched against a **chart** to determine the pH of the soil. Electronic **pH monitors** can also be used.
   - **Moisture content** — the **mass** of a sample of soil is measured **before** and **after** being **dried out** in an **oven** at **80-100 °C** (until it reaches a **constant mass**). The difference in mass as a **percentage** of the **original** mass of the soil is then calculated. This shows the water content of the soil sample.

5) Topography — the shape and features of the Earth's surface:

   - **Relief** (how the **height** of the land changes across a surface) can be measured by taking **height readings** using a **GPS** (global positioning system) device at **different points** across the surface. You can also use **maps** with **contour lines** (lines that join points that are the same height).
   - **Slope angle** (how **steep** a slope is) is measured using a **clinometer**. A simple clinometer is just a piece of **string** with a **weight** on the end attached to the centre of a **protractor**. You **point** the flat edge of the protractor **up the hill**, and read the slope angle off the protractor.
   - **Aspect** (the **direction** a slope is facing) is measured using a **compass**.

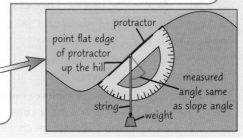

Practice Questions

Q1 What does percentage cover show?

Q2 Briefly describe how belt transects are different from line transects.

Q3 Describe how kite diagrams can be used to show the abundance and distribution of organisms in a habitat.

Exam Question

Q1 A student wants to sample a population of daffodils in a field.
   a) Describe how she could estimate the percentage cover of daffodils in the whole field using frame quadrats. [3 marks]
   b) The abundance of daffodils can be affected by different abiotic factors. State two ways climatic conditions could be measured. [2 marks]

What did the quadrat say to the policeman — I've been framed...

If you want to know what it's really like doing these investigations then read these pages outside in the pouring rain. Writing about them while you're tucked up in a nice warm, dry exam hall won't seem so bad then, take my word for it.

Succession

Repeat after me: successful succession involves several simple successive stages.

Succession is the Process of Ecosystem Change

Ecosystems (see p. 100) are **dynamic** — they are constantly **changing**. **Succession** is the process by which an **ecosystem changes** over **time**. The **biotic conditions** (e.g. **plant** and **animal communities**) change as the **abiotic conditions** (e.g. **water** availability) change. There are **two** types of succession:

Remember — biotic = living things, abiotic = non-living.

1) **Primary succession** — this happens on land that's been **newly formed** or **exposed**, e.g. where a **volcano** has erupted to form a **new rock surface**, or where **sea level** has **dropped** exposing a new area of land. There's **no soil** or **organic material** to start with, e.g. just bare rock.

2) **Secondary succession** — this happens on land that's been **cleared** of all the **plants**, but where the **soil remains**, e.g. after a **forest fire** or where a forest has been **cut down by humans**.

Succession Occurs in a Series of Stages

1) **Primary succession** starts when species **colonise** a new land surface. **Seeds** and **spores** are blown in by the **wind** and begin to **grow**. The **first species** to colonise the area are called **pioneer species**.

   - The **abiotic conditions** are hostile (**harsh**), e.g. there's no soil to **retain water**. Only pioneer species **grow** because they're **specially adapted** to cope with the harsh conditions, e.g. **marram grass** can grow on sand dunes near the sea because it has **deep roots** to get water and can **tolerate** the salty environment.

   - The pioneer species **change** the **abiotic conditions** — they **die** and **microorganisms decompose** the dead **organic material** (**humus**). This forms a **basic soil**.

   - This makes conditions **less hostile**, e.g. the basic soil helps to **retain water**, which means **new organisms** with **different adaptations** can move in and grow. These then die and are decomposed, adding **more** organic material, making the soil **deeper** and **richer in minerals**. This means **larger plants** like **shrubs** can start to grow in the deeper soil, which retains **even more** water.

   - Some new species may **change** the **environment** so that it becomes **less suitable** for the previous species. E.g. **sand sedge stabilises** the sand through the growth of **rhizomes** (underground stems). This makes the conditions **less suitable** for **marram grass**, which needs constant **reburial** by **sand** in order to grow healthily.

2) **Secondary succession** happens in the **same way**, but because there's already a **soil layer** succession starts at a **later stage** — the pioneer species in secondary succession are **larger plants**, e.g. shrubs.

3) At each stage, **different** plants and animals that are **better adapted** for the improved conditions move in, **out-compete** the plants and animals that are already there, and become the **dominant species** in the ecosystem.

4) As succession goes on, the ecosystem becomes **more complex**. New species move in **alongside** existing species, which means that **biodiversity** (the variety of living organisms) **increases**.

5) The **final stage** is called the **climax community** — the ecosystem is supporting the **largest** and **most complex** community of plants and animals it can. It **won't change** much more — it's in a **steady state**.

This example shows primary succession on bare rock, but succession also happens on sand dunes, salt marshes and even on lakes.

Example of primary succession — bare rock to woodland

1) **Pioneer species colonise** the rocks. E.g. **lichens** grow **on** and **break down** rocks, **releasing minerals**.

2) The lichens **die** and are **decomposed** helping to form a **thin soil**, which thickens as more **organic material** is formed. This means other species such as **mosses** can **grow**.

3) **Larger plants** that need **more water** can move in as the soil **deepens**, e.g. **grasses** and **small flowering plants**. The soil **continues to deepen** as the larger plants die and are decomposed.

4) **Shrubs, ferns** and **small trees** begin to grow, **out-competing** the grasses and smaller plants to become the **dominant** species. **Diversity increases**.

5) Finally, the soil is **deep** and **rich** enough in **nutrients** to support **large trees**. These become the dominant species, and the **climax community** is formed.

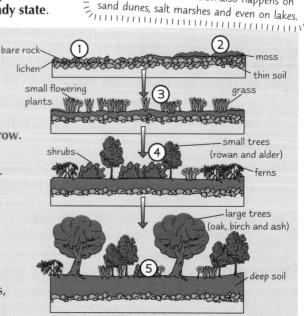

Succession

Different Ecosystems have Different Climax Communities

Which species make up the climax community depends on what the **climate** is like in an ecosystem. The climax community for a **particular** climate is called its **climatic climax**. For example:

- In a **temperate climate** there's **plenty** of **available water**, **mild temperatures** and not much **change** between the seasons. The climatic climax will contain **large trees** because they **can grow** in these conditions once **deep soils** have developed.

- In a **polar climate** there's **not much available water**, temperatures are **low** and there are **massive changes** between the seasons. Large trees **won't ever** be able to grow in these conditions, so the climatic climax contains only **herbs** or **shrubs**, but it's still the **climax community**.

Succession can be Prevented

Human activities can **prevent succession**, stopping a climax community from **developing**. When succession is stopped **artificially** like this the climax community is called a **plagioclimax**. For example:

A **regularly mown** grassy field **won't develop** shrubs and trees (**woody plants**), even if the climate of the ecosystem could support them. The **growing points** of the woody plants are **cut off** by the lawnmower, so larger plants **can't establish** themselves. The **longer** the interval between mowing, the **further** succession can progress and the more **diversity increases**. But with **more frequent** mowing, succession can't progress and diversity will be **lower** — only the grasses can **survive** being mowed.

A mighty weapon with which to tame the forces of nature.

Practice Questions

Q1 What is the difference between primary and secondary succession?

Q2 What is the name given to species that are the first to colonise an area during succession?

Q3 As succession continues, what happens to the biodiversity in the area?

Q4 What is meant by a climax community?

Q5 Give an example of how succession can be prevented.

Exam Questions

Q1 Succession occurs on sand dunes.
You can often see the different stages of succession as you move further inland from the shoreline.

a) Name the type of succession that is taking place when the first grasses start to appear on the dune.
Give a reason for your answer. [2 marks]

b) Explain how the growth of grasses can lead to the colonisation
of the dune by larger plants like shrubs. [2 marks]

Q2 A farmer has a field where he plants crops every year. When the crops are fully grown he removes them all and then ploughs the field (churns up all the plants and soil so the field is left as bare soil). The farmer has decided not to plant crops or plough the field for several years.

a)* Describe, in terms of succession, what will happen in the field over time. [6 marks]

b) Explain why succession doesn't usually take place in the farmer's field. [2 marks]

* You will be assessed on the quality of your written response in this question.

Revision succession — bare brain to a woodland of knowledge...

When answering questions on succession, examiners are keen on you using the right terminology — that means saying "pioneer species" instead of "the first plants to grow there". This stuff's quite wordy, but the concept of succession is simple enough — some plants start growing, change the environment so it's less hostile, then others can move in.

Photosynthesis and Energy Supply

OK, this isn't the easiest subject in the book, but 'cos I'm feeling nice today we'll take it slowly, one bit at a time...

You Need to **Know Some Technical Terms** Before You Start

Phosphorylation — **adding phosphate** to a molecule, e.g. **ADP** is phosphorylated to **ATP** (see below).

Photophosphorylation — **adding phosphate** to a molecule using **light**.

Photolysis — the **splitting** (lysis) of a molecule using **light** (photo) energy.

Hydrolysis — the **splitting** (lysis) of a molecule using **water** (hydro), e.g. **ATP** is hydrolysed to **ADP**.

Redox reactions — reactions that involve **oxidation** and **reduction**:

- If something is **reduced** it has **gained electrons** (e⁻), and may have **gained hydrogen** or lost oxygen.
- If something is **oxidised** it has **lost electrons**, and may have **lost hydrogen** or gained oxygen.
- Oxidation of one molecule **always** involves reduction of another molecule.

Biological Processes Need Energy

Plant and animal cells **need energy** for biological processes to occur:

- **Plants** need energy for things like **photosynthesis**, **active transport** (e.g. to take in minerals via their roots), **DNA replication**, **cell division** and **protein synthesis**.
- **Animals** need energy for things like **muscle contraction**, maintenance of **body temperature**, **active transport**, **DNA replication**, **cell division** and **protein synthesis**.

Without energy, these biological processes would stop and the plant or animal would die.

Photosynthesis Stores Energy in Glucose

1) **Photosynthesis** is the process where **energy** from **light** is used to **break apart** the **strong bonds** in H_2O molecules. **Hydrogen** from the breakdown of H_2O is **stored** in **glucose** (a **fuel**), which is formed when the hydrogen is **combined** with CO_2. O_2 is formed and **released** into the **atmosphere** during this process.

2) Photosynthesis occurs in a **series** of **reactions**, but the overall equation is:

$$6CO_2 + 6H_2O + Energy \longrightarrow C_6H_{12}O_6 \text{ (glucose)} + 6O_2$$

3) So, energy is **stored** in the **glucose** until the plants **release** it by **respiration** (see page 152).

4) Animals obtain glucose by **eating plants** (or **other animals**), then respire the glucose to release energy.

ATP is the Immediate Source of Energy in a Cell

1) A cell **can't** get its energy **directly** from glucose.

2) During respiration, glucose is **broken down** (see page 152). This process **releases energy**, which is then used to **make ATP** (adenosine triphosphate).

3) ATP **carries energy** around the cell to where it's **needed**.

4) It's **synthesised** by the **phosphorylation** of **ADP** using energy from an **energy-releasing** reaction, e.g. the **breakdown** of **glucose** in **respiration**. The energy is stored as **chemical energy** in the **phosphate bond**. The enzyme **ATP synthase** catalyses this reaction.

5) ATP **diffuses** to the part of the cell that **needs** energy.

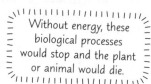

ENERGY USED

ADP + Pᵢ — ribose — phosphate — inorganic phosphate — ATP synthase — ATP

adenine — adenosine diphosphate i.e. it has 2 phosphates — ATPase — ENERGY RELEASED — adenosine triphosphate i.e. it has 3 phosphates

6) Here, it's **broken down** via hydrolysis back into **ADP** and **inorganic phosphate** (Pᵢ). Chemical energy is **released** from the phosphate bond and used by the cell. **ATPase** catalyses this reaction.

7) The ADP and inorganic phosphate are **recycled** and the process starts again.

ADP stands for adenine diphosphate — di because it has two phosphates. Inorganic phosphate (Pᵢ) is just the fancy name for a single phosphate.

Photosynthesis and Energy Supply

Photosynthesis Involves Enzymes and Coenzymes

1) Photosynthesis uses **lots** of different **enzymes**, e.g. RUBISCO (see p. 112). This means that the **rate** at which photosynthesis can occur is **affected** by the **same things** that affect the **rate** of other **enzyme-controlled reactions**, e.g. temperature (see p. 120).

2) Photosynthesis also relies on the action of **coenzymes**. A coenzyme is a molecule that **aids** the **function** of an **enzyme**. They work by **transferring** a **chemical group** from one molecule to another.

3) A coenzyme used in **photosynthesis** is **NADP**. NADP transfers **hydrogen** from one molecule to another — this means it can **reduce** (give hydrogen to) or **oxidise** (take hydrogen from) a molecule.

Photosynthesis Takes Place in the Chloroplasts of Plant Cells

You need to know about **chloroplasts** and how their structure is **related** to the **role** they play in **photosynthesis**.

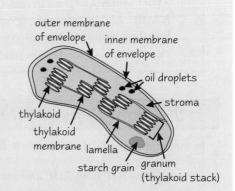

1) **Chloroplasts** are **flattened organelles** found in **plant cells**.

2) They have a **double membrane** called the **chloroplast envelope**. The **chloroplast envelope** keeps the **reactants** for photosynthesis **close** to their **reaction sites**.

3) The **thylakoids** (fluid-filled sacs) have a **large surface area** to allow as much **light energy** to be **absorbed** as possible. They're **stacked up** in the chloroplast into structures called **grana** (singular = **granum**). The grana are **linked** together by bits of thylakoid membrane called **lamellae** (singular = **lamella**). **Lots of ATP synthase** molecules are present in the thylakoid membranes to **produce ATP** in the light-dependent reaction (see pages 110-111).

4) Chloroplasts contain **photosynthetic pigments** (e.g. **chlorophyll a**, **chlorophyll b** and **carotene**). These are **coloured substances** that **absorb** the **light energy** needed for photosynthesis. The pigments are found in the **thylakoid membranes** — they're attached to **proteins**. The protein and pigment is called a **photosystem**.

5) There are **two** photosystems used by plants to capture light energy. **Photosystem I** (or PSI) absorbs light best at a wavelength of **700 nm** and **photosystem II** (PSII) absorbs light best at **680 nm**.

6) Contained within the inner membrane of the chloroplast and **surrounding** the thylakoids is a gel-like substance called the **stroma**. It contains all the **enzymes**, **sugars** and **organic acids** required for the light-independent reaction to take place (see pages 111-112), as well as **oil droplets** (which store **non-carbohydrate organic material**).

Practice Questions

Q1 Briefly describe how carbon dioxide and water produce glucose and oxygen during photosynthesis.

Q2 Name the process that is used to synthesise ATP from ADP.

Q3 How is ATP able to provide energy for metabolic processes in a cell?

Exam Question

Q1 Chloroplasts are organelles found in plant cells, which contain photosynthetic pigments. They are the site of photosynthesis.

    a) State the function of photosynthetic pigments in photosynthesis.   [1 mark]

    b) Other than the presence of photosynthetic pigments, explain **three** ways in which the structure of a chloroplast is adapted to carry out photosynthesis.   [3 marks]

Oh dear, I've used up all my energy on these two pages...

Well, I won't beat about the bush, this stuff is pretty tricky... nearly as hard as a cross between Hugh Jackman and concrete. With a little patience and perseverance (and plenty of [chocolate] [coffee] [marshmallows] — delete as you wish), you'll get there. Once you've got these pages straight in your head, the next ones will be easier to understand.

Photosynthesis Reactions

Right, pen at the ready. Check. Brain switched on. Check. Cuppa piping hot. Check. Sweets on standby. Check. Okay, I think you're all sorted to look at what happens in photosynthesis. Here we go...

Photosynthesis can be Split into Two Stages

See page 112 for the stages of the Calvin cycle.

There are actually **two stages** that make up **photosynthesis**:

1) The Light-Dependent Reaction

1) As the name suggests, this reaction **needs light energy**.

2) It takes place in the **thylakoid membranes** of the chloroplasts.

3) Here, light energy is absorbed by **photosynthetic pigments** in the **photosystems** and converted to **chemical energy**.

4) The light energy is used to add a phosphate group to ADP to form **ATP**, and to reduce NADP to form **reduced NADP**. **ATP transfers energy** and reduced **NADP transfers hydrogen** to the light-independent reaction.

5) During the process H_2O is oxidised to O_2.

2) The Light-Independent Reaction

1) This is also called the **Calvin cycle** and as the name suggests it **doesn't use light energy** directly. (But it does **rely on the products** of the light-dependent reaction).

2) It takes place in the **stroma** of the chloroplasts.

3) Here, the **ATP** and **reduced NADP** from the light-dependent reaction supply the **energy** and **hydrogen** to make **glucose** from CO_2.

In the *Light-Dependent Reaction*, ATP is Made by *Photophosphorylation*

In the light-dependent reaction, the **light energy** absorbed by the photosystems is used for **three** things:

1) Making **ATP** from **ADP** and **inorganic phosphate**. This reaction is called **photophosphorylation** (see p. 108).

2) Making **reduced NADP** from **NADP**.

3) Splitting **water** into **protons** (H^+ ions), **electrons** and **oxygen**. This is called **photolysis** (see below).

The light-dependent reaction actually includes **two types** of **photophosphorylation** — **non-cyclic** and **cyclic**. Each of these processes has **different products**.

Non-cyclic Photophosphorylation Produces ATP, Reduced NADP and O_2

To understand the process you need to know that the photosystems (in the thylakoid membranes) are **linked** by **electron carriers**. Electron carriers are **proteins** that **transfer electrons**. The photosystems and electron carriers form an **electron transport chain** — a **chain** of **proteins** through which **excited electrons flow**. All the processes in the diagrams are happening together — I've just split them up to make it easier to understand.

1) Light energy excites electrons in chlorophyll

- **Light energy** is absorbed by **PSII**.
- The light energy **excites electrons** in **chlorophyll**.
- The electrons move to a **higher energy level** (i.e. they have more energy).
- These high-energy electrons **move along the electron transport chain** to **PSI**.

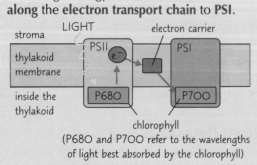

(P680 and P700 refer to the wavelengths of light best absorbed by the chlorophyll)

2) Photolysis of water produces protons (H^+ ions), electrons and O_2

- As the excited electrons **from chlorophyll leave PSII** to **move along** the electron transport chain, they must be **replaced**.
- **Light** energy splits **water** into **protons** (H^+ ions), **electrons** and **oxygen**. (So the O_2 in photosynthesis comes from water.) This process is called **photolysis**.
- The reaction is: $H_2O \rightarrow 2H^+ + \frac{1}{2}O_2$

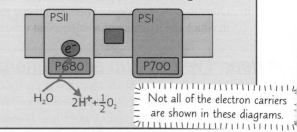

Not all of the electron carriers are shown in these diagrams.

Photosynthesis Reactions

(3) Energy from the excited electrons makes ATP...

- The excited electrons **lose energy** as they **move along** the **electron transport chain**.

- This energy is used to **transport protons into** the **thylakoids** so that the thylakoid has a **higher concentration** of protons than the stroma. This forms a **proton gradient** across the membrane.

- Protons move **down** their concentration gradient, into the stroma, **via** the enzyme **ATP synthase**. The energy from this movement combines **ADP** and **inorganic phosphate** (P_i) to form **ATP**.

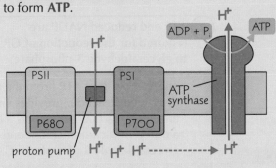

Chemiosmosis is the name of the process where the movement of H^+ ions across a membrane generates ATP. This process also occurs in respiration (see p. 155).

(4) ...and generates reduced NADP.

- Light energy is **absorbed** by PSI, which excites the electrons again to an **even higher** energy level.

- Finally, the electrons are **transferred** to NADP, along with a **proton** (H^+ ion) from the **stroma**, to form **reduced NADP**.

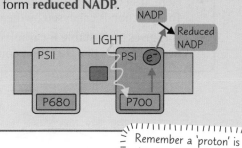

Remember a 'proton' is just another word for a hydrogen ion (H^+).

Cyclic Photophosphorylation Only Produces ATP

Cyclic photophosphorylation **only uses PSI**. It's called 'cyclic' because the electrons from the chlorophyll molecule **aren't** passed onto NADP, but are **passed back** to PSI via electron carriers. This means the electrons are **recycled** and can repeatedly flow through PSI. This process doesn't produce any reduced NADP or O_2 — it **only produces** small amounts of **ATP**.

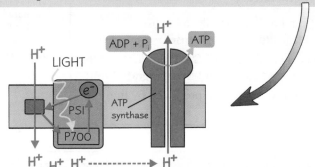

I wanted to put a 'cycling' joke here, but I couldn't think of one, so here's a picture of a man swallowing a bike.

The *Light-Independent* Reaction is also called the *Calvin Cycle*

1) The **Calvin cycle** takes place in the **stroma** of the chloroplasts.

2) It makes a molecule called **glyceraldehyde 3-phosphate** (GALP) from **CO_2** and **ribulose bisphosphate** (a 5-carbon compound). GALP can be used to make **glucose** and other **useful organic substances** (see next page).

   Glyceraldehyde 3-phosphate (GALP) is also known as triose phosphate (TP).

3) There are a few steps in the cycle, and it needs **ATP** and **H^+ ions** to keep it going. These are provided by **ATP** and **reduced NADP** from the **light-dependent reaction**.

4) The reactions are linked in a **cycle**, which means the starting compound, **ribulose bisphosphate**, is **regenerated**.

5) The Calvin cycle is also known as **carbon dioxide fixation** because carbon from **CO_2** is 'fixed' into an **organic molecule**.

Photosynthesis Reactions

The *Calvin Cycle Fixes Carbon* in *Organic Molecules*

Here's what happens at each stage in the Calvin cycle:

1 **Carbon dioxide is combined with ribulose bisphosphate to form two molecules of glycerate 3-phosphate**

- CO_2 enters the leaf through the **stomata** and diffuses into the **stroma** of the chloroplast.
- Here, it's combined with **ribulose bisphosphate** (RuBP).
  This reaction is catalysed by the enzyme **RUBISCO**.
- This gives an **unstable 6-carbon** compound, which quickly breaks down into
  two molecules of a **3-carbon** compound called **glycerate 3-phosphate** (GP).

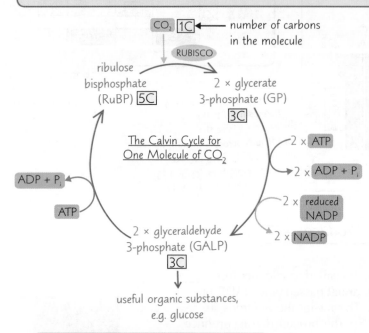

number of carbons in the molecule

The Calvin Cycle for One Molecule of CO_2

useful organic substances, e.g. glucose

2 **ATP and reduced NADP are required for the reduction of GP to glyceraldehyde 3-phosphate**

- The hydrolysis of **ATP** (from the **light-dependent** reaction) **provides energy** to turn the **3-carbon** compound, **GP**, into a **different** 3-carbon compound called **glyceraldehyde 3-phosphate** (GALP).
- This reaction also requires **H$^+$ ions**, which come from **reduced NADP** (also from the **light-dependent reaction**). **Reduced NADP** is recycled to NADP.
- Some **GALP** is then converted into **useful organic compounds** (e.g. **glucose**) and some **continues** in the **Calvin cycle** to regenerate RuBP (see below).

3 **Ribulose bisphosphate is regenerated**

- Two molecules of **GALP** can be used to make a **hexose sugar** (a sugar with six carbon atoms, e.g. **glucose**).
- However, **five** out of every **six** molecules of **GALP** produced in the cycle aren't used to make hexose sugars, but to **regenerate RuBP**.
- Regenerating RuBP uses the **rest** of the **ATP** produced by the **light-dependent reaction**.

Reduced NADP reduces GP to GALP — reduction reactions are explained on p. 108.

Calvin Cycle Products can be *Used* to *Make Other Organic Substances*

The Calvin cycle is the starting point for making **all** the organic substances a plant needs. **Glyceraldehyde 3-phosphate** (GALP) and **glycerate 3-phosphate** (GP) molecules are used to make essential **biological molecules**:

- **Carbohydrates** — **simple sugars** (e.g. glucose) are made by joining **two GALP molecules** together, and **polysaccharides** (e.g. starch and cellulose) are made by joining **hexose sugars** together in **different ways**. The production of **glucose** is very important as it's used in **respiration**, which provides the **energy** needed for biological processes (see page 152).
- **Lipids** — these are made using **glycerol**, which is synthesised from **GALP**, and **fatty acids**, which are synthesised from **GP**.
- **Amino acids** — some amino acids are made from **GP**.
- **Nucleic acids** — the sugar in **RNA** (**ribose**) is made using **GALP**.

The **simple sugars** produced by photosynthesis can be passed on to **animals** and **other organisms** via **food chains**. These organisms use the simple sugars for **respiration** and as a starting point to **synthesise** new **biological molecules**.

Photosynthesis Reactions

You Can *Investigate Photosynthesis* Using *Extracts* of *Chloroplasts*

1) In **photosystem I**, during the **light-dependent** stage of photosynthesis, **NADP** acts as an **electron acceptor** — it **accepts electrons** and a **proton** released from **split water molecules**, causing it to become **reduced**. **Oxygen** is released in the process. The reaction is called the **Hill reaction**, named after British biologist Robert Hill, who discovered it.

2) The **rate** of the **Hill reaction** can be **investigated** by adding a **redox indicator dye**, e.g. **DCPIP**, to isolated **chloroplasts**. Like **NADP**, the dye acts as an electron acceptor and gets reduced during the light-dependent reaction. As the dye gets reduced, you'll see a **colour change** (**DCPIP** changes from **blue** to **colourless**). Measuring the **rate** of the **colour change** gives an indication of the rate of the Hill reaction.

3) The experiment below describes how you can do this. For the experiment, you'll need a **colorimeter** — a machine that measures how much **light** a solution **absorbs** when a light source is **shone** directly **through** it.

1) **Cut** a few **leaves** (spinach works well) into pieces. Remove any tough stalks.

2) Using a pestle and mortar, **grind** up the **leaf pieces** with some **chilled isolation solution** (a solution of **sucrose**, **potassium chloride** and **phosphate buffer** at **pH 7**). **Filter** the **liquid** you make into a **beaker** through a **funnel** lined with **muslin cloth**. Transfer the liquid to **centrifuge tubes** and centrifuge them at **high speed** for **10 minutes**. This will make the **chloroplasts** gather at the **bottom** of each tube in a '**pellet**'.

3) **Get rid** of the **liquid** from the top of the tubes, **leaving** the **pellets** in the bottom.

4) **Re-suspend** the pellets in **fresh**, chilled **isolation solution**. This is your **chloroplast extract**. **Store** it on **ice** for the rest of the experiment.

5) Set up a **colorimeter** with a **red filter** and **zero** it using a cuvette (a cuboid-shaped vessel used in colorimeters) containing the **chloroplast extract** and **distilled water**.

6) Set up a **test tube rack** at a **set distance** from a **bench lamp**. Switch the lamp on.

7) Put a test tube in the rack, add a **set volume** of **chloroplast extract** to the tube and a **set volume** of **DCPIP**. **Mix** the contents of the tube together.

8) **Immediately** take a sample of the mixture from the tube and add it to a **clean cuvette**. Then place the cuvette in your colorimeter and **record** the **absorbance**. Do this every **2 minutes** for the next **10 minutes**.

9) **Repeat** the experiment twice more, ensuring that the **tubes** are **exposed** to the **light source** for the **same amount** of **time** and are the **same distance** from it, as these variables affect the **number** of **electrons released**.

Sucrose is included in the isolation solution to prevent water being drawn from the chloroplasts by osmosis.

pellet

As the Hill reaction takes place, the **absorbance** will **decrease** as the DCPIP gets **reduced** and **loses** its **blue colour**. The **faster** the absorbance decreases, the **faster** the **rate** of the **Hill reaction**. You can plot a **graph** of **absorbance against time** to help you visualise your results. This experiment can also be **adapted** to investigate the effects of **different variables** on the **rate** of photosynthesis. For example, the effect of **light intensity** can be investigated by altering the **distance** of the tubes from the **light source**.

You should also prepare two negative control tubes. The first should contain only DCPIP and chilled isolation solution. The second should contain both DCPIP and chloroplast extract, but it should be wrapped in tin foil (so no light reaches the tube). No change in absorbance should be seen for these two controls. They show that the DCPIP colour change only occurs because of the action of the chloroplasts and that the colour of DCPIP doesn't just naturally deteriorate over time.

Practice Questions

Q1 What three substances does non-cyclic photophosphorylation produce?

Q2 Where in the chloroplasts does the light-independent reaction occur?

Q3 How is glucose produced as a result of the Calvin cycle?

Q4 Describe how a redox indicator dye can be used to investigate the Hill reaction.

Exam Questions

Q1 RUBISCO is an enzyme that catalyses the first reaction of the Calvin cycle. CA1P is an inhibitor of RUBISCO.
   a) Describe how GALP is produced in the Calvin cycle. [5 marks]
   b) Briefly explain how ribulose bisphosphate (RuBP) is regenerated in the Calvin cycle. [2 marks]
   c) Explain the effect that CA1P would have on glucose production. [3 marks]

Calvin cycles — bikes made by people who normally make pants...

There's a lot to learn here, but it's all important. When you're done, maybe prepare a plan just in case zombies are real.

Energy Transfer and Productivity

Some organisms get their energy from the Sun, some get it from other organisms, and it's all very friendly. Yeah right. These pages tell you all you need to know about how energy is transferred through ecosystems.

Energy is Transferred Through Ecosystems

1) The main route by which energy **enters** an ecosystem is **photosynthesis** (e.g. by plants, see page 108).

2) During photosynthesis plants **convert sunlight energy** into a form that can be **used** by other organisms — plants are called **producers** (because they produce **organic molecules** using sunlight energy).

3) Producers store sunlight energy as **biomass**, so you can think of the following **energy transfers** through ecosystems as **biomass transfers**.

> Biomass is the <u>mass</u> of <u>living material</u>, e.g. the mass of plant material.

4) Energy is **transferred** through the **living organisms** of an ecosystem when organisms **eat** other organisms, e.g. producers are eaten by organisms called **primary consumers**. Primary consumers are then eaten by **secondary consumers** and secondary consumers are eaten by **tertiary consumers**. Each of the **stages** (e.g. producers, primary consumers) is called a **trophic level**.

Not All Energy gets Transferred to the Next Trophic Level

1) **Not all** the energy (e.g. from sunlight or food) that's available to the organisms in a trophic level is **transferred** to the **next** trophic level — around **90%** of the **total available energy** is **lost** in various ways.

2) Some of the available energy (**60%**) is **never taken in** by the organisms in the first place. E.g.

   - Plants **can't use** all the light energy that reaches their **leaves**, e.g. some is the **wrong wavelength**, some is **reflected**, and some **passes straight through** the leaves.

   - Some sunlight can't be used because it hits parts of the plant that **can't photosynthesise**, e.g. the bark of a tree.

   - Some **parts** of food, e.g. **roots** or **bones**, **aren't eaten** by organisms so the energy isn't taken in — they pass to **decomposers** (organisms that **break down dead** or **undigested** material).

   - Some parts of food are **indigestible** so **pass through** organisms and come out as **waste**, e.g. faeces — this also passes to **decomposers**.

> The percentages used are general figures — real values for a given ecosystem will vary.

3) The rest of the available energy (**40%**) is **taken in** (**absorbed**) — this is called the **gross productivity**. But not all of this is available to the next trophic level either.

   - **30%** of the **total energy** available (75% of the gross productivity) is **lost to the environment** when organisms use energy produced from **respiration** for **movement** or body **heat**. This is called **respiratory loss**.

   - **10%** of the **total energy** available (25% of the gross productivity) becomes **biomass** (e.g. it's **stored** or used for **growth**) — this is called the **net productivity**.

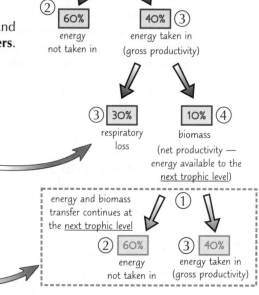

4) **Net productivity** (or **biomass**) is the amount of energy that's **available** to the **next trophic level**. The **flow** of energy transfer **continues** at the **next trophic level** — the process starts again from the beginning (back to step 1). Here's how net productivity is **calculated**:

> **net productivity = gross productivity − respiratory loss**

> **EXAMPLE:** The rabbits in an ecosystem receive **20 000 kJm⁻²yr⁻¹** of energy, but don't take in **12 000 kJm⁻²yr⁻¹** of it, so their gross productivity is **8000 kJm⁻²yr⁻¹** (20 000 − 12 000).
> They lose **6000 kJm⁻²yr⁻¹** using energy from **respiration**.
> You can use this to **calculate** the **net productivity** of the rabbits:
>
> **net productivity = 8000 − 6000 = 2000 kJm⁻²yr⁻¹**

5) You might be asked to **calculate** how **efficient** energy transfer from one trophic level to another is:

> The rabbits receive **20 000 kJm⁻²yr⁻¹**, and their **net productivity** is **2000 kJm⁻²yr⁻¹**. So the **percentage efficiency** of **energy transfer** is:
>
> **(net productivity ÷ energy received) × 100 = (2000 ÷ 20 000) × 100 = 10%**

Energy Transfer and Productivity

Primary Productivity can be Calculated too

When you're **just** talking about **producers** (e.g. plants), net productivity is called **net primary productivity** (**NPP**) and gross productivity is called **gross primary productivity** (**GPP**), so the equation is:

$$NPP = GPP - \text{plant respiration}$$

NPP is lower when it's cold or there's not a lot of light, as photosynthesis is slower.

Here's an example of how **net primary productivity** is **calculated**:

The **grass** in an ecosystem receives **950 000 kJm⁻²yr⁻¹** of sunlight energy. It doesn't take in **931 000 kJm⁻²yr⁻¹** of the energy received, so the gross primary productivity of the grass is **19 000 kJm⁻²yr⁻¹** (950 000 – 931 000). The grass loses **8000 kJm⁻²yr⁻¹** using energy from **respiration**. You can use this to **calculate** the **net primary productivity** of the grass:

net primary productivity = 19 000 – 8000
= 11 000 kJm⁻²yr⁻¹

Energy Transfer Between Trophic Levels can be Measured

1) To **measure** the **energy transfer** between two trophic levels you need to **calculate** the **difference** between the amount of **energy** in each level (the net productivity of each level).

2) You can **calculate** the **amount of energy** in a trophic level by measuring the **dry mass** of the organisms (their **biomass**). Remember, energy is stored as biomass, so it indicates **how much energy** an organism **contains**.

3) First you calculate the amount of biomass in a **sample** of the organisms, e.g. a 1 m² area of **wheat** or a single **mouse** that feeds on the wheat. This can be done by **drying** the organisms, often in an **oven** set to a **low temperature**. The sample is then weighed at **regular intervals** (e.g. every day). Once the mass becomes **constant**, you know that all the **water** has been **removed**.

In reality, the dry mass of animals may need to be estimated, as killing them to find their dry mass is not very ethical.

4) Then you **multiply** the results from the **sample** by the **size** of the **total population** (e.g. a 10 000 m² **field** of wheat or the **number** of mice in the population) to give the **total** amount of energy in the organisms at that **trophic level**.

5) The **difference** in **energy** between the trophic levels is the amount of energy **transferred**.

6) There are **problems** with this method though. For example, the consumers (mice) might have **taken in energy** from sources **other than** the producer measured (wheat). This means the difference between the two figures calculated **wouldn't** be an **accurate** estimate of the energy transferred between **only those two** organisms. For an **accurate estimate** you'd need to include **all** the individual organisms at each trophic level.

Practice Questions

Q1 Briefly explain why not all the energy from one trophic level gets transferred to the next trophic level.

Q2 What is meant by 'gross primary productivity'?

Q3 State the formula for net primary productivity.

Exam Question

Grass 13 883 kJ m⁻²yr⁻¹	→	Arctic hare 2345 kJ m⁻²yr⁻¹	→	Arctic fox 137 kJ m⁻²yr⁻¹

Q1 The diagram above shows the net productivity of different trophic levels in a food chain.

a) Explain why the net productivity of the Arctic hare is less than the net primary productivity of the grass.

[4 marks]

b) Calculate the percentage efficiency of energy transfer from the Arctic hare to the Arctic fox.

[1 mark]

Boy, do I need an energy transfer this morning...

It's really important to remember that energy transfer through an ecosystem isn't 100% efficient — most gets lost along the way so the next organisms don't get all the energy. Make sure you can calculate productivity and the efficiency of energy transfers — you might not like maths, but they're fairly easy marks in the exam if you remember the methods.

Introduction to Climate Change

A-level student, meet climate change — take a few pages to get to know each other...

Climate Change is Long-Term Changes in Global Weather Patterns

1) **Climate change** is the term used to describe a significant change in the **weather** of a region usually over a period of **several decades**.

2) It includes **natural variations** in climate but is commonly used to refer to the changes caused by **humans** (see page 118).

3) **Global warming** is a type of climate change — it's the **rapid increase** in **global temperature** seen over the **last century**.

4) Global warming **causes other types** of climate change, e.g. changing **rainfall patterns** and **seasonal cycles**.

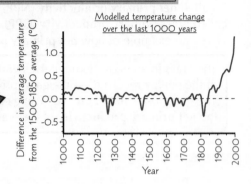

You Need to be able to Interpret Evidence for Climate Change

There are **different types** of **evidence** that can be used to show that climate change **is happening**. Here are **three** types of evidence for climate change that you need to be able to understand:

(1) Temperature Records

1) Since the 1850s **temperature** has been **measured** around the world using **thermometers**.

2) This gives a **reliable** but **short-term** record of global temperature change.

3) Here's an example of how a **temperature record** from thermometer measurements **shows** that climate change **is happening**:

> 1) The graph on the right shows the **temperature record** from thermometer measurements.
>
> 2) Average global temperature **fluctuated** around **13.6 °C** between **1850** and **1910**.
>
> 3) It has **steadily increased** (with a couple of fluctuations) from **13.6 °C** in **1910** to around **14.4 °C** today.
>
> 4) The **general trend** of **increasing** global temperature over the last century (since 1910) is **evidence** for **climate change**.

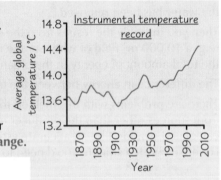

(2) Dendrochronology (Tree rings)

1) **Dendrochronology** is a method for figuring out **how old** a **tree** is using **tree rings** (the rings formed within the trunk of a tree as it grows).

2) Most trees produce **one ring** within their trunks **every year**.

3) The **thickness** of the ring depends on the **climate** when the ring was formed — when it's **warmer** the rings are **thicker** (because the conditions for growth are better).

4) Scientists can take **cores** through **tree trunks** then **date** each ring by **counting** them **back** from when the core was taken. By looking at the **thickness** of the rings they can see what the **climate** was like **each year**.

5) Here's an example of how dendrochronology **shows** that climate change **is happening**:

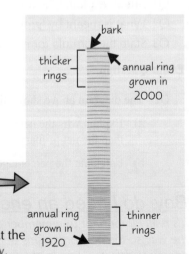

> 1) The diagram on the right shows a **core** taken from a **tree** in 2000.
>
> 2) The **most recent** rings are the **thickest** and the rings get **steadily thinner** the further in the **past** they were formed.
>
> 3) The **trend** of increasingly thicker rings from **1920** to **2000** suggests that the climate where the tree lived had become **warmer** over the **last century**.

Introduction to Climate Change

③ Pollen in Peat Bogs

Pollen in peat bogs can be used to show how **temperature** has **changed** over **thousands** of years.
Here's how it works:

1) **Pollen** is often **preserved** in **peat bogs** (acidic wetland areas).

2) Peat bogs accumulate in **layers** so the **age** of the preserved **pollen increases** with **depth**.

3) Scientists can take **cores** from peat bogs and extract **pollen grains** from the different aged layers.
   They then **identify** the **plant species** the pollen came from.

4) Only **fully grown** (mature) plant species **produce pollen**, so the samples only show the species that were **successful** at that time.

5) Scientists know the **climates** that different plant species live in **now**. When they find preserved pollen from **similar plants**, it indicates that the **climate** was **similar** when that pollen was **produced**.

6) Because plant species **vary** with **climate** the preserved pollen will **vary** as climate **changes** over time.

7) So a gradual **increase** in **pollen** from a plant species that's **more successful** in **warmer climates** would show a **rise** in **temperature** (a decrease in pollen from a plant that needs cold conditions would show the same thing).

8) Here's an example of how pollen in peat bogs can provide **evidence** for climate change in the **past**:

---

1) The table shows data on **samples** of **pollen** taken from a **core** of a **peat bog**.

2) Between **7100** and **3100 years ago** the number of **oak tree** pollen grains **increased** from **51** grains to **253** grains.

3) This suggests that the **climate** in the area had become **better** for **oak trees** — more oak trees **reached maturity** and **produced pollen**.

4) Between **7100** and **3100** years ago the number of **fir tree** pollen grains in the sample **decreased** from **231** grains to **28** grains.

5) This suggests that the **climate** in the area had become **worse** for **fir trees** — **fewer** fir trees **reached maturity** and **produced pollen**.

6) Today, **oak trees** are mainly found in **temperate** (mild) regions, and **fir trees** are mainly found in **cooler** regions.

7) This suggests that the **temperature** around the peat bog **increased** over this time period — a **warming event** had occurred.

Depth of sample (metres)	Approximate age of sample (years)	Number of pollen grains in sample	
		Oak	Fir
0.5	3100	253	28
1.0	4200	194	121
1.5	5700	138	167
2.0	7100	51	231

> You can also use pollen to see how moisture levels have changed. You can tell if the climate was wetter/drier by the types of plant pollen present in the peat.

Practice Questions

Q1 What is climate change?

Q2 Explain how temperature records can be used as evidence for climate change.

Q3 Explain why only pollen from successful plant species is preserved in peat bogs.

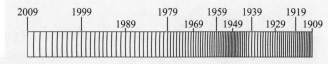

2009   1999   1989   1979   1969   1959   1949   1939   1929   1919   1909

Exam Questions

Q1 The diagram above shows a core taken from a pine tree in 2009.
Analyse the data shown in the diagram to explain how the core provides evidence for climate change. [4 marks]

Q2 Explain how the pollen of present-day species can be used to show what the climate was like in the past. [4 marks]

I'm actually a dendrochronologist by trade — oh, you've fallen asleep...

A lot of people get climate change confused with global warming — make sure you know that climate change is a significant change in weather patterns in a region and not just a change in temperature. Tree rings and pollen aren't obvious sources of evidence for climate change, but they're important, so make sure you understand what they show.

Causes of Climate Change

Now you know what climate change is, it's time to find out what causes it...

Climate Change *Can be* Caused *by* Human Activity

1) The **scientific consensus** is that the recent, rapid increase in global temperature (global warming) has **anthropogenic causes** — this means that it's been caused by **human activity**.

2) Human activity has caused global warming by **enhancing** the **greenhouse effect** — the effect of **greenhouse gases** absorbing outgoing **energy**, so that less is **lost** to space.

3) The greenhouse effect is **essential** to keep the planet warm, but **too much** greenhouse gas in the atmosphere means the planet **warms up**.

4) Two of the main greenhouse gases (and the ones you need to learn about) are CO_2 and **methane**:

Carbon dioxide (CO_2)

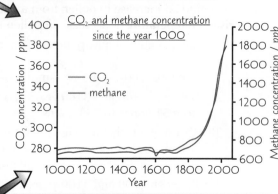

- Atmospheric CO_2 concentration has **increased** by **over 100 ppm** (parts per million) since the **mid-19th century**. The concentration had been **stable** for the previous **10 000 years**.

- CO_2 concentration is **increasing** as more **fossil fuels** like coal, oil, natural gas and petrol are **burnt**, e.g. in power stations or in cars. Burning fossil fuels **releases** CO_2.

- CO_2 concentration is also **increased** by the **destruction** of **natural sinks** (things that keep CO_2 **out** of the atmosphere by storing **carbon**). E.g. trees are a big CO_2 sink — they store the carbon as **organic compounds**. CO_2 is **released** when trees are **burnt**, or when **decomposers break down** the organic compounds and **respire** them.

Methane (CH_4)

- Atmospheric methane concentration has **more than doubled** since the **mid-19th century**. The level had been **stable** for the previous **850 years**.

- Methane concentration is **increasing** because **more** methane is being **released** into the atmosphere, e.g. because **more fossil fuels** are being **extracted**, there's more **decaying waste** and there are **more cattle** which give off methane as a **waste gas**.

- Methane can also be released from **natural stores**, e.g. **frozen ground** (permafrost). As temperatures **increase** it's thought these stores will **thaw** and release **large amounts** of methane into the atmosphere.

An increase in **human activities** like **burning fossil fuels** (for industry and in cars), **farming** and **deforestation** has **increased** atmospheric concentrations of CO_2 and methane. This has **enhanced** the greenhouse effect and **caused** a rise in average global temperature — **global warming**.

You Need to be Able to *Interpret Evidence* for the *Causes* of *Climate Change*

You need to be able to **interpret data** on things like atmospheric CO_2 concentration and temperature, and recognise **correlations** (a **relationship** between two variables) and **causal relationships** (where a change in one variable **causes** a change in another variable). Here's an example of how it's done:

There's more on correlation and cause on page 206.

1) **Describe the data:**
The **temperature fluctuated** between **1950 and 2006**, but the general trend was a **steady increase** from around **13.8 °C** to around **14.5 °C**. The atmospheric CO_2 concentration also showed a trend of **increasing** from around **310 ppm** in **1950** to around **380 ppm** in **2006**.

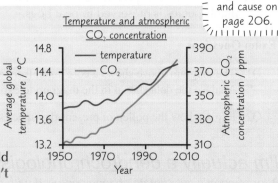

2) **Draw a conclusion:**
There's a **positive correlation** between the temperature and CO_2 concentration. The increasing CO_2 concentration could be **linked** to the increasing **temperature**. However, you **can't conclude** from this data alone that it's a **causal relationship** — **other factors** may have been involved, e.g. changing solar activity. **Other studies** would need to be carried out to **investigate** the effects of other factors.

Causes of Climate Change

Data about Climate Change can be Extrapolated to make Predictions

Data that's **already** been collected on atmospheric greenhouse gas concentrations can be **extrapolated** — used to make **predictions** about how it will **change** in the **future**. These predictions can then be used to produce **models** of how the **global climate** might change in the **future**. For example:

1) An **international** group of scientists called the Intergovernmental Panel on Climate Change (**IPCC**) has **extrapolated data** on atmospheric greenhouse gas concentrations to produce a number of **emissions scenarios** — **predictions** of how human greenhouse gas emissions might **change** up until 2100.

2) The scenarios considered by the IPCC include:

   • **Scenario 1: minimum emissions** — in this scenario, concentrations of greenhouse gases peak, then reduce (i.e. humans significantly reduce their greenhouse gas emissions).

   • **Scenarios 2 and 3** — these are stabilising scenarios in which greenhouse gas concentrations continue to increase, but eventually level off (after steps are taken to reduce emissions).

   • **Scenario 4: maximum emissions** — the worst case scenario, in which the rate of production of emissions continues to increase and greenhouse gas concentrations end up very high.

3) They can put all these different scenarios into **global climate models** (computer models of how the climate works), to see how different aspects of **global climate**, e.g. temperature, will be affected in each scenario.

Models of future climate change based on extrapolated greenhouse gas concentration data have **limitations**:

1) We don't actually know how greenhouse gas emissions will **change**, i.e. which emissions scenario is most **accurate**.

2) We don't know exactly how much each emissions scenario will **cause** the global **temperature to rise by**.

3) The change in atmospheric greenhouse gas concentrations due to **natural causes** (without human influence) **isn't known**.

4) We don't know what attempts there will be to **manage** the atmospheric concentration of greenhouse gases, or how **successful** they'll be.

5) We don't know what effect increasing greenhouse gas concentrations will actually have on the **climate** because of the **complex feedback systems** involved.

In this scenario, an athlete is floored by emissions.

Practice Questions

Q1 What is the greenhouse effect?

Q2 State one human activity that increases atmospheric carbon dioxide concentration.

Q3 State two human activities that increase atmospheric methane concentration.

Q4 Give two limitations of models for climate change.

Exam Question

Q1 The graph shows the average global temperature and atmospheric CO_2 concentration from 1970 to 2006. A student concludes that the increasing atmospheric CO_2 concentration has led to an increase the global average temperature.

Analyse the data shown in the graph to comment on this conclusion. [4 marks]

Earth not hot enough for you — spice it up with a dash of CO_2...

Another fine mess that humanity's gotten itself into — too much of things like driving, leaving TVs on standby, making big piles of rubbish and cows farting has caused global warming. I suspect you've come to the conclusion that revising climate change causes boredom. However, I suspect they're just correlated — better try the next page to check...

Effects of Climate Change

*I thought it was about time we started discussing living things for a change — this is Biology after all.
Here's how climate change could affect everything from plants and animals to microscopic bacteria...*

Global Warming Affects Plants and Animals

Climate change in the form of **global warming** has a direct impact on **plants**, **animals** and other **organisms**.

An Increasing Temperature Affects the Rate of Enzyme Activity...

1) Normally the **rate** of an enzyme-controlled reaction **increases** when the **temperature's increased**. This is because more heat means **more kinetic energy**, so molecules **move faster**. This makes the enzymes **more likely** to **collide** with the substrate molecules. The **energy** of these collisions also **increases**, which means each collision is more likely to **result** in a **reaction**.

2) But, if the temperature gets too high, the **reaction stops**. Here's why:

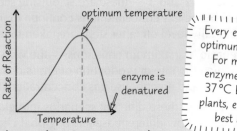

- The rise in temperature makes the enzyme's molecules **vibrate more**.
- If the temperature goes above a certain level, this vibration **breaks** some of the **bonds** that hold the enzyme in shape.
- The **active site changes shape** and the enzyme and substrate **no longer fit together**.
- At this point, the enzyme is **denatured** — it no longer functions as a catalyst.

Every enzyme has an optimum temperature. For most human enzymes it's around 37 °C but in many plants, enzymes work best at 25 °C.

...which Can Affect Organisms' Life Cycles, Development and Distribution

1) An organism's **metabolism** is all the **chemical reactions** that take place in its cells in order to keep it alive. Metabolic reactions are controlled by **enzymes**. An **increase** in **temperature** will mean that the metabolic reactions in some organisms will **speed up**, so their **rate** of **growth** will **increase**. This also means they'll **develop** and **progress** through their **life cycle faster**.

> **Examples**
> - **Enzymes** are involved in **photosynthesis** (see p. 109). This means that **plants** have an **optimum temperature** for photosynthesis and for **growth**. Up to this optimum, increases in temperature **increase** the **rate of photosynthesis** — so if they have enough water, CO_2, etc. plants **grow faster**.
> - **Cyanobacteria** (also known as **blue-green algae**), are bacteria that are able to **photosynthesise**. Some species of cyanobacteria also produce **toxins**. **Warmer water** increases the cyanobacterial growth rate, which may lead to **more harmful algal blooms** — rapid increases in populations of aquatic algae, which are harmful to human health.

2) But the temperature will become **too high** for some organisms. Their metabolic reactions will **slow down**, so their **rate** of **growth** will **decrease**. This also means they'll **progress** through their **life cycle slower**.

> **Examples**
> - Above about **25 °C**, wheat develops **fewer grains** and **yields** begin to **fall**.
> - The **eggs** of many **cold water fish** (e.g. trout, salmon) **develop best** at **low temperatures** and **won't hatch** if the water temperature gets **too high**, e.g. the eggs of brown trout won't hatch above **13 °C**.

3) Global warming will also affect the **distribution** of some species — all species exist where their **ideal conditions** for survival are, e.g. their ideal temperature. When these conditions **change**, they'll have to **move** to a **new area** where the conditions are better. If they **can't move** they may **die out** in that area. Also, the **range** of some species may **expand** if the conditions in previously uninhabitable areas change.

> **Examples**
> - **Alpine plants** prefer the relatively **cool** conditions found in the **mountains**. As temperatures have increased, their **zone of growth** has moved up the mountains to **higher altitudes** where it is **cooler**.
> - As **sea surface temperatures** in the North Atlantic have **increased**, **subtropical plankton species** (which prefer relatively warm seas) have been found **further north**.
> - Many European **butterflies**, typically found in **southern Europe**, have shifted their range **northwards**.

Effects of Climate Change

121

Other Types of *Climate Change* Also *Affect Plants* and *Animals*

As you may remember from page 116, global warming causes other types of climate change, e.g. **global rainfall patterns** and the **timing of seasonal cycles**, which will also affect plants and animals:

1 *Changing Rainfall Patterns*

1) Global warming will **alter** global **rainfall patterns** — some areas will get **more rain**, others will get **less rain**.
2) Changing rainfall patterns will affect the **development** and **life cycles** of some organisms, e.g. ocotillo is a desert plant — it's dormant during dry periods, but after rainfall it becomes active and grows new leaves. Reduced rainfall will cause ocotillo plants to remain dormant for longer periods.
3) Changing rainfall patterns will also affect the **distribution** of some species, e.g. deserts could increase in area because of decreases in rainfall — species that aren't adapted to live in deserts will have to move to new areas or they'll die out.

2 *Seasonal Cycles*

1) Global warming is thought to be changing the **timing of the seasons**, e.g. when winter changes to spring.
2) Organisms are **adapted** to the timing of the seasons and the **changes** that happen, e.g. changes in temperature, rainfall and the availability of food.
3) Changing seasonal cycles will affect the **development** and **life cycles** of some organisms, e.g. some red squirrels in Canada are giving birth nearly three weeks earlier than usual because of an earlier availability of food.
4) Changing seasonal cycles will also affect the **distribution** of some species, for example:

> 1) Some swallows live in South Africa over the winter and fly to different parts of Europe to breed at the start of spring (when more food is available).
> 2) An early British spring will produce flowers and insects earlier than usual, so the swallows that migrate to Britain at the normal time will arrive when there isn't as much food available (there'll be fewer insects because the flowers will have disappeared earlier).
> 3) This will reduce the number of swallows that are born in Britain, and could eventually mean that the population of swallows that migrate to Britain will die out. The distribution of swallows in Europe will have changed.

I told you we should've come back earlier.

Practice Questions

Q1 Give one example of how an increase in temperature could affect the development of a plant, animal or microorganism.

Q2 Give one example of how changing rainfall patterns could affect the distribution of a plant or an animal.

Q3 Give one example of how the timing of the seasonal cycles could affect the life cycle of a plant or an animal.

Exam Question

Q1 Potato tuber moths infest potato crops in warm climates, such as southern Europe.
   a) They complete their life cycle faster at 21 °C than at 16 °C. Explain why this is the case. [4 marks]
   b) Describe what may happen to their range in Europe over the next 25 years if global warming continues. [2 marks]

Climate change effects — not as much fun as special effects...

Higher temperatures make a weekend at an English coastal town sound more appealing, but many plants and animals won't appreciate it much. Because enzymes are so sensitive to temperature, and are involved in so many reactions in living things, temperature changes can have a big impact. And that's before you get to earlier seasons and so on...

Investigating the Effects of Climate Change

You can do some lab experiments to see how climate change might affect different organisms....

You Need to Know how to **Investigate** the Effect of **Temperature** on **Organisms**

Global warming will affect the **development** of **plants** and **animals** (see page 120). You can **investigate** the effect of **temperature** on both **seedling growth rate** and **brine shrimp hatch rate**:

1) Seedling Growth Rate

1) **Plant** some seedlings (of the same variety and age) in **soil trays** and **measure** the **height** of each seedling.

2) Put the trays in **incubators** at **different temperatures**.

3) Make sure **all other variables** (e.g. the water content of the soil, light intensity and CO_2 concentration) are the **same** for **each tray** as these will all affect seedling growth.

4) After a period of incubation record the **change in height** of each seedling. The **average growth rate** in each tray can be calculated in the following way:

$$\frac{\text{average change in seedling height in each tray}}{\text{incubation period}}$$

Using multiple plants and calculating an average helps to make your results more reliable.

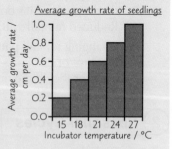

Average growth rate of seedlings

5) For example, the **graph on the right** shows that as **temperature increases**, seedling **growth rate increases** — from **0.2 cm per day** at **15 °C** to **1.0 cm per day** at **27 °C**. You can **conclude** that **higher temperatures** cause **faster growth rates** (it's a **causal relationship**) because **all** other variables were **controlled**.

2) Brine Shrimp Hatch Rate

Brine shrimp are also known as Sea-Monkeys®.

1) Put an **equal number** of brine shrimp eggs in **water baths** set at **different temperatures**.

2) Make sure **all other variables** (e.g. the volume of water, the salinity of the water and O_2 concentration) are the **same** for **each water bath**.

3) The **number** of **hatched brine shrimp** in each water bath are recorded every five hours. The **hatch rate** in each water bath can be calculated in the following way:

$$\frac{\text{number of hatched brine shrimp in each water bath}}{\text{number of hours}}$$

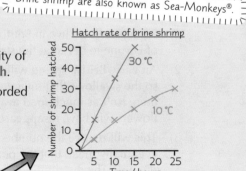

Hatch rate of brine shrimp

4) For example, the **graph on the right** shows that as **temperature increases**, brine shrimp **hatch rate increases**, e.g. at **30 °C** the initial hatch rate is **3 per hour** and at **10 °C** it's **1 per hour**. You can **conclude** that **higher temperatures** cause **faster hatch rates** (it's a **causal relationship**) because **all** other variables were **controlled**.

Temperature Effects the Initial Rate of Enzyme-Catalysed Reactions

You may remember investigating the effect of **enzyme** and **substrate concentration** on the **initial rate** of **enzyme-catalysed reactions** from Year 1 of your course. You could do a **similar experiments** to investigate the **effect** of **temperature** on initial rate. For example, you could investigate how the initial rate of the enzyme **catalase** (which catalyses the breakdown of **hydrogen peroxide** into **water** and **oxygen**) is affected by temperature:

1) Set up boiling tubes containing the **same volume** and **concentration** of **hydrogen peroxide**. To keep the **pH** constant, add **equal volumes** of a suitable **buffer solution** to each tube.

2) Set up the rest of the **apparatus** as shown in the diagram.

3) Put each boiling tube in a **water bath** set to a different temperature (e.g. 10 °C, 20 °C, 30 °C and 40 °C) along with another tube containing **catalase** (*wait 5 minutes before moving onto the next step so the enzyme gets up to temperature*).

4) Use a pipette to add the **same volume** and **concentration** of **catalase** to each boiling tube. Then **quickly attach** the **bung** and **delivery tube**.

5) **Record** how much oxygen is produced every 10 seconds in the **first minute** (60 s) of the reaction. Use a **stopwatch** to measure the time.

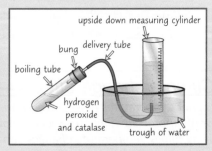

Investigating the Effects of Climate Change

You Can *Calculate* the *Initial Rate* of *Reaction* by Drawing a *Tangent*

Once you've got your results, you'll need to plot a **graph** of the **volume of O$_2$ produced** against **time** for **each temperature** you investigated. You can then use the graph to calculate the **initial rate of reaction** at each temperature. Remember, the initial rate is the rate of reaction right at the **start**, close to time equals zero ($t = 0$).

1) **Draw** a **tangent** to the curve at **$t = 0$**, using a ruler. (For more on drawing tangents see page 205.)

2) Then calculate the **gradient** of the **tangent** — this is the **initial rate of reaction**.

$$\text{gradient} = \frac{\text{change in y axis}}{\text{change in x axis}} = \frac{40 \text{ cm}^3}{30 \text{ s}} = \textbf{1.3 cm}^3\textbf{ s}^{-1}$$

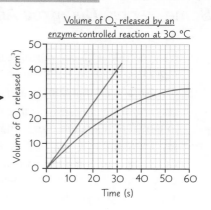

Volume of O$_2$ released by an enzyme-controlled reaction at 30 °C

Q$_{10}$ Shows How *Rate Changes* with *Temperature*

1) The **temperature coefficient** or **Q$_{10}$** value for a reaction shows **how much** the **rate** of a **reaction changes** when the **temperature** is **raised** by **10 °C**.

2) You can calculate it using this **equation**:

$$Q_{10} = \frac{\text{rate at higher temperature}}{\text{rate at lower temperature}}$$

3) The graph on the right shows the **rate** of a reaction between 0 °C and 50 °C. Here's how to **calculate** the Q$_{10}$ value of the reaction using the rate at **30 °C** and at **40 °C**:

$$Q_{10} = \frac{\text{rate at 40 °C}}{\text{rate at 30 °C}} = \frac{8}{4} = 2$$

4) At temperatures **before** the **optimum**, a Q$_{10}$ value of **2** means that the **rate doubles** when the temperature is raised by 10 °C. A Q$_{10}$ value of **3** would mean that the **rate trebles**.

5) Most **enzyme-controlled reactions** have a Q$_{10}$ value of **around 2**.

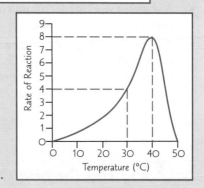

Practice Questions

Q1 Give three variables you would need to control if investigating the effect of temperature on the hatch rate of brine shrimp.

Q2 What does the temperature coefficient (Q$_{10}$) tell you about a reaction?

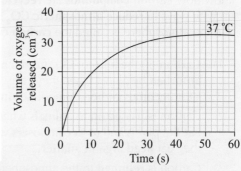

Exam Questions

Q1 A scientist carries out an enzyme-controlled reaction at 37 °C. Her results are shown in the graph above.

   a) Find the initial rate of reaction at 37 °C. [2 marks]

   b) The initial rate of reaction at 27 °C was found to be 2.3 cm^3 s^{-1}.
   Use the initial rates at 27 °C and 37 °C to calculate Q$_{10}$ between these two temperatures. [1 mark]

Q2 Describe a method that could be used to investigate the effect of increasing temperature on seedling growth rate. [4 marks]

I know what you're thinking — why do I need to know about brine shrimp...

...and what on earth can they tell me about climate change? It is actually pretty important to be able to investigate the effect of temperature on things like seedling growth, the good ol' brine shrimp and enzyme-controlled reactions in the lab — this gives scientists the data they need to start working out how climate change might affect the planet. Useful.

Reducing Climate Change

Since climate change could have some dire consequences, some people are having a pop at reducing it.

Some People Disagree About Whether Humans are Causing Climate Change

1) It's agreed that **global warming** is **happening** — there **has** been a rapid rise in global temperature over the past century.

2) It's also agreed that **human activity** is **increasing** the **atmospheric CO_2 concentration**.

3) The **scientific consensus** is that the **increase** in atmospheric CO_2 concentration **is causing** the **increase** in global temperature (i.e. humans are causing climate change in the form of global warming).

4) But a **handful** of scientists have drawn a **different conclusion** from the **data** on atmospheric CO_2 concentration and temperature — they think that the **increase** in atmospheric CO_2 concentration **isn't** the **main cause** of the **increase** in global temperature.

5) The conclusions scientists reach can be affected by **how good** the **data** is that they're basing their conclusions on (i.e. how **reliable** it is), **how much evidence** there is for a certain theory, and also sometimes by **bias**.

6) Biased conclusions **aren't objective** — they've been **influenced** by an **opinion**, instead of being **purely** based on **scientific evidence**.

7) For example, the conclusions research scientists reach may be **biased towards** the goals of the **organisation funding** their work:

Trust me, humans definitely aren't causing global warming. Now let's talk about where to build my new oil refinery.

- A scientist working for an **oil company** may be more likely to say humans **aren't** causing climate change — this would help to **keep oil sales high**.

- A scientist working for a **renewable energy company** may be more likely to say humans **are** causing climate change — this would **increase sales** of energy produced from renewable sources, e.g. from wind turbines.

Understanding The Carbon Cycle Helps to Reduce Atmospheric CO_2

Increasing atmospheric CO_2 concentration is one of the **causes** of global warming. Scientists need to know how **carbon compounds** are **recycled** between **organisms** and the **atmosphere** so they can come up with ways to **reduce atmospheric CO_2 concentration**. The **movement** of carbon **between organisms** and the **atmosphere** is called the **carbon cycle**:

1) **Carbon** (in the form of **CO_2** from the **atmosphere**) is **absorbed** by plants when they carry out **photosynthesis** — it becomes carbon compounds in **plant tissues**.

2) Carbon is **passed on** to **animals** when they **eat the plants** and to **decomposers** when they eat **dead organic matter**.

3) Carbon is **returned** to the atmosphere as **all living organisms** carry out **respiration**, which **produces CO_2**.

4) If dead organic matter ends up in places where there **aren't any decomposers**, e.g. deep oceans or bogs, the carbon compounds can be turned into **fossil fuels** over **millions of years** (by heat and pressure).

5) The carbon in fossil fuels is **released** as **CO_2** when they're **burnt** — this is called **combustion**.

```
━━ = removing CO₂ from the atmosphere
━━ = adding CO₂ to the atmosphere

          carbon dioxide in atmosphere

PHOTOSYNTHESIS    RESPIRATION    COMBUSTION

carbon compounds   carbon compounds   carbon turned
  in plants          in animals       into fossil fuels
          feeding
          DECOMPOSITION

              carbon compounds
               in decomposers
```

To **reduce atmospheric CO_2 concentration** either the **amount** of CO_2 **going into** the atmosphere (due to **respiration** and **combustion**) needs to be **decreased** or the **amount** of CO_2 being **taken out** of the atmosphere (by **photosynthesis**) needs to be **increased**.

Reducing Climate Change

Biofuels and Reforestation Decrease the Atmospheric CO_2 Concentration

Unfortunately, finding ways to **reduce** the **atmospheric CO_2 concentration** isn't as easy as it might seem. Humans use energy from **fossil fuels** for **transport**, **cooking** and making **electricity**. They also need **land to build on** and for **growing crops** or **grazing animals**, which leads to **deforestation** — reducing **photosynthesis**. This creates a **conflict** between **human needs** and **conservation**. You need to know **two examples** of how this conflict has been **managed effectively**:

Biofuels

1) Biofuels are **fuels** produced from **biomass** — material that **is** or **was recently living**. They're often made from crops, which can be **replanted** after harvesting — making biofuels a **sustainable resource**.
2) Biofuels are **burnt** to release energy, which **produces CO_2**.
3) There's **no net increase** in atmospheric CO_2 concentration when biofuels are burnt — the amount of CO_2 **produced** is the **same** as the amount of CO_2 **taken in** when the material was **growing**.
4) So using biofuels as an **alternative** to fossil fuels **stops** the **increase** in atmospheric CO_2 concentration caused by burning fossil fuels.

Reforestation

1) Reforestation is the planting of **new trees** in **existing forests** that have been **depleted**.
2) **More trees** means **more CO_2 is removed** from the atmosphere by **photosynthesis**.
3) CO_2 is **converted** into carbon compounds and **stored** as plant tissues in the trees. This means more carbon is **kept out** of the atmosphere, so there's **less CO_2** contributing to global warming.

People Disagree About How to Reduce Climate Change

Scientists have come up with lots of **strategies** to **reduce global warming**. There's **debate** about which strategies are the **right** ones to use because **different people** have **different viewpoints**. Here are a few examples of why different people might support or oppose **increasing** the use of **biofuels** and **wind turbines** for energy production:

Increase the use of biofuels

- Some **farmers** might **support** this strategy — some governments **fund** the **farming** of **crops** for biofuels.
- **Drivers** might **support** this strategy — the **price** of **biofuels** is usually **lower** than **oil-based fuels**.
- **Consumers** might **oppose** this strategy — using **farmland** to grow **crops** for biofuels could cause **food shortages**.
- **Conservationists** might **oppose** this strategy — **forests** have been **cleared** to grow **crops** for biofuels.

Increase the use of wind turbines

- Companies that make **wind turbines** would **support** this strategy — their **sales** would **increase**.
- **Environmentalists** might **support** this strategy — wind turbines produce electricity **without increasing** atmospheric CO_2 concentration.
- **Local communities** might **oppose** this strategy — some people think wind turbines **ruin** the **landscape**.
- **Bird conservationists** might **oppose** this strategy — many **birds** are **killed** by **flying into** wind turbines.

Practice Questions

Q1 What is reforestation?
Q2 Suggest one group of people who might support increasing the use of wind turbines to reduce global warming.

Exam Question

Q1* Some scientists have proposed using biofuels instead of fossil fuels to help reduce climate change and to manage the conflict between human needs and conservation.

With reference to the carbon cycle, evaluate how effective this strategy is likely to be. [9 marks]

* You will be assessed on the quality of your written response in this question.

Strategy for reducing climate change — stop respiring...

...on seconds thoughts, that's not really a plan that's going to work. We might have melted by the time everyone agrees on the best way to reduce climate change, but you can start doing your bit now — stop using your private jet to attend lessons and dedicate your life to planting trees. Make sure you know these two pages inside out before you move on.

Evolution, Natural Selection and Speciation

Climate change may cause organisms to evolve as the environment they live in changes. It could even cause new species to develop. You should remember a lot of this stuff on evolution and speciation from Year 1 of your course, but you need to learn it again now and in a bit more detail...

Evolution *is a* Change *in* Allele Frequency

Evolution is when the **frequency** of an **allele** in a **population changes** over time. It occurs by **natural selection**.

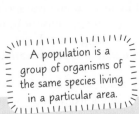
A population is a group of organisms of the same species living in a particular area.

1) **Individuals** within a population **vary** because they have **different alleles**. The different alleles are due to **gene mutations** (changes in the DNA base sequence of genes).

2) This means some individuals are **better adapted** to their environment than others.

3) Individuals that have an allele that **increases** their **chance of survival** are **more likely** to **survive**, **reproduce** and **pass on** their genes (including the beneficial allele), than individuals with different alleles.

4) This means that a **greater proportion** of the next generation **inherit** the **beneficial allele**.

5) They, in turn, are **more likely** to **survive**, **reproduce** and **pass on** their genes. So the **frequency** of the beneficial allele **increases** from generation to generation.

Isolation Reduces Gene Flow *Leading to* Speciation

1) You may remember from Year 1 that a **species** is a group of **similar organisms** that can **reproduce** to give **fertile offspring**, and that **speciation** is the development of a **new species**.

2) Speciation happens when **populations** of the **same species** become **reproductively isolated**, reducing **gene flow** (transfer of genes) between two populations. This means that **natural selection** acts on each population **separately** — so **new species** can develop.

3) **Reproductive** isolation may occur because of **geographical isolation** (**allopatric speciation**) or because **random mutations** produce changes in **phenotype** that prevent populations from mating (**sympatric speciation**).

Allopatric Speciation *Requires* Geographical Isolation

1) Populations that are geographically separated will experience slightly **different conditions**. E.g. there might be a **different climate** on each side of the physical barrier.

2) The populations will experience **different selection pressures** and so **different changes** in allele frequencies could occur:

   - Different **alleles** will be **more advantageous** in the different populations. E.g. if geographical separation places one population in a **colder climate** than before, **longer fur length** will be **beneficial**. **Natural selection** will then act on the **alleles** for fur length in this population, increasing the frequency of this allele.

   - Allele frequencies will also change as **mutations** (see above) occur **independently** in each population.

3) The changes in allele frequency will lead to **differences** accumulating in the **gene pools** of the separated populations, causing changes in **phenotype frequencies**.

4) Eventually, the different populations will have become **genetically distinct** — their DNA will have become significantly different. Individuals from the different populations will have changed so much that they won't be able to breed with one another to produce **fertile** offspring — they'll have become **reproductively isolated**. The two groups will have become **separate species**, as shown in the diagram.

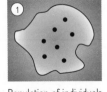
Population of individuals
● = individual organism

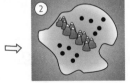
Physical barriers stop interbreeding and gene flow between populations.

Populations adapt to new environments.

Allele and phenotype frequency change leading to development of new species.

Evolution, Natural Selection and Speciation

Reproductive Isolation Occurs in Many Ways

Reproductive isolation occurs because the **changes** in the alleles and phenotypes of the two populations **prevent** them from **successfully breeding together**. These changes include:

1) **Seasonal changes** — individuals from the same population develop different **flowering** or **mating** seasons, or become **sexually active** at **different times** of the year.

2) **Mechanical changes** — changes in **genitalia** prevent successful mating.

3) **Behavioural changes** — a group of individuals develop **courtship rituals** that **aren't attractive** to the main population.

Sympatric Speciation Doesn't Require Geographical Isolation

A population **doesn't** have to become **geographically isolated** to become **reproductively isolated**. Random mutations could occur **within a population**, resulting in the changes mentioned above, **preventing** members of that population breeding with other members of the species. Speciation without geographical isolation is called **sympatric speciation**.

Example:

1) Most eukaryotic organisms are **diploid** — they have **two sets** of **homologous** (matched) **chromosomes** in their cells. Sometimes, **mutations** can occur that **increase** the number of **chromosomes**. This is known as **polyploidy**.

2) Individuals with different numbers of chromosomes **can't reproduce** sexually to give **fertile offspring** — so if a polyploid organism emerges in a diploid population, the polyploid organism will be **reproductively isolated** from the diploid organisms.

3) If the polyploid organism then reproduces **asexually**, a **new species** could develop.

4) Polyploidy can only lead to speciation if it **doesn't prove fatal** to the organism and more polyploid organisms can be produced. It's **more common** in **plants** than animals.

Practice Questions

Q1 What is speciation?

Q2 What is the difference between allopatric and sympatric speciation?

Exam Question

Q1   The Galápagos Islands contain many species of finch that evolved from one original species.

  a) Which of the following statements best defines evolution.

    A   Evolution is the change in gene flow in a population over time.

    B   Evolution is the change in allele frequency in a population over time.

    C   Evolution is the change in mutation frequency in a population over time.

    D   Evolution is the development of a new species over time.   [1 mark]

  b) Finches on one of the Galápagos islands have larger beaks than finches on other islands. Large-beaked finches are able to eat larger, tougher seeds than finches with smaller beaks. Explain how the larger beak size may have evolved.   [5 marks]

  c) Give two possible reasons why finches from different islands are not able to breed together any more, even if they come into contact with one another.   [2 marks]

If they were ever separated, Al and Patrick would be heartbroken...

It's a bit of a toughie getting your head round the different mechanisms that can produce a new species. Isolation reduces gene flow between populations, setting the stage for speciation. To remember which sort allopatric is, I imagine someone on an island shouting 'allo (hello) to their friend Patrick on a separate island. Just thought it might help...

Evidence for Evolution

In science, you can't just do some research and then wave it about like it's pure fact. Oh no. A load of other scientists stick their noses in first — then if you're lucky, your evidence will be accepted. Take evolution for example...

There's **Plenty of Evidence** to **Support Evolution**

The theory of evolution has been around for quite a long time now and there's plenty of **evidence** to support it. Fairly **new** evidence includes some from **molecular biology** — the study of **molecules** such as **DNA** and **proteins**:

Genomics

1) **Genomics** is a branch of science that uses **DNA technology** to determine the **base sequence** of an organism's **genome** and the **functions** of its genes. This allows scientists to make **comparisons** between organisms' **DNA**.

An organism's genome is its entire set of DNA, including its genes.

2) The theory of evolution suggests that all organisms have **evolved** from shared **common ancestors**.

3) Closely related species **diverged** (evolved to become different species) **more recently**.

4) Evolution is caused by **gradual changes** in the **base sequence** of organisms' DNA.

5) Organisms that diverged away from each other more recently should have **more similar DNA**, as **less time** has passed for changes in the DNA sequence to occur. This is exactly what scientists have found.

Example — Humans, chimps and mice all evolved from a common ancestor. Humans and mice diverged a **long time ago**, but humans and chimps diverged **quite recently**. The **DNA base sequence** of humans and chimps is 94% the same, but human and mouse DNA is only 85% the same.

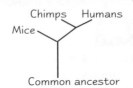

Proteomics

1) **Proteomics** is the study of **proteins**, e.g. the study of the **size**, **shape** and **amino acid sequence** of **proteins**.

2) The **sequence** of **amino acids** in a protein is **coded for** by the DNA sequence in a gene.

3) **Related** organisms have **similar DNA sequences** and so **similar amino acid sequences** in their proteins.

4) So organisms that diverged away from each other **more recently** should have **more similar proteins**, as **less time** has passed for changes to occur. This is what scientists have found.

The **Scientific Community Validates Evidence** About **Evolution**

1) The job of a scientist is to collect **data** and use it to **test theories** and **ideas** — the data either **supports** the theory (it's **evidence for it**) or it doesn't (it's **evidence to disprove it**). E.g. genomic and proteomic data has been collected that provides evidence for the theory of evolution.

2) The **scientific community** is all the scientists around the world, e.g. researchers, technicians and professors.

3) Scientists within the scientific community **accept** the theory of **evolution** because they've **shared** and **discussed** the evidence for evolution to make sure it's **valid** and **reliable**.

4) Scientists share and discuss their work in **three main ways**:

① Scientific Journals

Examples of scientific journals include Science, Nature, the British Medical Journal and the Journal of Biological Chemistry.

1) **Scientific journals** are **academic magazines** where scientists can publish **articles** describing their work.

2) They're used to share new **ideas, theories, experiments, evidence** and **conclusions**.

3) Scientific journals allow other scientists to repeat experiments and see if they get the **same results** using the **same methods**.

4) If the results are **replicated** over and over again, the scientific community can be pretty confident that the evidence collected is **reliable**.

Evidence for Evolution

② *Peer Review*

1) **Before** scientists can get their work **published** in a journal it has to undergo something called the **peer review process**.

2) This is when **other scientists** who work in that area (**peers**) read and **review** the work.

3) The peer reviewer has to **check** that the work is **valid** and that it **supports** the **conclusions**.

4) Peer review is used by the scientific community to try and make sure that any scientific evidence that's published is **valid** and that experiments are carried out to the **highest possible standards**.

How this object of sheer beauty could have been left out of this year's pier review was a mystery to many.

③ Conferences

1) **Scientific conferences** are **meetings** that scientists attend so they can **discuss** each other's work.

2) Scientists with important or interesting results might be invited to present their work in the form of a **lecture** or **poster presentation**.

3) Other scientists can then **ask questions** and **discuss** their work with them **face to face**.

4) Conferences are valuable because they're an **easy way** for the latest theories and evidence to be **shared** and **discussed**.

Practice Questions

Q1 What is proteomics?

Q2 What is the scientific community?

Q3 Give one way a scientist might present their work at a scientific conference.

Q4 Why are conferences valuable to the scientific community?

Exam Questions

Q1 Describe and explain how the theory of evolution is supported by genomics. [4 marks]

Q2 Scientific journals publish evidence for theories, such as the theory of evolution. Explain how the scientific community checks that evidence published in scientific journals is valid and reliable. [4 marks]

Peer review — checking out who's got the latest mobile phone...

Congratulations, you've finally made it to the end of this section. All you need to do now is keep testing yourself on the information on these two pages until you're so sick of it you want to throw the book out of the window (takes about 3 goes). Then you need to retrieve your book for the next section...

Microbial Decomposition and Time of Death

Wowsers, this is pretty morbid stuff. Make sure you read these pages before you've had your lunch...

Microorganisms **Decompose Organic Matter**

1) **Microorganisms**, e.g. **bacteria** and **fungi**, are an important part of the **carbon cycle** (see p. 124).

2) When plants and animals die, microorganisms on and in them **secrete enzymes** that decompose the **dead organic matter** into **small molecules** that they can **respire**.

3) When the microorganisms respire these small molecules, **methane** (CH_4) and CO_2 are released — this **recycles** carbon back into the atmosphere.

Scientists can **Estimate** the **Time of Death** of a **Body**

Police and **forensic scientists** often need to establish a body's **time of death** (TOD). This can give them a lot of information about the **circumstances** of the death, e.g. if they know when someone died they might be able to figure out who was present. The TOD can be established by looking at **several different factors** together — on their **own** these factors **aren't accurate** enough to give a reliable time of death. The **five** factors you need to know about are:

1) Body Temperature

1) All mammals **produce heat** from metabolic **reactions** like **respiration**, e.g. the **human body** has an internal temperature of around **37 °C**.

2) From the TOD the metabolic reactions **slow down** and eventually **stop**, causing **body temperature** to **fall** until it **equals** the temperature of its **surroundings** — this process is called *algor mortis*.

3) Forensic scientists know that **human bodies** cool at a rate of around **1.5 °C** to **2.0 °C per hour**, so from the temperature of a dead body they can **work out** the approximate TOD. E.g. a dead body with a temperature of **35 °C** might have been **dead** for about an **hour**.

4) Conditions such as **air temperature, clothing** and **body weight** can **affect** the **cooling rate** of a body. E.g. the cooling rate of a **clothed body** will be **slower** than one without clothing, because it's **insulated**.

2) Degree of Muscle Contraction

About **4-6 hours** after death, the **muscles** in a dead body **start** to **contract** and become **stiff** — this is called *rigor mortis*:

1) *Rigor mortis* begins when **muscle cells** become **deprived** of **oxygen**.

2) **Respiration** still takes place in the muscle cells, but it's **anaerobic**, which causes a build-up of **lactic acid** in the muscle (see p. 157).

3) The **pH** of the cells **decreases** due to the lactic acid, **inhibiting enzymes** that produce ATP.

4) **No ATP** means the **bonds** between the **myosin** and **actin** in the muscle cells (see p. 149) become **fixed** and the body **stiffens**.

It usually takes around 12-18 hours after the TOD for every muscle in the body to contract.

Smaller muscles in the head **contract first**, with **larger muscles** in the lower body being the **last** to contract. *Rigor mortis* is affected by **degree of muscle development** and **temperature**. E.g. *rigor mortis* occurs **more quickly** at **higher** temperatures because the chemical reactions in the body are **faster**.

3) Forensic Entomology

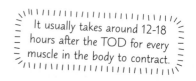

Rigor mortis wears off around 24-36 hours after the TOD.

1) When somebody dies the body is quickly **colonised** by a **variety** of **different insects** — the study of this is called **forensic entomology**.

2) TOD can be estimated by identifying the **type of insect** present on the body — e.g. **flies** are often the **first** insects to appear, usually a **few hours** after death. Other insects, like **beetles**, colonise a body at **later** stages.

3) TOD can also be estimated by identifying the **stage of life cycle** the insect is in — e.g. **blowfly larvae hatch** from eggs about **24 hours** after they're **laid**. If **only** blowfly **eggs** are found on a body you could estimate that the TOD was **no more than 24 hours ago**.

4) Different conditions will **affect** an insect's **life cycle**, such as **drugs, humidity, oxygen** and **temperature**. E.g. the **higher** the temperature, the **faster** the **metabolic rate** and the **shorter** the **life cycle**.

Microbial Decomposition and Time of Death

4) Extent of Decomposition

1) **Immediately** after death **bacteria** and **enzymes** begin to **decompose** the **body**.

2) Forensic scientists can use the **extent** of decomposition to establish a **TOD**:

Approximate time since TOD	Extent of decomposition
Hours to a few days	Cells and tissues are being broken down by the body's own enzymes and bacteria that were present before death. The skin on the body begins to turn a greenish colour.
A few days to a few weeks	Microorganisms decompose tissues and organs. This produces gases (e.g. methane), which cause the body to become bloated. The skin begins to blister and fall off.
A few weeks	Tissues begin to liquefy and seep out into the area around the body.
A few months to a few years	Only a skeleton remains.
Decades to centuries	The skeleton begins to disintegrate until there's nothing left of the body.

3) Different conditions **affect** the **rate** of decomposition, such as **temperature** and **oxygen availability**. E.g. **aerobic** microorganisms need **oxygen**, so decomposition could be **slower** if there's a **lack** of oxygen.

5) Stage of Succession

1) The **types of organism** found in a dead body **change over time**, going through a number of **stages** — this is called **succession**.

2) Forensic scientists can establish a **TOD** from the particular **stage of succession** that the body's in.

3) If a dead body is left to decompose **above ground** succession will usually follow these stages:

- **Immediately after** the TOD conditions in a dead body are **most favourable** for **bacteria**.
- As bacteria **decompose tissues**, conditions in a dead body become favourable for **flies** and their **larvae**.
- When fly larvae **feed** on a dead body they make conditions favourable for **beetles**, so beetles move in.
- As a dead **body dries out** conditions become **less favourable** for flies — they leave the body. Beetles **remain** as they can decompose **dry tissue**.
- When **no tissues** remain, conditions are **no longer favourable** for **most organisms**.

4) Succession in a dead body is **similar** to plant succession (see p. 106) — the **only difference** is that most of the **early insects** (e.g. beetles) **remain** on the body as other insects colonise it.

5) The stage of succession of a dead body (and so the type of organism that's present) is affected by many things including the **location** of the body, such as above ground, under ground, in water or sealed away. E.g. a body that's been **sealed away won't** be **colonised** by any species of insect.

Practice Questions

Q1 Describe how microorganisms recycle carbon from dead plants and animals.

Q2 What is forensic entomology?

Exam Question

Q1 A human body with a temperature of 29 °C was found at 22:45. *Rigor mortis* was only present in the face and shoulders. There was no visible decomposition of the body. Blowfly eggs, but no larvae, were found on the body. Analyse the evidence above to estimate the person's time of death, giving reasons for your answer. [4 marks]

CSI: Cumbria — *it doesn't really have the same ring to it, does it...*

Well, that was just lovely. Admittedly, I found it all rather interesting cos I like to watch repeats of Silent Witness on the TV. The main aim of all this grim stuff is to estimate the time of death of a body — remember that it's only an estimate, and lots of things (especially temperature) affect a dead body. Maybe if I pickle myself now, I'll never decompose...

DNA Profiling

We've been able to identify people from their fingerprints for over 100 years, but now we can use their DNA instead. DNA can also be used to figure out who's related to who... clever stuff.

A DNA Profile is a Genetic Fingerprint

1) A **DNA profile** is a **fingerprint** of an organism's DNA.

2) Everyone's DNA is **different** (except identical twins), so your DNA profile is **unique** to you.

3) DNA profiling can be used to **identify people** (see p. 133) and to **determine genetic relationships** between humans, between animals and between plants (see p. 134).

4) Here's how a DNA profile is made:

> **You should remember from Topic 2...**
> • DNA is made up of **nucleotides**.
> • Each nucleotide contains one of four **bases** (A, T, C or G).
> • A molecule of DNA consists of two strands of nucleotides joined by **complementary base pairing** (A with T, and C with G).
> The sequence of bases is what makes your DNA **unique**.

1) A DNA Sample is Obtained

A **sample of DNA** is obtained from the organism the DNA profile is being made for (e.g. from **blood**, **saliva**, etc.).

2) PCR is Used to Amplify the DNA

The **polymerase chain reaction** (PCR) is used to make **millions of copies** of **specific regions** of the DNA in just a few hours. The DNA needs to be amplified so there's **enough** to **make a DNA profile** (see the next page). PCR has **several stages** and is **repeated** over and over to make lots of copies:

1) A reaction mixture is set up that contains the **DNA sample, free nucleotides, primers** and **DNA polymerase**.

- **Primers** are short pieces of DNA that are **complementary** to the bases at the **start** of the fragment you want.

- **DNA polymerase** is an **enzyme** that creates new DNA strands.

2) The DNA mixture is **heated** to **95 °C** to break the **hydrogen bonds** between the two strands of DNA.

3) The mixture is then **cooled** to between **50 and 65 °C** so that the primers can **bind** (**anneal**) to the strands.

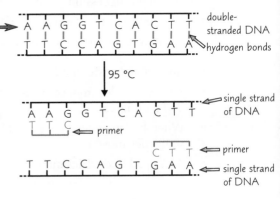

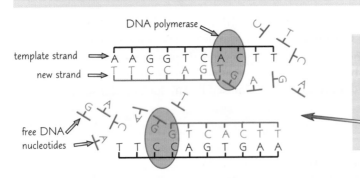

4) The reaction mixture is heated to **72 °C**, so **DNA polymerase** can **work**.

5) The DNA polymerase **lines up** free DNA nucleotides **alongside** each **template strand**. Complementary **base pairing** means **new complementary strands** are formed.

6) **Two new copies** of the fragment of DNA are formed and **one cycle** of PCR is **complete**.

7) The cycle starts again, with the mixture being heated to 95 °C and this time **all four strands** (two original and two new) are used as **templates**.

8) Each PCR cycle **doubles** the amount of DNA, e.g. **1st cycle = 2 × 2 = 4 DNA fragments, 2nd cycle = 4 × 2 = 8 DNA fragments, 3rd cycle = 8 × 2 = 16 DNA fragments**, and so on.

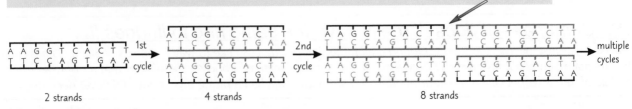

DNA Profiling

3) A Fluorescent Tag is Added

In a sequencing lab, a **fluorescent tag** can be added to all the DNA fragments so they can be viewed under **UV light**. In class, you're more likely to **stain** the fragments once they've been separated (see page 135).

4) Gel Electrophoresis is Used to Separate the DNA

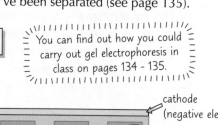
You can find out how you could carry out gel electrophoresis in class on pages 134 - 135.

Gel electrophoresis is used to **separate** out the DNA fragments according to their **length**. Here's how it works:

1) The DNA is placed into a **well** in a slab of **gel** and covered in a **buffer solution** that **conducts electricity**.

2) An **electrical current** is passed through the gel — DNA fragments are **negatively charged**, so they **move towards** the **anode** (positive electrode) at the far end of the gel.

3) **Short** DNA fragments move **faster** and travel **further** through the gel, so the DNA fragments **separate** according to **length**.

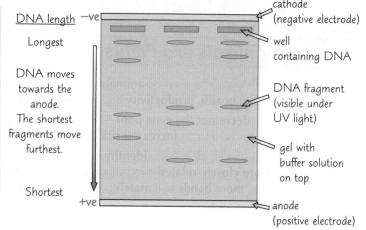

DNA length −ve
Longest
DNA moves towards the anode. The shortest fragments move furthest.
Shortest
+ve

cathode (negative electrode)
well containing DNA
DNA fragment (visible under UV light)
gel with buffer solution on top
anode (positive electrode)

5) The Gel is Viewed Under UV Light

1) The DNA fragments appear as **bands** under **UV light** — this is the **DNA profile**.

2) Two DNA profiles can be **compared** to see how **similar** the **pattern** of bands on the gel is — a **match** could help **identify** a person (see below) or determine a **genetic relationship** (see next page).

DNA length
Longest
Shortest

person 1   person 2
−ve
+ve

DNA fragments from different regions of the DNA

Different people have different sized fragments.

DNA Profiling can be Used to Identify People in Forensic Science

Forensic scientists use DNA profiling to **compare** samples of **DNA** collected from **crime scenes** (e.g. DNA from **blood, semen, skin cells, saliva, hair**, etc.) to samples of DNA from **possible suspects**, to **link them** to crime scenes.

1) The **DNA** is **isolated** from all the collected samples (from the crime scene and from the suspects).

2) Each sample is **amplified** using **PCR** (see previous page).

3) The **PCR products** are run on an **electrophoresis gel** and the DNA profiles produced are **compared** to see if any match.

4) If the samples match, it **links** a **person** to the **crime scene**. E.g. this gel shows that the DNA profile from **suspect C matches** that from the crime scene, **linking** them to the crime scene.

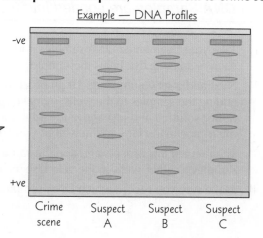

Example — DNA Profiles
−ve
+ve
Crime scene   Suspect A   Suspect B   Suspect C

DNA Profiling

DNA Profiling is also Used to Determine Genetic Relationships in Humans...

1) We **inherit** our DNA from our **parents** — roughly **half** comes from **each parent**.

2) This means the **more bands** on two DNA profiles that **match**, the more **closely-related** (genetically similar) those two people are.

3) For example, **paternity tests** are used to determine the **biological father** of a child by comparing DNA profiles. If lots of bands on the profile **match**, then that person is **most probably** the child's father.

Even without the hats, Cheryl and Beryl didn't think they needed a DNA profile to prove they were related...

...and in Animals and Plants

1) DNA profiling can be used on **animals** and **plants** to **prevent inbreeding**, which causes **health**, **productivity** and **reproductive problems**.

2) Inbreeding **decreases** the **gene pool** — the number of **different alleles** (versions of a gene) in a population — which can lead to an **increased risk** of **genetic disorders**, leading to **health problems**, etc.

3) DNA profiling can be used to **identify** how **closely-related** individuals are — the **more closely-related** two individuals are, the **more similar** their DNA profiles will be (e.g. **more bands** will **match**). The **least related** individuals will be **bred together**.

Here's How you can Carry Out Gel Electrophoresis

You saw on the previous page that gel electrophoresis can be used to **separate out DNA fragments** depending on their **length**. Here's how you can carry out electrophoresis in the lab using samples of **fragmented DNA** — there are several stages involved...

Firstly you add a Gel Tray to a Gel Box (or Tank)

1) Electrophoresis is commonly performed using **agarose gel** that has been poured into a **gel tray** and left to **solidify**. A **row of wells** is created at **one end** of the gel.

2) To perform electrophoresis, firstly you need to put the **gel tray** into a **gel box** (or tank). You need to make sure the end of the gel tray with the wells is closest to the **cathode** (negative electrode) on the gel box.

3) Then add **buffer solution** to the **reservoirs** at the **sides** of the gel box so that the **surface of the gel** becomes **covered** in the buffer solution.

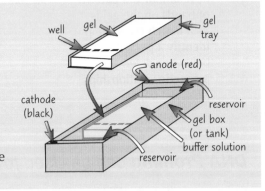

Next DNA Samples are Loaded Into the Wells

1) Take your fragmented DNA samples and, using a micropipette, add the same volume of **loading dye** to each — loading dye helps the samples to **sink to the bottom** of the wells and makes them **easier to see**.

2) Next add a set volume (e.g. **10 μl**) of a DNA sample to the first well. You have to be **really careful** when adding the samples to the wells — make sure the **tip** of your micropipette is in the **buffer solution** and **just above** the **opening of the well**. **Don't** stick the tip of the micropipette too far into the well or you could **pierce the bottom** of it.

3) Then repeat this process and add the same volume of each of your **other DNA samples** to **other wells** in the gel. Use a **clean micropipette tip** each time.

4) Make sure you **record** which DNA sample you have added to each well.

DNA Profiling

Then **Electrophoresis** is Carried Out

1) Put the **lid** on the **gel box** and **connect the leads** from the gel box to the **power supply**.

2) **Turn on** the power supply and **set it to the required voltage**, e.g. 100 V. This causes an **electrical current** to be **passed through the gel**.

3) The current will cause the DNA fragments to **separate** according to **length** (see page 133).

4) Let the gel run for about **30 minutes** (or until the dye is **about 2 cm** from the end of the gel) then **turn off** the power supply.

5) **Remove** the gel tray from the gel box and **tip off** any **excess buffer solution**.

6) Wearing **gloves**, **stain** the DNA fragments by covering the surface of the gel with a staining solution then **rinsing** the gel with water. The **bands** of the different **DNA fragments** will now be **visible**.

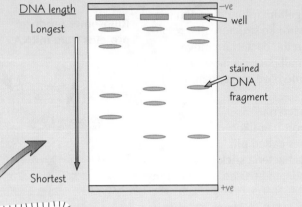

The length of a DNA fragment is measured in bases, e.g. ATCC = 4 bases or base pairs. 1000 bases is one kilobase (1 kb).

Practice Questions

Q1 What is a DNA profile?

Q2 What does PCR stand for?

Q3 In gel electrophoresis, which electrode do DNA fragments move towards?

Q4 Why might DNA profiling be used in forensic science?

Q5 Briefly describe the procedure you would use to separate DNA fragments by electrophoresis.

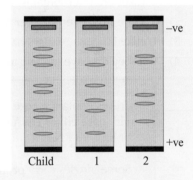

Exam Questions

Q1 The diagram on the right shows three DNA profiles — one from a child and two from possible fathers.

a) Describe how a DNA profile is made in a sequencing lab. [3 marks]

b) Explain which DNA profile is most likely to be from the child's father. [1 mark]

c) Give another use of DNA profiling. [1 mark]

Q2 In the EU there is a ban on the import and export of any products made from dog fur. Authorities enforcing the ban only need to analyse DNA from a single hair found within a product they suspect to contain dog fur, to identify if the product is illegal.

Explain a procedure that allows scientists to successfully isolate and amplify DNA from such a small original sample. [3 marks]

DNA profiling should give conclusive proof of who stole the biscuits...

Who would have thought that tiny pieces of DNA on a gel would be that important? Well, they are and you need to know all about them. Make sure you know the techniques used to make a DNA profile as well as its applications. And remember, it's very unlikely that two people will have the same DNA profile (except identical twins that is).

Bacterial and Viral Infections

Unfortunately, some microorganisms have got nothing better to do than cause disease...

You need to **Know** the **Structure** of **Bacteria**...

1) Bacteria are **single-celled**, **prokaryotic** microorganisms (prokaryotic means they have **no nucleus**).

2) Most bacteria are only a **few micrometers** (μm) long, e.g. the TB bacterium is about 1 μm.

3) Bacterial cells have a **plasma membrane**, **cytoplasm**, **ribosomes** and other features:

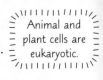
Animal and plant cells are eukaryotic.

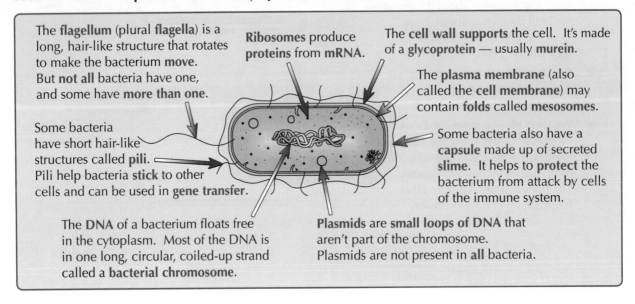

The **flagellum** (plural **flagella**) is a long, hair-like structure that rotates to make the bacterium **move**. But **not all** bacteria have one, and some have **more than one**.

Some bacteria have short hair-like structures called **pili**. Pili help bacteria **stick to other** cells and can be used in **gene transfer**.

Ribosomes produce **proteins from mRNA**.

The **DNA** of a bacterium floats free in the cytoplasm. Most of the DNA is in one long, circular, coiled-up strand called a **bacterial chromosome**.

The **cell wall supports** the cell. It's made of a **glycoprotein** — usually **murein**.

The **plasma membrane** (also called the **cell membrane**) may contain **folds** called **mesosomes**.

Some bacteria also have a **capsule** made up of secreted **slime**. It helps to **protect** the bacterium from attack by cells of the immune system.

Plasmids are **small loops of DNA** that aren't part of the chromosome. Plasmids are not present in **all** bacteria.

...And **Viruses**

1) Viruses are microorganisms but they're **not cells** — they're just **nucleic acids** surrounded by **protein**.

2) They're **tiny**, even **smaller** than bacteria, e.g. HIV is about 0.1 μm across.

3) **Unlike** bacteria, viruses have **no** plasma membrane, **no** cytoplasm and **no** ribosomes.

4) But they do have **nucleic acids** (like bacteria) and some other features:

Remember — DNA and RNA are nucleic acids.

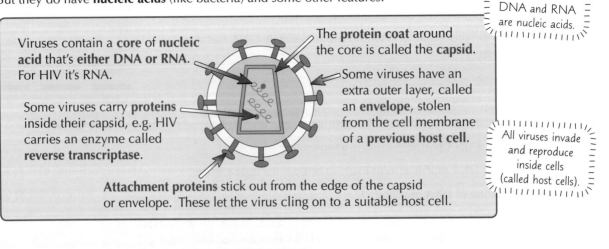

Viruses contain a **core of nucleic acid** that's **either DNA or RNA**. For HIV it's RNA.

Some viruses carry **proteins** inside their capsid, e.g. HIV carries an enzyme called **reverse transcriptase**.

The **protein coat** around the core is called the **capsid**.

Some viruses have an extra outer layer, called an **envelope**, stolen from the cell membrane of a **previous host cell**.

Attachment proteins stick out from the edge of the capsid or envelope. These let the virus cling on to a suitable host cell.

All viruses invade and reproduce inside cells (called host cells).

Pathogens Cause **Infectious Diseases**

1) A **pathogen** is **any organism** that **causes disease**.

2) Diseases caused by pathogens are called **infectious diseases**.

3) Pathogenic microorganisms include **some bacteria**, **some fungi** and **all viruses**.

4) As an infectious disease **develops** in an organism it causes a **sequence of symptoms**, which **may** lead to **death**.

5) You need to know the sequence of symptoms for the diseases caused by the **human immunodeficiency virus** (HIV — see next page) and ***Mycobacterium tuberculosis*** (see page 138).

Bacterial and Viral Infections

The *Human Immunodeficiency Virus (HIV) Affects the* Immune System

The **human immunodeficiency virus** (**HIV**) infects and destroys a type of **white blood cell** called a **T helper cell** (see page 141), which act as a **host cell** for the virus. T helper cells **activate** other immune system cells so they're **hugely important** in the immune response.

HIV *Replicates Inside its* Host's T Helper Cells

1) **HIV** is spread through **infected bodily fluids**. Infection of a new host occurs when these fluids come into contact with **mucosal surfaces** (e.g. of the genitals) or **damaged tissue**, or are injected into the **bloodstream**. One of the most common ways that HIV infects a new host is via **sexual intercourse**.

2) **HIV** (and all other viruses) can only **reproduce** inside the cells of the organism it has infected. HIV replicates inside the **T helper cells** of the host. It doesn't have the equipment (such as **enzymes** and **ribosomes**) to replicate on its own, so it uses those of the **host cell**.

Here's how **HIV** replicates:

1) The attachment protein **attaches** to a **receptor molecule** on the cell membrane of the host T helper cell.

2) The capsid is released into the cell, where it **uncoats** and releases the **genetic material** (RNA) into the cell's cytoplasm.

3) Inside the cell, reverse transcriptase is used to make a **complementary** strand of DNA from the **viral RNA template**.

4) From this, **double-stranded DNA** is made and **inserted** into the human DNA.

5) Host cell enzymes are used to make **viral proteins** from the **viral DNA** found within the human DNA.

6) The viral proteins are **assembled** into **new viruses**, which **bud** from the cell and go on to infect other cells.

During the initial infection period, HIV replicates rapidly and the infected person may experience severe flu-like symptoms. After this period, HIV replication drops to a lower level. This is the **latency period**. During the latency period (which can last for years), the infected person **won't experience** any **symptoms**.

HIV Causes AIDS

1) HIV infection eventually leads to **acquired immune deficiency syndrome** (**AIDS**).

2) AIDS is a condition where the immune system **deteriorates** and eventually **fails**.

3) People with HIV are classed as having AIDS when **symptoms** of their **failing immune system** start to **appear** or their **T helper cell count drops** below a certain level.

4) People with AIDS generally develop diseases and infections that **wouldn't** cause serious problems in people with a **healthy** immune system — these are called **opportunistic infections**.

5) The length of time between **infection** with HIV and the **development** of AIDS **varies** between individuals but without treatment it's usually around **10 years**. The disease then progresses through a **sequence of symptoms**:

   1) The **initial symptoms** of AIDS include **minor infections** of mucous membranes (e.g. the inside of the nose, ears and genitals), and recurring respiratory infections. These are caused by a **lower than normal** number of **T helper cells**.

   2) As AIDS **progresses** the number of **T helper cells decreases** further. Patients become susceptible to **more serious infections** including chronic diarrhoea, severe bacterial infections and tuberculosis (see next page).

   3) During the **late stages** of AIDS, patients have a **very low number** of T helper cells and suffer from a **range of serious infections** such as toxoplasmosis of the brain (a parasite infection) and candidiasis of the respiratory system (fungal infection). It's these serious infections that kill AIDS patients, not HIV itself.

The infections become more and more serious as there are fewer and fewer immune system cells to fight them.

The length of time that people survive with AIDS varies. Factors that affect progression of HIV to AIDS and survival time with AIDS include **existing infections**, the **strain of HIV** they're infected with, **age** and access to **healthcare**.

TOPIC 6B — MICROORGANISMS AND IMMUNITY

Bacterial and Viral Infections

The *Bacterium* Mycobacterium tuberculosis *Causes Tuberculosis (TB)*

1) *Mycobacterium tuberculosis* causes the disease **tuberculosis** (**TB**).

2) Infection occurs when tiny **droplets** containing the bacteria (e.g. from an **infected person's** cough/sneeze) are **inhaled** into the lungs.

3) In the lungs, the bacteria are taken up by a type of white blood cell called a **phagocyte** (see page 140).

4) The bacteria **survive** and **replicate** inside the phagocytes.

Phagocytes usually engulf and then digest bacteria, but M. tuberculosis is able to evade digestion once it's inside the phagocyte.

5) Most people **don't develop TB straight away** — their immune system **seals off** the **infected phagocytes** in structures in the lungs called **tubercles**.

6) When sealed inside the tubercles, the bacteria become **dormant** and the infected person shows **no obvious symptoms**.

7) Later on, the **dormant bacteria** may become **reactivated** and **overcome** the **immune system**, causing TB.

8) **Reactivation** is **more likely** in people with **weakened immune systems**, e.g. people with **AIDS** (see previous page).

9) The length of **time** between the **infection** with *M. tuberculosis* and the **development** of TB **varies** between individuals — it can be **weeks** to **years**. TB then progresses through a **sequence of symptoms**:

> 1) The **initial symptoms** of TB include **fever**, **general weakness** and **severe coughing**, caused by **inflammation** of the lungs.
>
> 2) As TB **progresses** it **damages** the **lungs** and if it's left **untreated** it can cause **respiratory failure**, which can lead to **death**.
>
> 3) TB can also **spread** from the lungs to **other parts** of the body, e.g. the **brain** and **kidneys**. If it's left **untreated** it can cause **organ failure**, which can lead to **death**.

See next page for more on inflammation.

Practice Questions

Q1 What type of cell does HIV replicate in?

Q2 How does HIV infect a host cell?

Q3 What is the name of the bacterium that causes tuberculosis?

Q4 Describe two ways in which tuberculosis can cause death.

Exam Questions

Q1 HIV and *Mycobacterium tuberculosis* both contain nucleic acids.

a) Look at the table on the right.

i) Which row (A-D) represents the nucleic acid content of HIV? [1 mark]

ii) Which row (A-D) represents the nucleic acid content of *Mycobacterium tuberculosis*? [1 mark]

	Contains RNA	Contains DNA
A	✓	✓
B	✗	✗
C	✓	✗
D	✗	✓

b) Other than the nucleic acid content, state three differences between the structure of HIV and the structure of *Mycobacterium tuberculosis* (TB). [3 marks]

Q2 People infected with HIV eventually develop AIDS.
Describe and explain the likely sequence of symptoms found in a person infected with the HIV virus. [6 marks]

My computer has a virus — I knew I shouldn't have sneezed on it...

Not the nicest of topics, but one you have to learn about. You need to know how HIV and M. tuberculosis cause disease — from the initial infection, right through the sequence of symptoms that may eventually lead to death. I always find it weird just how simple a virus is — they're not cells, or even living things, but they can do a lot of damage to us.

Infection and the Non-Specific Immune Response

Infections are never fun. Luckily, your body's got some pretty clever ways of keeping those pesky pathogens at bay...

Pathogens Need to Enter the Body to Cause Disease...

Pathogens can **enter** the body via four major routes:

1) Through **cuts** in the **skin**.
2) Through the **digestive system** via **contaminated food** or **drink**.
3) Through the **respiratory system** by being **inhaled**.
4) Through other **mucosal surfaces**, e.g. the **inside** of the **nose**, **mouth** and **genitals**.

...but there are Several Barriers to Prevent Infection

Stomach acid — If you **eat** or **drink** something that contains **pathogens**, most of them will be **killed** by the **acidic** conditions of the **stomach**. However, some may **survive** and pass into the intestines where they can **invade cells** of the **gut wall** and cause disease.

Skin — Your skin acts as a **physical barrier** to pathogens. But if you **damage** your skin, **pathogens** on the surface can **enter** your **bloodstream**. The blood **clots** at the area of damage to **prevent** pathogens from entering, but some may get in **before** the clot forms.

Gut and skin flora — Your **intestines** and **skin** are **naturally covered** in billions of **harmless microorganisms** (called **flora**). They **compete** with **pathogens** for **nutrients** and **space**. This **limits** the **number** of **pathogens** living in the gut and on the skin and makes it **harder** for them to **infect** the body.

Lysozyme — Mucosal surfaces (e.g. eyes, mouth and nose) produce **secretions** (e.g. tears, saliva and mucus). These secretions all **contain** an **enzyme** called **lysozyme**. Lysozyme **kills bacteria** by **damaging** their **cell walls** — it makes the bacteria **burst open** (**lyse**).

Foreign Antigens Trigger an Immune Response

Antigens are **molecules** (usually proteins or polysaccharides) found on the **surface** of **cells**. When a **pathogen invades** the body, the **antigens** on its cell surface are **recognised as foreign**, which **activates** cells in the **immune system**. The body has **two types** of immune response — **specific** (see page 141) and **non-specific** (see below).

The Non-Specific Immune Response Happens First

The non-specific response happens in the **same** way for **all microorganisms** (regardless of the foreign antigen they have) — it's **not** antigen-specific. It starts attacking the microorganisms **straight away**. You need to know about **three mechanisms** that are part of the non-specific immune response:

① Inflammation at the Site of Infection

The **site** where a **pathogen enters** the body (the **site of infection**) usually becomes **red**, **warm**, **swollen** and **painful** — this is called **inflammation**. Here's how it happens:

1) Immune system cells **recognise foreign antigens** on the surface of a pathogen and **release molecules** that trigger inflammation.
2) The molecules cause **vasodilation** (**widening** of the blood vessels) around the site of infection, **increasing** the **blood flow** to it.
3) The molecules also **increase** the **permeability** of the **blood vessels**.
4) The increased blood flow brings **loads** of **immune system cells** to the **site of infection** and the increased permeability allows those cells to **move out** of the blood vessels and **into** the infected tissue.
5) The immune system cells can then start to **destroy** the **pathogen**.

Trevor's throat infection triggered a small amount of inflammation.

Infection and the Non-Specific Immune Response

2) Production of **Anti-Viral Proteins** Called **Interferons**

1) When cells are **infected** with **viruses**, they produce **proteins** called **interferons**.
2) Interferons help to **prevent** viruses **spreading** to **uninfected cells**.
3) They do this in several ways:

> • They **prevent** viral **replication** by **inhibiting** the production of **viral proteins**.
> • They **activate** cells involved in the **specific** immune response (see next page) to **kill** infected cells.
> • They **activate** other mechanisms of the **non-specific** immune response, e.g. they **promote inflammation** to bring immune system cells to the **site of infection** (see previous page).

3) **Phagocytosis** and **Lysozyme Action**

A **phagocyte** (e.g. a macrophage) is a type of **white blood cell** that carries out **phagocytosis** (**engulfment** of pathogens). They're found in the **blood** and in **tissues** and are the **first cells** to **respond** to a pathogen inside the body. Here's how they work:

1) A phagocyte **recognises** the **antigens** on a pathogen.
2) The cytoplasm of the phagocyte moves round the pathogen, **engulfing** it.
3) The pathogen is now contained in a **phagocytic vacuole** (a bubble) in the cytoplasm of the phagocyte.
4) A **lysosome** (an organelle that contains **digestive enzymes**, including **lysozymes**) **fuses** with the phagocytic vacuole. The enzymes **break down** the pathogen.
5) The phagocyte then **presents** the pathogen's **antigens**. It sticks the antigens on its **surface** to **activate** other immune system cells (see next page) — so it's also called an **antigen-presenting cell**.

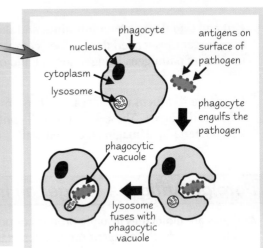

Practice Questions

Q1 State four ways in which pathogens can enter the body.

Q2 State two barriers that prevent infection.

Q3 What are antigens?

Q4 Describe two ways in which interferons prevent viruses from spreading to uninfected cells.

Exam Questions

Q1 Inflammation is part of the non-specific immune response.
  a) Describe how inflammation is triggered at the site of infection. [1 mark]
  b) Explain how inflammation aids the immune response. [4 marks]

Q2 Describe the process of phagocytosis. [3 marks]

Studying for exams interferons with your social life...

There's a lot to remember here, but fear not, you just need to know about your body's barriers to pathogens and how the non-specific immune response works. It's also important that you know what an antigen is — it'll help you to understand how the specific immune response works. Next stop, T and B cells — and no, you can't get off...

The Specific Immune Response

Most pathogens will regret even thinking about sneaking into your body when the specific response gets going...

The **Specific Immune Response** Involves **T** and **B** Cells

The **specific immune response** is **antigen-specific** — it produces responses that are **aimed** at **specific pathogens**. It involves white blood cells called **T** and **B cells**:

1 Phagocytes **Activate T Cells**

1) A **T cell** is a type of **white blood cell**.

2) Their surface is covered with **receptors**.

3) The receptors **bind to antigens** displayed by **antigen-presenting cells**, such as **macrophages** (a type of phagocyte).

4) Each T cell has a **different shaped receptor** on its surface.

5) When the receptor on the surface of a T cell meets a **complementary antigen**, it binds to it — so each T cell will bind to a **different antigen**.

6) This **activates** the T cell. The activated T cell then **divides** to produce **clones** of itself.

7) **Different types** of T cells carry out **different functions**:

- **T helper cells** — **release substances** to **activate B cells** (see below), **T killer cells** and macrophages.
- **T killer cells** — **attach** to antigens on a pathogen-infected cell and **kill** the cell.
- **T memory cells** — see p. 144.

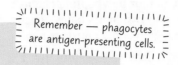
Remember — phagocytes are antigen-presenting cells.

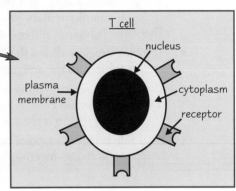
T cell — nucleus, plasma membrane, cytoplasm, receptor

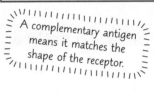
A complementary antigen means it matches the shape of the receptor.

2 T Helper Cells **Activate B Cells**

1) **B cells** are another type of **white blood cell**.

2) They're covered with proteins called **antibodies**.

3) Antibodies **bind to antigens** to form an **antigen-antibody complex**.

4) Each B cell has a **different shaped antibody** on its surface.

5) When the antibody on the surface of a B cell meets a **complementary antigen**, it binds to it — so each B cell will bind to a **different antigen**.

6) This, together with substances **released** from the T cell, **activates** the B cell.

7) The activated B cell **divides**, by **mitosis**, into **plasma cells** (also called **B effector cells**) and **B memory cells** (see p. 144).

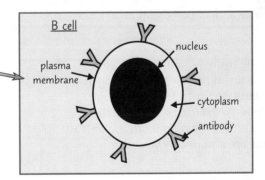
B cell — nucleus, plasma membrane, cytoplasm, antibody

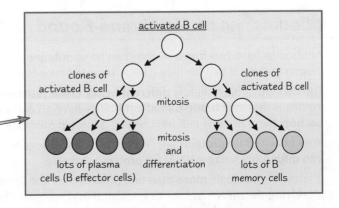
activated B cell — clones of activated B cell, clones of activated B cell, mitosis, mitosis and differentiation, lots of plasma cells (B effector cells), lots of B memory cells

The Specific Immune Response

Plasma Cells Make Antibodies to a Specific Antigen

1) **Plasma cells** are **clones** of the **B** cells (they're **identical** to the B cells).

2) They secrete **loads** of the **antibody**, specific to the antigen, into the blood.

3) These antibodies will bind to the antigens on the surface of the
pathogen to form **lots** of **antigen-antibody complexes**:

Don't forget — plasma cells are also called B effector cells.

- Antibodies are made of **four polypeptide chains**
— **two heavy** chains and **two light** chains. Each
chain has a **variable** region and a **constant** region.

- The **variable regions** of the antibody form the
antigen binding sites. The **shape** of the variable
region is **complementary** to a particular antigen.
The variable regions **differ** between antibodies.

- The **hinge region** allows **flexibility** when the
antibody binds to the antigen.

- The **constant regions** allow binding to **receptors**
on **immune system cells**, e.g. phagocytes.
The constant region is the **same in all** antibodies.

- **Disulfide bridges** (a type of bond) hold the
polypeptide chains together.

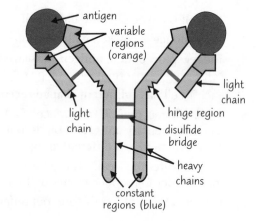

An Antigen-Antibody Complex

antigen
variable regions (orange)
light chain
light chain
hinge region
disulfide bridge
heavy chains
constant regions (blue)

Antibodies Help to Clear Infections

Antibodies **help** to **clear** an **infection** by:

1) <u>Agglutinating pathogens</u> — each antibody has **two
binding sites**, so an antibody can **bind** to **two pathogens**
at the **same time** — the pathogens become **clumped
together**. Phagocytes then bind to the antibodies and
phagocytose a lot of pathogens **all at once**.

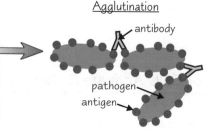

Agglutination

antibody
pathogen
antigen

2) <u>Neutralising toxins</u> — antibodies can
bind to the **toxins** produced by pathogens.
This **prevents** the toxins from **affecting
human cells**, so the toxins are **neutralised**
(inactivated). The toxin-antibody
complexes are also phagocytosed.

3) <u>Preventing the pathogen binding to human cells</u>
— when antibodies bind to the antigens on
pathogens, they may **block** the cell surface
receptors that the pathogens need to **bind to**
the host cells. This means the pathogen **can't
attach to** or **infect** the host cells.

Antibodies can be Membrane-Bound or Secreted

1) Antibodies have **two forms** — they can be **membrane-bound** (attached to the
membrane of a B cell) or they can be **secreted** (free from any attachment).

2) The two forms have slightly **different heavy chain proteins** — one of the reasons
for this is that **membrane-bound antibodies** have an **extra section** of protein that
anchors them to the B cell membrane. Secreted antibodies don't need this.

3) Both **heavy chain proteins** are coded for by **a single gene**, which is copied
into **mRNA** (messenger RNA) for **protein synthesis**.

4) It's possible to create **more than one protein** from **the heavy chain gene** by
modifying the **mRNA** before it's translated into protein. This process is
explained in more detail on the next page.

Remember, the process of copying a gene into mRNA is called transcription. It takes place in the nucleus before translation.

The Specific Immune Response

mRNA is Modified Before Translation

1) Genes contain sections that **don't code** for amino acids.

2) These sections of DNA are called **introns**. All the bits that **do** code for amino acids are called **exons**.

3) During transcription the introns and exons are both **copied** into mRNA. mRNA strands containing both introns and exons are called **pre-mRNA**.

4) The introns are then **removed** by a process called **splicing** — introns are removed and exons joined forming **mRNA** strands. This takes place in the **nucleus** and is a **post-transcriptional change**.

5) Sometimes, **certain exons** are **removed**, as well as the introns, to form **different** mRNA strands. This is called **alternative splicing**.

6) This means **more than one amino acid sequence** and so **more than one protein** can be produced from **one gene**. For example:

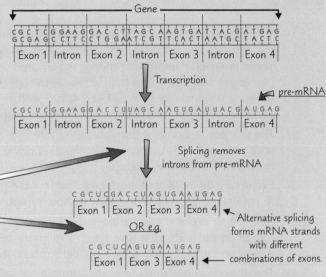

There are **many exons** in the gene for an **antibody heavy chain**. Two of these exons code for the part of the heavy chain protein that **anchors** the antibody to the **B cell membrane**. To produce the heavy chain for the **secreted antibody**, these **two exons** are **removed** from the **pre-mRNA**. An exon that's unique to the secreted antibody is removed when producing the heavy chain for the membrane-bound antibody.

It is thought that about **95%** of **human genes** that have **more than one exon** undergo **alternative splicing**. This means that our genome can produce a **lot more proteins** than it could if each gene made only one protein.

Practice Questions

Q1 Name the structures found on the surface of T cells that bind to antigens.

Q2 What is the role of a macrophage in T cell activation?

Q3 Briefly describe how a B cell is activated.

Q4 What cells do activated B cells divide into?

Q5 What is an exon?

Exam Questions

Q1 a) Describe how a T cell is activated. [2 marks]

b) Which of the following statements about T helper cells is true?

   A They divide to form plasma cells.   **B** They engulf pathogens.

   C They activate B cells.   **D** They kill pathogen-infected cells. [1 mark]

Q2 Describe the function of antibodies. [3 marks]

Q3 Describe how one gene can give rise to more than one protein. [5 marks]

The student-revision complex — only present the night before an exam...

So phagocytes activate T cells, T cells activate B cells, and B cells clone themselves to make plasma cells. Plasma cells then secrete lots of antibodies. Seems a bit of a long winded way to get rid of a few pathogens but, hey, who am I to argue. How about using 'phew, this Biology paper — aced' to help remember the order of the specific immune response.

Developing Immunity

Your immune system has a memory — it's handy for fighting infections, not for remembering Biology notes...

The Production of **Memory Cells** Gives **Immunity**

1) When a pathogen enters the body for the **first time** the antigens on its surface **activate** the **immune system**. The **non-specific immune response** is activated first (see pages 139-140). This then activates the **specific immune response** (see pages 141-142). Together these two immune responses make up the **primary response**.

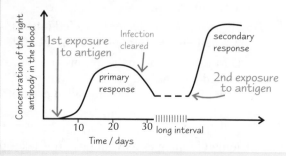

2) The primary response is **slow** because there **aren't many B cells** that can make the antibody needed to bind to the antigen.

3) Eventually the body will produce **enough** of the right antibody to overcome the infection. Meanwhile the infected person will show **symptoms** of the disease.

4) After being exposed to an antigen, both T and B cells produce **memory cells**. These memory cells **remain in the body** for a **long** time. T memory cells remember the **specific antigen** and will recognise it a second time round. B memory cells record the specific **antibodies** needed to bind to the antigen.

5) The person is now **immune** — their immune system has the **ability** to respond **quickly** to a second infection.

6) If the **same pathogen** enters the body again, the immune system will produce a **quicker, stronger** immune response — the **secondary response**.

7) **T memory cells** divide into the **correct type** of T cells to kill the cell carrying the antigen. **B memory cells** divide into plasma cells (also called **B effector cells**) that produce the right antibody to the antigen.

8) The secondary response often gets rid of the pathogen **before** you begin to show any **symptoms**.

Immunity *can be* **Active** *or* **Passive**

ACTIVE IMMUNITY

This is the type of immunity you get when **your immune system makes its own antibodies** after being **stimulated** by an **antigen**. There are **two** different types of active immunity:

1) **Natural** — this is when you become immune after **catching a disease**.

2) **Artificial** — this is when you become immune after you've been given a **vaccine** containing a harmless dose of antigen (see below).

Active immunity gives you long-term protection, but it takes a while for the protection to develop.

PASSIVE IMMUNITY

This is the type of immunity you get from being **given antibodies made by a different organism** — your immune system **doesn't** produce any antibodies of its own. Again, there are **two** types:

1) **Natural** — this is when a **baby** becomes immune due to the antibodies it receives from its **mother**, through the **placenta** and in **breast milk**.

2) **Artificial** — this is when you become immune after being **injected** with **antibodies**, e.g. if you contract tetanus you can be injected with antibodies against the tetanus toxin.

Passive immunity gives you short-term protection, but the protection is immediate.

Vaccines *Give You* **Immunity Without Getting** *the* **Disease**

1) While your B cells are busy **dividing** to build up their numbers to deal with a pathogen (i.e. the **primary response** — see above), you **suffer** from the disease. Vaccination can help avoid this.

2) Vaccines **contain antigens** that stimulate the **primary immune response** against a **particular pathogen, without** the pathogen **causing disease**. This results in your body producing **memory cells**, and means that you become **immune** without getting any **symptoms** of the disease.

3) Some vaccines contain **many different antigens** to protect against **different strains** of pathogens. Different strains of pathogens are created by **antigenic variation** (see next page).

Developing Immunity

Pathogens Evolve Mechanisms to Evade the Immune System

1) Over **millions** of **years** vertebrates (e.g. humans) have **evolved** better and better **immune systems** — ones that **fight** a **greater variety** of pathogens in lots of **different ways**.

2) At the same time, **pathogens** have **evolved** better and better ways to **evade** (**avoid**) the immune systems of their **hosts** (the **organisms** that they **infect**).

3) This struggle between **pathogens** and their **hosts** to outdo each other is known as an **evolutionary race**.

4) An evolutionary race is **similar** to an **arms race** — where **two countries** constantly **develop better weapons** in an attempt to **overpower** each other.

5) **Evidence** to **support** the **theory** of an **evolutionary race** comes from the **evasion mechanisms** that pathogens have **developed**. For example:

HIV's evasion mechanisms

- HIV **kills** the **immune system cells** that it **infects**. This **reduces** the overall **number** of immune system cells in the body, which **reduces** the **chance** of HIV being **detected**.

- HIV has a **high rate** of **mutation** in the **genes** that code for **antigen proteins**. The mutations **change** the **structure** of the antigens and this forms **new strains** of the virus — this process is called **antigenic variation**. The **memory cells** produced for **one strain** of HIV **won't recognise** other strains with **different antigens**, so the immune system has to produce a **primary response** against **each new strain**.

- HIV **disrupts antigen presentation** in infected cells. This **prevents** immune system cells from **recognising** and **killing** the **infected cells**.

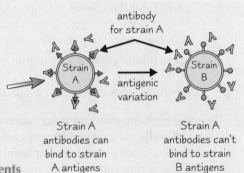

antibody for strain A

Strain A → antigenic variation → Strain B

Strain A antibodies can bind to strain A antigens

Strain A antibodies can't bind to strain B antigens

Mycobacterium tuberculosis' evasion mechanisms

- When *M. tuberculosis* bacteria **infect** the **lungs** they're **engulfed** by **phagocytes**. Here, they **produce substances** that **prevent** the **lysosome fusing** with the **phagocytic vacuole** (see p. 140). This means the bacteria **aren't broken down** and they can **multiply undetected** inside phagocytes.

- This bacterium also **disrupts antigen presentation** in infected cells, which **prevents** immune system cells from **recognising** and **killing** the **infected phagocytes**.

Practice Questions

Q1 Describe the role of B memory cells in the secondary response.

Q2 State two differences between active and passive immunity.

Q3 Describe how a vaccine gives immunity to a pathogen.

Q4 Describe one way in which *Mycobacterium tuberculosis* evades the immune system.

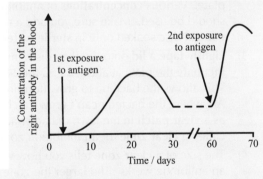

Concentration of the right antibody in the blood

1st exposure to antigen

2nd exposure to antigen

Time / days

Exam Questions

Q1* The graph shows the concentration of antibody in a person's bloodstream following two separate exposures to the same antigen. Describe and explain the changes in the concentration of antibody. [6 marks]

Q2 Give one evasion mechanism of HIV and explain how it helps HIV to avoid destruction by the immune system. [2 marks]

*You will be assessed on the quality of your written response in this question.

Even if you could change your antigens, you can't evade your exams...

Who would've thought there were so many ways to become immune to a microorganism. I don't like the sound of being injected with antibodies (I'm not keen on needles), but if it stops me dying from something like tetanus, then I'll give it a go. We're in an evolutionary race with loads of nasty microbes at the minute... let's hope we're the first past the post...

TOPIC 6B — MICROORGANISMS AND IMMUNITY

Antibiotics

You've probably taken antibiotics at some point. Now you get to learn about how they work — the fun never ends...

Antibiotics Kill or Prevent the Growth of Microorganisms

1) **Antibiotics** are **chemicals** that **kill** or **inhibit** the **growth** of microorganisms.
2) There are **two different types** of antibiotics:
3) Antibiotics are **used** by humans as **drugs** to **treat bacterial infections**.

- **Bacteriocidal** antibiotics **kill** bacteria.
- **Bacteriostatic** antibiotics **prevent** bacteria growing.

Antibiotics Work by Inhibiting Bacterial Metabolism

Antibiotics kill bacteria (or inhibit their growth) because they **interfere** with **metabolic reactions** that are **crucial** for the growth and life of the cell:

1) Some **inhibit enzymes** that are needed to make the chemical **bonds** in bacterial **cell walls**. This prevents the bacteria from **growing** properly. It can also lead to **cell death** — the weakened cell wall can't take the **pressure** as water moves into the cell by **osmosis**. This can cause the cell to **burst**.
2) Some **inhibit protein production** by binding to bacterial **ribosomes**. All **enzymes** are proteins, so if the cell can't make proteins, it can't make enzymes. This means it can't carry out important **metabolic processes** that are needed for growth and development.

Bacterial cells are **different** from **mammalian** cells (e.g. human cells) — mammalian cells are **eukaryotic**, they **don't** have **cell walls**, they have **different enzymes** and they have different, **larger ribosomes**. This means antibiotics can be designed to **only target** the **bacterial cells**, so they don't damage mammalian cells. **Viruses don't** have their **own** enzymes and ribosomes — they use the ones in the host's cell, so antibiotics **don't affect them**.

You Can Investigate the Effects of Antibiotics on Bacterial Growth

You need to know how to **investigate** the effect of **antibiotics** on **bacterial growth**, using **aseptic techniques**. It's similar to the investigation you did into the **antimicrobial properties** of **plants** in Year 1. Here's how you could do it:

1) Use a **sterile pipette** to **transfer** the bacteria you've been given to an **agar plate**. Spread the bacteria over the plate using a sterile spreader.
2) Use sterile forceps to place paper discs **soaked** with different **antibiotics** spaced apart on the plate. Various **concentrations** of antibiotics should be used. Make sure you add a **negative control** disc soaked only in **sterile water**.
3) **Lightly tape** a lid onto the Petri dish, invert, and **incubate** the plate at about **25 °C** for **24-48 hours**. This allows the bacteria to **grow** (forming a 'lawn'). Anywhere the bacteria **can't grow** can be seen as a **clear patch** in the lawn of bacteria. This is called a **clear zone** (or an inhibition zone).
4) The size of a **clear zone** tells you how well an antibiotic works. The **larger** the zone, the **more** the bacteria were inhibited from growing.

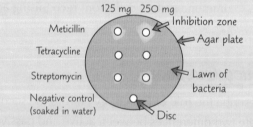

This diagram shows an agar plate with **meticillin, tetracycline** and **streptomycin** discs **after** it has been **incubated**.

125 mg   250 mg
Meticillin — Inhibition zone
— Agar plate
Tetracycline
Streptomycin — Lawn of bacteria
Negative control (soaked in water) — Disc

- The **tetracycline** discs have **no** clear zones, so the bacteria are **resistant** to tetracycline up to 250 mg.
- The **streptomycin** discs have **small** clear zones, with the zone at 250 mg slightly larger than the one at 125 mg. So streptomycin has **some effect** on the bacteria.
- The **meticillin** discs have the **largest** clear zones, so meticillin has the **strongest effect** on these bacteria.

When carrying out this investigation, you need to use **aseptic techniques** to prevent your bacterial cultures becoming **contaminated** with **unwanted microorganisms**. This is important as contamination could **affect your results** by interfering with the **growth** of the bacteria that you're working with. It's also important to avoid contamination with **human pathogens** that could make you **ill**. Aseptic techniques include:

- Regularly **disinfecting surfaces** to minimise contamination.
- Using **sterile equipment**, which is discarded safely after use.
- Working near a **Bunsen burner** flame, so any **microbes** in the air are **drawn away** from your culture.

You should have met aseptic techniques back in the first year of your course when investigating the antimicrobial properties of plants — the same ones apply here.

Antibiotics

Hospital Acquired Infections (HAIs) can be Transmitted by Poor Hygiene

1) **Hospital acquired infections** (HAIs) are **infections** that are **caught** while a patient is being treated **in hospital**.

2) HAIs are **transmitted** by poor hygiene, such as:

- Hospital **staff** and **visitors not washing** their **hands** before and after visiting a patient.
- **Coughs** and **sneezes not** being **contained**, e.g. in a tissue.
- **Equipment** (e.g. beds or surgical instruments) and **surfaces not** being **disinfected** after they're used.

3) People are **more likely** to catch infections in hospital because many patients are ill, so have **weakened immune systems**, and they're **around** other **ill people**.

4) **Codes of practice** have been developed to **prevent** and **control HAIs**. They include:

- Hospital **staff** and **visitors** should be **encouraged** to **wash** their **hands**, **before** and **after** they've been with a patient.
- **Equipment** and **surfaces** should be **disinfected** after they're used.
- **People with HAIs** should be **moved** to an **isolation ward** so they're **less likely** to **transmit** the infection to **other patients**.

Despite his protests, Huxley wasn't allowed in the ward with his mucky trotters.

Some HAIs are Antibiotic-Resistant

1) Some **HAIs** are caused by bacteria that are **resistant** to **antibiotics**, e.g. MRSA.

2) These HAIs are **difficult** to **treat** because antibiotics **don't** get rid of the infection. This means these HAIs can lead to **serious health problems** or even **death**.

3) Infections caused by antibiotic-resistant bacteria are **more common** in **hospitals** because **more** antibiotics are used there, so bacteria in hospitals are **more likely** to have **evolved resistance** against them.

4) **Codes of practice** have also been developed to **prevent** and **control** HAIs caused by antibiotic-resistant bacteria:

- Doctors **shouldn't** prescribe antibiotics for **minor** bacterial infections or **viral** infections.
- Doctors **shouldn't** prescribe antibiotics to **prevent** infections.
- Doctors **should** use **narrow-spectrum antibiotics** (which only affect a specific bacterium) if possible, e.g. when the **strain** of bacteria the person has been infected with has been **identified**.
- Doctors **should rotate** the **use** of **different** antibiotics.
- Patients **should** take **all** of the antibiotics that they're **prescribed** so infections are **fully cleared**.

These codes reduce the likelihood that bacteria will evolve antibiotic resistance.

Practice Questions

Q1 What are bacteriostatic antibiotics?

Q2 Name two processes in a bacterial cell that antibiotics can inhibit.

Q3 What is a hospital acquired infection?

Negative control (N)
Penicillin 125 mg (A)
Amoxicillin 125 mg (B)
Erythromycin 125 mg (C)
Streptomycin 125 mg (D)

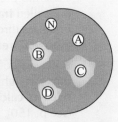

Exam Questions

Q1 The agar plate on the right shows the effects of different antibiotics on a strain of bacteria.
 a) Describe how the plate could have been prepared. [4 marks]
 b) Which antibiotic is most effective against this strain of bacterium? Explain your answer. [2 marks]

Q2 Describe one way in which poor hygiene can cause HAIs, and a code of practice designed to prevent it. [2 marks]

The Market Research Society of Australia — not a deadly bacterium...

It's just typical, scientists discover all these fancy chemicals that get rid of bacteria and then some of the swines decide they won't be affected by them. Spoilsports. So, if you ever visit a hospital, make sure you use the alcohol gel to clean your hands. You'll not only be preventing those pesky infections, but you'll experience a cooling sensation like no other.

Muscles and Movement

Muscles are pretty darn useful — they contract so you can move. But before we get into the gritty detail of exactly how they contract, you need to know a bit more about them and how they're involved in movement...

Movement *Involves* Skeletal Muscles, Tendons, Ligaments *and* Joints

1) **Skeletal muscle** is the type of muscle you use to **move**, e.g. the biceps and triceps move the lower arm.
2) Skeletal **muscles** are **attached** to **bones** by **tendons**.
3) **Ligaments attach bones** to **other bones**, to hold them together.
4) Skeletal muscles **contract** and **relax** to **move bones** at a **joint**.
    To understand how this works it's best to look at an example:

- The bones of your lower arm are attached to a biceps muscle and a triceps muscle by tendons.
- The biceps and triceps work together to move your arm — as one contracts, the other relaxes:

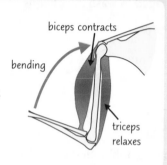

When your **biceps contracts** your **triceps relaxes**. This pulls the bone so your **arm bends** (**flexes**) at the elbow. A muscle that **bends** a joint when it contracts is called a **flexor**.

biceps contracts

bending

triceps relaxes

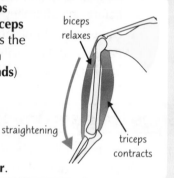

When your **triceps contracts** your **biceps relaxes**. This pulls the bone so your **arm straightens** (**extends**) at the **elbow**. A muscle that **straightens** a joint when it contracts is called an **extensor**.

biceps relaxes

straightening

triceps contracts

- Muscles that work together to move a bone are called antagonistic pairs.

Muscles work in pairs because they can only pull (when they contract) — they can't push. So you need two muscles, creating opposite forces, to move a bone.

Skeletal Muscle *is made up of* Long Muscle Fibres

1) Skeletal muscle is made up of **large bundles** of **long cells**, called **muscle fibres**.
2) The cell membrane of muscle fibre cells is called the **sarcolemma**.
3) Bits of the sarcolemma **fold inwards** across the muscle fibre and stick into the **sarcoplasm** (a muscle cell's cytoplasm). These folds are called **transverse (T) tubules** and they help to **spread electrical impulses** throughout the sarcoplasm so they **reach** all parts of the **muscle fibre**.
4) A network of **internal membranes** called the **sarcoplasmic reticulum** runs through the sarcoplasm. The sarcoplasmic reticulum **stores** and **releases calcium ions** that are needed for muscle contraction (see p. 150).
5) Muscle fibres have lots of **mitochondria** to **provide** the **ATP** that's needed for **muscle contraction**.
6) They are **multinucleate** (contain many nuclei).
7) Muscle fibres have lots of **long, cylindrical organelles** called **myofibrils**. They're made up of proteins and are **highly specialised** for **contraction**.

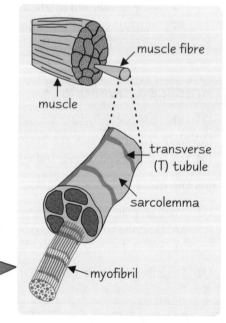

muscle fibre

muscle

transverse (T) tubule

sarcolemma

myofibril

Muscles and Movement

Myofibrils Contain Thick Myosin Filaments and Thin Actin Filaments

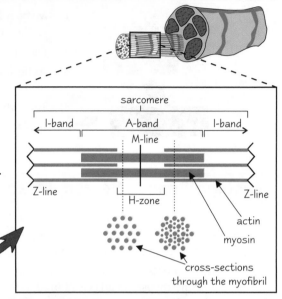

1) Myofibrils contain bundles of **thick** and **thin myofilaments** that **move past each other** to make muscles **contract**.
   - **Thick myofilaments** are made of the protein myosin.
   - **Thin myofilaments** are made of the protein actin.

2) If you look at a **myofibril** under an **electron microscope**, you'll see a pattern of alternating **dark** and **light bands**:
   - Dark bands contain the **thick myosin filaments** and some overlapping thin actin filaments — these are called **A-bands**.
   - **Light** bands contain **thin actin filaments** only — these are called **I-bands**.

3) A myofibril is made up of **many** short units called **sarcomeres**.

4) The **ends** of each **sarcomere** are marked with a **Z-line**. Sarcomeres are **joined together** lengthways at their **Z-lines**.

5) In the **middle** of each sarcomere is an **M-line**. The M-line is the **middle** of the **myosin** filaments.

6) **Around** the M-line is the **H-zone**. The H-zone **only** contains **myosin** filaments.

Muscle Contraction is Explained by the Sliding Filament Theory

1) **Myosin** and **actin** filaments **slide** over one another to make the **sarcomeres contract** — the **myofilaments** themselves **don't contract** and the myosin and actin molecules stay the **same length**.

2) The **simultaneous contraction** of lots of **sarcomeres** means the **myofibrils** and **muscle fibres contract**.

3) Sarcomeres return to their **original length** as the muscle **relaxes**.

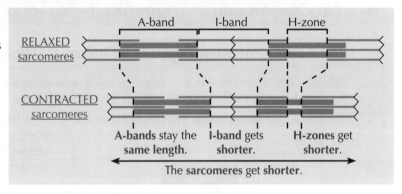

Practice Questions

Q1 What is skeletal muscle?

Q2 What are transverse (T) tubules?

Q3 Name the two proteins that make up myofibrils.

Exam Questions

Q1 Describe how myofilaments, muscle fibres, myofibrils and muscles are related to each other. [3 marks]

Q2 When walking, your quadriceps (muscles at the front of the thigh) contract to straighten the leg, whilst your hamstrings (muscles at the back of the thigh) relax. Then your hamstrings contract to bend the leg, whilst the quadriceps relax.
   a) State which of these muscles are the extensors and which are the flexors. [1 mark]
   b) State the name given to muscles that work together to move a bone. [1 mark]

Q3 The diagram above shows a sketch of a muscle myofibril, which was examined under an electron microscope. What are the correct names for labels A, B and C? [3 marks]

Sarcomere — a French mother with a dry sense of humour...

Muscles involved in movement work in antagonistic pairs — one contracts as the other relaxes and vice versa. So let's practise — lower arm up, lower arm down, lower arm up... okay, that's enough exercise for one day. Anyway, you need to get on with learning the similar-sounding names on these pages and what they mean, like myofilament and myofibril.

Muscle Contraction

Brace yourself — here comes the detail of muscle contraction...

Myosin Filaments Have Globular Heads and Binding Sites

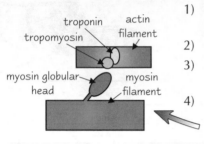

troponin, tropomyosin, actin filament, myosin globular head, myosin filament

1) **Myosin filaments** have **globular heads** that are **hinged**, so they can move **back** and **forth**.

2) Each myosin head has a **binding site** for actin and a **binding site** for **ATP**.

3) **Actin filaments** have **binding sites** for **myosin heads**, called **actin-myosin** binding sites.

4) Two other **proteins** called **tropomyosin** and **troponin** are found between actin filaments. These proteins are **attached** to **each other** and they **help** myofilaments **move** past each other.

Binding Sites in Resting Muscles are Blocked by Tropomyosin

1) In a **resting** (unstimulated) muscle the **actin-myosin binding site** is **blocked** by **tropomyosin**, which is held in place by **troponin**.

2) So **myofilaments can't slide** past each other because the **myosin heads can't bind** to the actin-myosin binding site on the actin filaments.

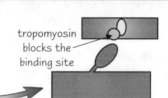

tropomyosin blocks the binding site

Muscle Contraction is Triggered by an Action Potential

Depolarisation means that the difference in charge across the sarcolemma is reduced.

1) The Action Potential Triggers an Influx of Calcium Ions

1) When an action potential from a motor neurone **stimulates** a muscle cell, it **depolarises** the **sarcolemma**. Depolarisation **spreads** down the **T-tubules** to the **sarcoplasmic reticulum** (see p. 148).

2) This causes the **sarcoplasmic reticulum** to **release** stored **calcium ions** (Ca^{2+}) into the **sarcoplasm**.

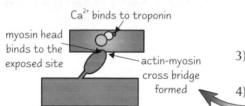

Ca^{2+} binds to troponin, myosin head binds to the exposed site, actin-myosin cross bridge formed

Calcium ions **bind** to **troponin**, causing it to **change shape**. This **pulls** the attached **tropomyosin out** of the **actin-myosin binding site** on the actin filament.

3) This **exposes** the **binding site**, which allows the **myosin head** to **bind**.

4) The bond formed when a **myosin head** binds to an **actin filament** is called an **actin-myosin cross bridge**.

2) ATP Provides the Energy Needed to Move the Myosin Head...

1) **Calcium** ions also **activate** the enzyme **ATPase**, which **breaks down ATP** (into ADP + P$_i$) to **provide** the **energy** needed for muscle contraction.

2) The **energy** released from ATP **moves** the **myosin head**, which **pulls** the **actin filament** along in a kind of **rowing action**.

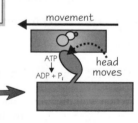

movement, ATP, ADP + P$_i$, head moves

3) ...and to Break the Cross Bridge

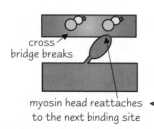

cross bridge breaks, myosin head reattaches to the next binding site

1) **ATP** also provides the **energy** to **break** the **actin-myosin cross bridge**, so the **myosin head detaches** from the actin filament **after** it's moved.

2) The **myosin head** then **reattaches** to a **different binding site** further along the actin filament. A **new actin-myosin cross bridge** is formed and the **cycle** is **repeated** (attach, move, detach, reattach to new binding site...).

3) **Many** cross bridges **form** and **break** very **rapidly**, pulling the actin filament along — which **shortens** the **sarcomere**, causing the **muscle** to **contract**.

4) The cycle will **continue** as long as **calcium ions** are **present** and **bound** to **troponin**.

Muscle Contraction

When **Excitation Stops**, **Calcium Ions Leave** Troponin Molecules

1) When the muscle **stops** being **stimulated**, **calcium ions leave** their **binding sites** on the **troponin** molecules and are moved by **active transport** back into the **sarcoplasmic reticulum** (this needs **ATP** too).

2) The **troponin** molecules return to their **original shape**, pulling the attached **tropomyosin** molecules with them. This means the **tropomyosin** molecules **block** the actin-myosin **binding sites** again.

3) Muscles **aren't contracted** because **no myosin heads** are **attached** to **actin** filaments (so there are no actin-myosin cross bridges).

4) The **actin** filaments **slide back** to their **relaxed** position, which **lengthens** the **sarcomere**.

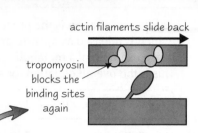

actin filaments slide back

tropomyosin blocks the binding sites again

Skeletal Muscles are Made of Slow and Fast Twitch Muscle Fibres

Skeletal muscles are made up of **two types** of muscle fibres — **slow twitch** and **fast twitch**.
Different muscles have **different proportions** of slow and fast twitch fibres. The two types have **different properties**:

SLOW TWITCH MUSCLE FIBRES	FAST TWITCH MUSCLE FIBRES
Muscle fibres that contract slowly.	Muscle fibres that contract very quickly.
Muscles you use for posture, e.g. those in the back, have a high proportion of them.	Muscles you use for fast movement, e.g. those in the eyes and legs, have a high proportion of them.
Good for endurance activities, e.g. maintaining posture, long-distance running.	Good for short bursts of speed and power, e.g. eye movement, sprinting.
Can work for a long time without getting tired.	Get tired very quickly.
Energy's released slowly through aerobic respiration. Lots of mitochondria and blood vessels supply the muscles with oxygen.	Energy's released quickly through anaerobic respiration using glycogen (stored glucose). There are few mitochondria or blood vessels.
Reddish in colour because they're rich in myoglobin — a red-coloured protein that stores oxygen.	Whitish in colour because they don't have much myoglobin (so can't store much oxygen).

Morgan used his sharp suit and his fast twitch muscle fibres to quickly hail a taxi.

Practice Questions

Q1 Which molecule blocks the actin-myosin binding site in resting muscles?

Q2 What's the name of the bond that's formed when a myosin head binds to an actin filament?

Q3 State three differences between slow and fast twitch skeletal muscle fibres.

Exam Questions

Q1 Rigor mortis is the stiffening of muscles in the body after death. It happens when ATP reserves are exhausted. Explain why a lack of ATP leads to muscles being unable to relax. [3 marks]

Q2 Bepridil is a drug that blocks calcium ion channels.
Describe and explain the effect this drug will have on muscle contraction. [3 marks]

What does muscle contraction cost? 80p...

Sorry, that's my favourite sciencey joke so I had to fit it in somewhere — a small distraction before you revisit this page. It's tough stuff but you know the best way to learn it — shut the book and scribble down what you can remember. If you can't remember much, read it again till you can (and if you remember loads read it again anyway, just to be sure).

Aerobic Respiration

Energy is needed for muscle contraction — this energy comes from respiration (so you have to learn it, unlucky).

Aerobic Respiration Releases Energy

1) **Aerobic respiration** is the process where a **large amount** of **energy** is **released** by **splitting glucose** into CO_2 (which is released as a **waste product**) and H_2 (which combines with atmospheric O_2 to produce H_2O). It's an example of a **metabolic pathway** because it's made up of a **series** of **chemical reactions**. This is the **overall equation** for aerobic respiration:

$$C_6H_{12}O_6 \text{ (glucose)} + 6O_2 \longrightarrow 6CO_2 + 6H_2O + \textbf{Energy}$$

Recap of mitochondrial structure:

inner membrane
outer membrane
matrix
fold (crista)

2) The energy released is **used** to **phosphorylate ADP to ATP**. ATP is then used to **provide energy** for all the **biological processes** inside a cell.

3) There are **four stages** in aerobic respiration — **glycolysis**, the **link reaction**, the **Krebs cycle** and **oxidative phosphorylation**. The **first three** stages of respiration are a **series of reactions**. The **products** from these reactions are **used** in the **final stage** to produce loads of ATP.

4) The **first** stage happens in the **cytoplasm** of cells and the **other three** stages take place in the **mitochondria**.

5) **Each reaction** in respiration is **controlled** and **catalysed** by a **specific intracellular enzyme**. The enzyme with the **slowest** activity is **rate limiting** — it determines the **overall rate** of **respiration**.

6) **Coenzymes** (see page 109) are used in respiration. For example:
   - **NAD** and **FAD** transfer **hydrogen** from one molecule to another — this means they can **reduce** (give hydrogen to) or **oxidise** (take hydrogen from) a molecule.
   - **Coenzyme A** transfers **acetate** between molecules (see pages 153-154).

7) All cells use **glucose** to **respire**, but organisms can also **break down** other **complex organic molecules** (e.g. fatty acids, amino acids), which can then be respired.

Glucose is a respiratory substrate — a molecule that can be respired.

Respiration Map

Glycolysis ← *You are here*
↓
Link Reaction
↓
Krebs Cycle
↓
Oxidative Phosphorylation

Stage 1 — Glycolysis Makes Pyruvate from Glucose

1) Glycolysis involves splitting **one molecule** of **glucose** (a **hexose** sugar, so it has 6 carbons — 6C) into **two** smaller molecules of **pyruvate** (3C).

2) The process happens in the **cytoplasm** of cells.

3) Glycolysis is the **first stage** of both aerobic and anaerobic respiration and **doesn't need oxygen** to take place — so it's an **anaerobic** process.

There are Two Stages in Glycolysis — Phosphorylation and Oxidation

First, **ATP** is **used** to **phosphorylate glucose** to triose phosphate. Then **triose phosphate** is **oxidised**, **releasing ATP**. Overall there's a **net gain** of **2 ATP**.

① Stage One — Phosphorylation

1) Glucose is **phosphorylated** by adding 2 phosphates from 2 molecules of **ATP**.

2) This creates 2 molecules of **triose phosphate** and 2 molecules of **ADP**.

② Stage Two — Oxidation

1) Triose phosphate is **oxidised** (loses hydrogen), forming 2 molecules of **pyruvate**.

2) **NAD** collects the hydrogen ions, forming **2 reduced NAD**.

3) **4 ATP** are **produced**, but 2 were used up in stage one, so there's a **net gain** of **2 ATP**.

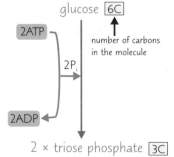

glucose 6C
2ATP
number of carbons in the molecule
2Pᵢ
2ADP
2 × triose phosphate 3C
4ADP + 4Pᵢ 2H⁺ 2NAD
4ATP 2 reduced NAD
2 × pyruvate 3C

You're probably wondering what now happens to all the products of glycolysis...

1) The **two** molecules of **reduced NAD** are used in the **last stage** (oxidative phosphorylation — see page 155).

2) The **two pyruvate** molecules go into the **matrix** of the **mitochondria** for the **link reaction** (see the next page).

Glycolysis involves the partial oxidation of glucose (via triose phosphate). To completely oxidise glucose, you need oxygen and the rest of the steps in aerobic respiration.

Aerobic Respiration

Stage 2 — the *Link Reaction* converts *Pyruvate* to *Acetyl Coenzyme A*

The **enzymes** and **coenzymes** needed for the **link reaction** are located in the **mitochondrial matrix**, so that's where the link reaction takes place. This means that the **reduced NAD** produced by the link reaction is made in the **right place** to be used by **oxidative phosphorylation** (see next page), which occurs **across** the **inner mitochondrial membrane**.

1) **Pyruvate** is **decarboxylated** (**carbon** is **removed**) — **one carbon atom** is **removed** from pyruvate in the form of CO_2.
2) **NAD** is **reduced** — it collects **hydrogen** from pyruvate, changing **pyruvate** into **acetate**.
3) **Acetate** is combined with **coenzyme A** (CoA) to form **acetyl coenzyme A** (**acetyl CoA**).
4) **No ATP** is produced in this reaction.

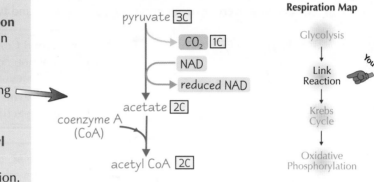

The *Link Reaction* occurs *Twice* for every *Glucose Molecule*

Two pyruvate molecules are made for **every glucose molecule** that enters glycolysis. This means the **link reaction** and the third stage (the **Krebs cycle**) happen **twice** for every glucose molecule. So for each glucose molecule:

- Two molecules of **acetyl coenzyme A** go into the Krebs cycle (see the next page).
- Two CO_2 molecules are released as a waste product of respiration.
- Two molecules of **reduced NAD** are formed and are used in the last stage (oxidative phosphorylation, see the next page).

Practice Questions

Q1 How many stages are there in aerobic respiration?

Q2 Name one coenzyme involved in respiration.

Q3 Where in the cell does glycolysis occur?

Q4 Is glycolysis an anaerobic or aerobic process?

Q5 How many ATP molecules are used up in glycolysis?

Q6 What is the product of the link reaction?

Exam Question

Q1 a) Which of the following statements about glycolysis is true?
    A ATP is phosphorylated to form ADP.
    B NAD is reduced to form reduced NAD.
    C Reduced NAD is oxidised to form NAD.
    D ADP is reduced to form ATP. [1 mark]

   b) What is the overall net gain of ATP from glycolysis?
    A 1   **B** 4   **C** 2   **D** 6 [1 mark]

   c) Once produced by glycolysis, describe the movement of pyruvate within the cell. [2 marks]

No ATP was harmed during this reaction...

Ahhhh... too many reactions. I'm sure your head hurts now, 'cause mine certainly does. Just think of revision as like doing exercise — it can be a pain while you're doing it (and maybe afterwards too), but it's worth it for the well-toned brain you'll have. Just keep going over and over it, until you get the first two stages of respiration straight in your head.

Aerobic Respiration

As you've seen, glycolysis produces a net gain of two ATP. Pah, we can do better than that.
The Krebs cycle and oxidative phosphorylation are where it all happens — ATP galore.

Stage 3 — the Krebs Cycle Produces Reduced Coenzymes and ATP

The Krebs cycle involves a series of **oxidation-reduction reactions**. Each of these reactions is controlled by a **specific intracellular enzyme**, which is found in the **matrix** of the **mitochondria** — so that's where the Krebs cycle takes place. The cycle happens **once** for **every pyruvate** molecule, so it goes round **twice** for **every glucose** molecule.

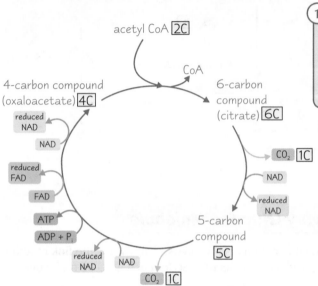

1
- **Acetyl CoA** from the link reaction combines with **oxaloacetate** to form **citrate**.
- **Coenzyme A** goes back to the **link reaction** to be used again.

2
- The **6C citrate molecule** is converted to a **5C molecule**.
- **Decarboxylation** occurs, where CO_2 **is removed**.
- **Dehydrogenation** also occurs — this is where **hydrogen** is removed.
- The hydrogen is used to **produce reduced NAD** from NAD.

Respiration Map

Glycolysis

↓

Link Reaction

You are here

↓

Krebs Cycle

↓

Oxidative Phosphorylation

3
- The **5C molecule** is then converted to a **4C molecule**. (There are some intermediate compounds formed during this conversion, but you don't need to know about them.)
- **Decarboxylation** and **dehydrogenation** occur, producing **one molecule** of **reduced FAD** and **two** of **reduced NAD**.
- **ATP is produced** by the **direct transfer** of a **phosphate** group from an **intermediate** compound to **ADP**. When a phosphate group is directly transferred from one molecule to another it's called **substrate-level phosphorylation**. **Citrate** has now been **converted** into **oxaloacetate**.

Some Products of the Krebs Cycle are Used in Oxidative Phosphorylation

Some products are **reused**, some are **released** and others are used for the **next stage** of respiration:

Product from one Krebs cycle	Where it goes
1 coenzyme A	Reused in the next link reaction
Oxaloacetate	Regenerated for use in the next Krebs cycle
2 CO_2	Released as a waste product
1 ATP	Used for energy
3 reduced NAD	To oxidative phosphorylation
1 reduced FAD	To oxidative phosphorylation

Remember — 1 molecule of acetyl CoA goes into the Krebs cycle, so these are the products of 1 molecule of acetyl CoA. More ATP is eventually produced from the reduced NAD and FAD in oxidative phosphorylation.

Respiration Map

Glycolysis

↓

Link Reaction

↓

Krebs Cycle

↓

Oxidative Phosphorylation *You are here*

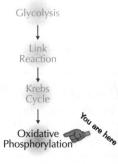

Stage 4 — Oxidative Phosphorylation Produces Lots of ATP

1) Oxidative phosphorylation is the process where the **energy** carried by **electrons**, from **reduced coenzymes** (reduced NAD and reduced FAD), is used to **make ATP**. (The whole point of the previous stages is to make reduced NAD and reduced FAD for the final stage.)

2) Oxidative phosphorylation involves two processes — the **electron transport chain** and **chemiosmosis** (see the next page).

Aerobic Respiration

Protons are Pumped Across the Inner Mitochondrial Membrane

So now on to how **oxidative phosphorylation** actually **works**:

1) **Hydrogen atoms** are released from **reduced NAD** and **reduced FAD** as they're **oxidised** to NAD and FAD. The H atoms **split** into **protons (H⁺)** and **electrons (e⁻)**.

2) The **electrons** move down the **electron transport chain** (made up of **electron carriers**), **losing energy** at each carrier.

3) This energy is used by the electron carriers to **pump protons** from the **mitochondrial matrix into** the **intermembrane space** (the space **between** the inner and outer **mitochondrial membranes**).

4) The **concentration** of **protons** is now **higher** in the **intermembrane space** than in the mitochondrial matrix — this forms an **electrochemical gradient** (a **concentration gradient** of **ions**).

5) Protons **move down** the **electrochemical gradient**, back into the mitochondrial matrix, via the enzyme **ATP synthase** (see p. 108). This **movement** drives the synthesis of **ATP** from **ADP** and **inorganic phosphate** (P_i).

> The regenerated coenzymes are reused in the Krebs cycle.

6) The movement of H⁺ ions across a membrane, which generates ATP is called **chemiosmosis**.

7) In the mitochondrial matrix, at the end of the transport chain, the **protons**, **electrons** and **O₂** (from the blood) combine to form **water**. Oxygen is said to be the final **electron acceptor**.

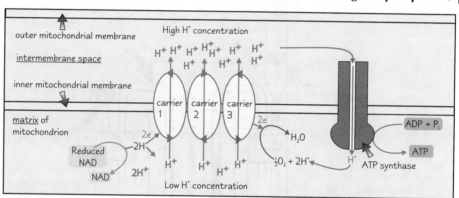

Some **metabolic poisons** target the **electron carriers** in oxidative phosphorylation, **preventing** them from **passing on electrons**. This **stops** electrons **moving down the electron transport chain**, which **stops chemiosmosis**. Reduced NAD and reduced FAD are no longer oxidised, so **NAD** and **FAD aren't regenerated** for the **Krebs cycle** — causing it to **stop** too. ATP synthesis in the cell ends up **hugely reduced**, so there's **not enough** ATP to fuel **ATP-requiring cellular processes**, e.g. the contraction of heart muscle. This can be **fatal** for the organism.

38 ATP Can be Made from One Glucose Molecule

As you know, **oxidative phosphorylation makes ATP** using energy from the reduced coenzymes — **3 ATP** are made from each **reduced NAD** and **2 ATP** are made from each **reduced FAD**. The table on the right shows **how much** ATP a cell can make from **one molecule** of glucose in **aerobic respiration**. (Remember, one molecule of glucose produces 2 pyruvate, so the link reaction and Krebs cycle happen twice.)

Stage of respiration	Molecules produced	Number of ATP molecules
Glycolysis	2 ATP	2
Glycolysis	2 reduced NAD	2 × 3 = 6
Link Reaction (×2)	2 reduced NAD	2 × 3 = 6
Krebs cycle (×2)	2 ATP	2
Krebs cycle (×2)	6 reduced NAD	6 × 3 = 18
Krebs cycle (×2)	2 reduced FAD	2 × 2 = 4
		Total ATP = 38

Practice Questions

Q1 Where in the cell does the Krebs cycle occur?

Q2 How many carbon dioxide molecules are produced during one turn of the Krebs cycle?

Q3 What do the electrons lose as they move along the electron transport chain in oxidative phosphorylation?

Exam Question

Q1 Carbon monoxide inhibits the final electron carrier in the electron transport chain.
  a) State how this affects ATP production via the electron transport chain. [2 marks]
  b) Explain how this affects ATP production via the Krebs cycle. [2 marks]

The electron transport chain isn't just a FAD with the examiners...

Oh my gosh, I didn't think it could get any worse. You may be wondering how to learn these pages of crazy chemistry, but basically you just have to put in the time and go over and over it. Don't worry though, it will pay off. Hooray.

Respirometers and Anaerobic Respiration

Congratulations — you've nearly finished respiration. You just need to get to grips with an 'exciting' respiration experiment and the tiny subject of anaerobic respiration, then it's all over. (When I say 'exciting' I'm using the word loosely, but I've got to say something positive to keep the morale up.)

The Rate of Respiration can be Measured using a Respirometer

1) The volume of **oxygen taken up** or the volume of **carbon dioxide produced** in a given time **indicates** the **rate** of **respiration**.

2) A **respirometer** measures the volume of **oxygen** being **taken up** in a given time — the **more** oxygen taken up, the **faster** the rate of respiration.

3) Here's how you can use a **respirometer** to **measure** the volume of **oxygen taken up** by some **woodlice**:

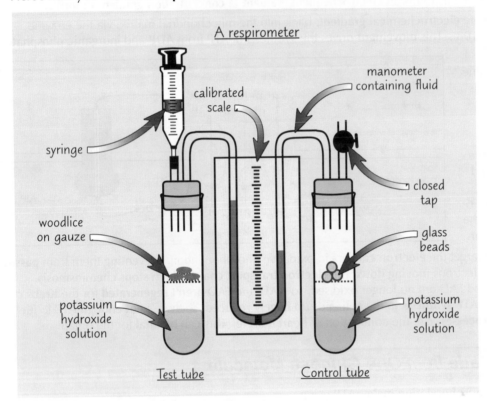

A respirometer

- syringe
- calibrated scale
- manometer containing fluid
- closed tap
- woodlice on gauze
- glass beads
- potassium hydroxide solution
- potassium hydroxide solution
- Test tube
- Control tube

Other small invertebrates can be used, e.g. aphids.

Alfred the aphid thought holding his breath in the respirometer would be really funny. The students didn't.

1) The apparatus is set up as shown above.

2) **Each tube** contains **potassium hydroxide** solution (or soda lime), which **absorbs carbon dioxide**.

3) The **control tube** is set up in exactly the **same way** as the test tube, but **without the woodlice**, to make sure the **results** are **only** due to the woodlice **respiring** (e.g. it contains beads that have the same mass as the woodlice).

4) The **syringe** is used to set the **fluid** in the **manometer** to a **known level**.

5) The apparatus is **left** for a **set** period of **time** (e.g. 20 minutes).

6) During that time there'll be a **decrease** in the **volume** of the **air** in the test tube, due to **oxygen consumption** by the **woodlice** (all the CO_2 produced is absorbed by the potassium hydroxide).

7) The decrease in the volume of the air will **reduce the pressure** in the tube and cause the **coloured liquid** in the manometer to **move towards** the test tube.

8) The **distance moved** by the **liquid** in a **given time** is **measured**. This value can then be used to **calculate** the **volume of oxygen** taken in by the woodlice **per minute**.

9) Any **variables** that could **affect** the results are **controlled**, e.g. temperature, volume of potassium hydroxide solution in each test tube.

Remember, when working with living organisms, you must treat them with respect and ensure that they're not harmed or distressed unnecessarily.

4) To produce more **precise** results the experiment is **repeated** and a **mean volume** of O_2 is calculated.

Respirometers and Anaerobic Respiration

Lactate Fermentation is a Type of Anaerobic Respiration

1) **Anaerobic** respiration **doesn't use oxygen**.
2) It **doesn't** involve the **link reaction**, the **Krebs cycle** or **oxidative phosphorylation**.
3) There are **two types** of anaerobic respiration, but you only need to know about one of them — **lactate fermentation**.
4) Lactate fermentation occurs in **animals** and produces **lactate**.
5) Here's how it works:

Some bacteria carry out lactate fermentation.

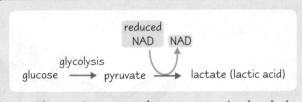

glycolysis
glucose → pyruvate → lactate (lactic acid)
reduced NAD → NAD

- **Glucose** is converted to **pyruvate** via **glycolysis**.
- **Reduced NAD** (from glycolysis) transfers **hydrogen** to **pyruvate** to form **lactate** and **NAD**.
- **NAD** can then be reused in **glycolysis**.

6) The production of lactate **regenerates NAD**. This means **glycolysis** can **continue** even when there **isn't** much oxygen around, so a **small amount of ATP** can still be **produced** to keep some biological process going... clever.

Lactic Acid Needs to be Broken Down

After a period of anaerobic respiration **lactic acid builds up**. Animals can **break down lactic acid** in **two** ways:

1) **Cells** can **convert** the lactic acid back to **pyruvate** (which then re-enters aerobic respiration at the **Krebs cycle**).
2) **Liver cells** can **convert** the lactic acid back to **glucose** (which can then be **respired** or **stored**).

Practice Questions

Q1 What does a respirometer measure?

Q2 Lactate fermentation is an example of what type of respiration?

Q3 Give one way that animals can break down lactate.

Exam Questions

Q1 A respirometer is set up as shown in the diagram on the previous page.
   a) Explain the purpose of the control tube. [1 mark]
   b) Explain what would happen if there was no potassium hydroxide in the tubes. [2 marks]
   c) What other substance could be measured to find out the rate of respiration? [1 mark]

Q2 A culture of mammalian cells was incubated with glucose, pyruvate and antimycin C.
   Antimycin C inhibits an electron carrier in the electron transport chain of aerobic respiration.
   Explain why these cells can still produce lactate. [1 mark]

Respiration experiments — they're a gas...

Okay, that wasn't very funny, but these pages don't really give me any inspiration. You probably feel the same way. It's just one of those times where you have to plough through. You could try drawing a few pretty diagrams to get the experiment or fermentation reaction in your head. Then you could do something fun, like sticking your toe in your ear.

Electrical Activity in the Heart

These pages are all about how the electrical activity in the heart keeps it pumping — if you need a reminder of the structure of the heart, look back at your Topic 1 notes.

Cardiac Muscle Controls the Regular Beating of the Heart

Cardiac (heart) muscle is '**myogenic**' — it can contract and relax without receiving signals from neurones. This **electrical activity** in the heart creates the **pattern of contractions** which coordinates the **regular heartbeat**.

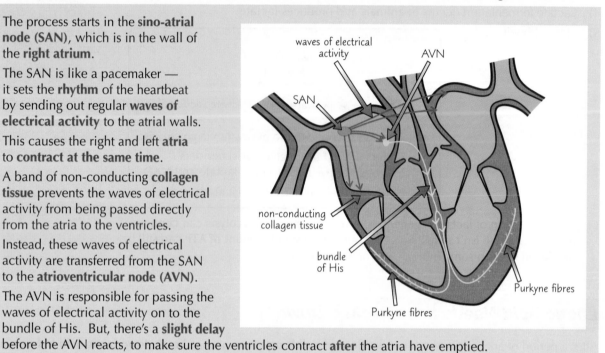

1) The process starts in the **sino-atrial node (SAN)**, which is in the wall of the **right atrium**.

2) The SAN is like a pacemaker — it sets the **rhythm** of the heartbeat by sending out regular **waves of electrical activity** to the atrial walls.

3) This causes the right and left **atria** to **contract at the same time**.

4) A band of non-conducting **collagen tissue** prevents the waves of electrical activity from being passed directly from the atria to the ventricles.

5) Instead, these waves of electrical activity are transferred from the SAN to the **atrioventricular node (AVN)**.

6) The AVN is responsible for passing the waves of electrical activity on to the bundle of His. But, there's a **slight delay** before the AVN reacts, to make sure the ventricles contract **after** the atria have emptied.

7) The **bundle of His** is a group of muscle fibres responsible for conducting the waves of electrical activity to the finer muscle fibres in the right and left ventricle walls, called the **Purkyne fibres**.

8) The Purkyne fibres carry the waves of electrical activity into the muscular walls of the right and left ventricles, causing them to **contract simultaneously**, from the bottom up.

An Electrocardiograph Records the Electrical Activity of the Heart

A doctor can check someone's **heart function** using an **electrocardiograph** — a machine that **records** the **electrical activity** of the heart. The heart muscle **depolarises** (loses electrical charge) when it **contracts**, and **repolarises** (regains charge) when it **relaxes**. An electrocardiograph records these changes in electrical charge using **electrodes** placed on the chest.

When Ed did that special thing to her beak, Polly's heart activity increased 10-fold.

The trace produced by an electrocardiograph is called an **electrocardiogram**, or **ECG**. A **normal** ECG looks like this:

1) The **P wave** is caused by **contraction** (depolarisation) of the **atria**.

2) The main peak of the heartbeat, together with the dips at either side, is called the **QRS complex** — it's caused by **contraction** (depolarisation) of the **ventricles**.

3) The **T wave** is due to **relaxation** (repolarisation) of the **ventricles**.

4) The **height** of the wave indicates how much electrical charge is passing through the heart — a **bigger wave** means more electrical charge, so (for the P and R waves) a bigger wave means a **stronger contraction**.

Electrical Activity in the Heart

Doctors *use ECGs to* Diagnose Heart Problems

Doctors **compare** their patients' ECGs with a **normal trace**. This helps them to **diagnose** any **problems** with the heart's **rhythm**, which may indicate **cardiovascular disease** (heart and circulatory disease) or other **heart conditions** (e.g. muscle damage or the AVN not conducting properly). Here are some examples of **abnormal traces**:

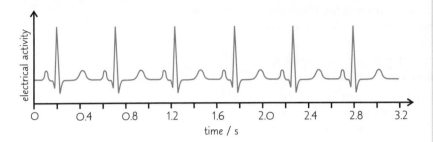

This heartbeat is **too fast** — around 120 beats per minute. It's called **tachycardia**. That might be OK during **exercise**, but at **rest** it shows that the heart **isn't pumping blood efficiently**. A heartbeat can also be **too slow** — below 60 beats per minute at rest. This is called **bradycardia**.

The 5th heartbeat on this ECG is an **ectopic heartbeat** — an 'extra' heartbeat. Here it's caused by an **earlier contraction of the atria** than in the previous heartbeats (you can see that the P wave is different and that it comes earlier than it should). However, it can be caused by **early contraction of the ventricles** too. Occasional ectopic heartbeats in a healthy person don't cause a problem.

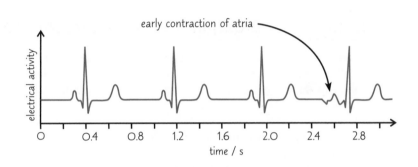

early contraction of atria

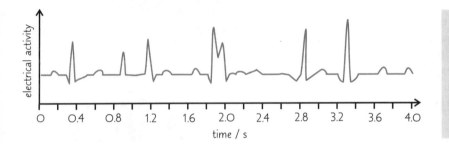

This is **fibrillation** — a really **irregular heartbeat**. The atria or ventricles completely **lose their rhythm** and **stop contracting properly**. It can result in anything from chest pain and fainting to lack of pulse and death.

Practice Questions

Q1 What prevents impulses from the atria travelling straight into the ventricles?

Q2 What is the name of the structure that picks up impulses from the atria and passes them on to the ventricles?

Q3 What is the function of the Purkyne fibres?

Q4 What causes the P wave of an ECG trace?

Exam Questions

Q1 Describe the function of:
   a) the sinoatrial node.   [1 mark]
   b) the bundle of His.   [1 mark]

Q2 Give one possible cause of an ECG which has a QRS complex that is not as high as normal.   [2 marks]

My heart rate seems to be controlled by the boy next door...

It's pretty incredible that your heart manages to go through all those stages in the right order, at exactly the right time, without getting it even slightly wrong. It does it perfectly, about 70 times every minute. That's about 100 800 times a day. If only my brain was that efficient. I'd have all this revision done in five minutes, then I could go and watch TV...

Variations in Breathing Rate

Your breathing rate changes throughout the day, depending on how active you are. And when you exercise you probably get quite out of breath — not so good when you want to look really fit in front of that special someone...

Breathing Rate and Heart Rate Increase When you Exercise

When you exercise your **muscles contract more frequently**, which means they use **more energy**. To replace this energy your body needs to do **more aerobic respiration**, so it needs to **take in more oxygen** and **breathe out more carbon dioxide**. The body does this by:

1) **Increasing breathing rate** and **depth** — to **obtain more oxygen** and to **get rid of more carbon dioxide**.

2) **Increasing heart rate** — to **deliver oxygen** (and glucose) to the muscles **faster** and **remove extra carbon dioxide** produced by the increased rate of **respiration** in muscle cells.

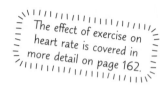
The effect of exercise on heart rate is covered in more detail on page 162.

The Medulla Oblongata Controls Breathing Rate

The **medulla oblongata** (a part of the **brain** — see p. 186) has areas called **ventilation centres**. There are two ventilation centres — the **inspiratory** centre and the **expiratory** centre. They control the **rate of breathing**:

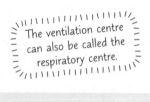
The ventilation centre can also be called the respiratory centre.

1) The **inspiratory centre** in the **medulla oblongata** sends nerve impulses to the **intercostal** and **diaphragm** muscles to make them **contract**.

2) This **increases** the **volume** of the lungs, which **lowers the pressure** in the lungs. (The inspiratory centre also sends nerve impulses to the **expiratory centre**. These impulses **inhibit** the action of the **expiratory centre**.)

3) **Air enters** the lungs due to the **pressure difference** between the lungs and the air outside.

4) As the **lungs inflate, stretch receptors** in the lungs are **stimulated**. The stretch receptors send nerve impulses back to the **medulla oblongata**. These impulses **inhibit** the action of the **inspiratory centre**.

5) The expiratory centre (no longer inhibited) then sends nerve impulses to the **diaphragm** and **intercostal muscles** to **relax**. This causes the **lungs to deflate**, expelling air. As the lungs deflate, the **stretch receptors** become **inactive**. The inspiratory centre is no longer inhibited and the cycle starts again.

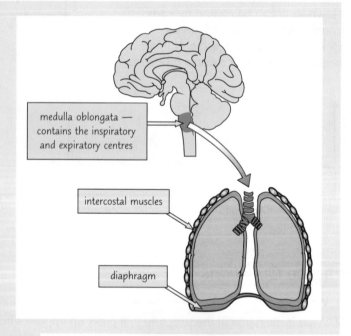

medulla oblongata — contains the inspiratory and expiratory centres

intercostal muscles

diaphragm

Jeremy's new slippers sent Max's ventilation centres into overdrive.

Variations in Breathing Rate

Exercise Triggers an Increase in Breathing Rate by Decreasing Blood pH

1) During exercise, the level of carbon dioxide (CO_2) in the blood increases. This decreases the pH of the blood.

2) There are chemoreceptors (receptors that sense chemicals) in the medulla oblongata, aortic bodies (clusters of cells in the aorta) and carotid bodies (clusters of cells in the carotid arteries) that are sensitive to changes in blood pH.

3) If the chemoreceptors detect a decrease in blood pH, they send nerve impulses to the medulla oblongata, which sends more frequent nerve impulses to the intercostal muscles and diaphragm. This increases the rate and depth of breathing.

4) This causes gaseous exchange to speed up. The CO_2 level drops and extra O_2 is supplied for the muscles — the pH returns to normal and breathing rate decreases.

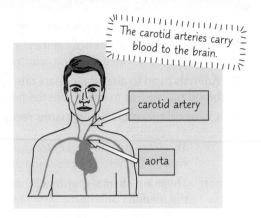

The carotid arteries carry blood to the brain.

carotid artery

aorta

Ventilation Rate Increases with Exercise

1) Ventilation rate is the volume of air breathed in or out in a period of time, e.g. a minute.

2) It increases during exercise because breathing rate and depth increase.

Don't worry Sam, we're not watching you. Honest...

Practice Questions

Q1 What effect does exercise have on breathing rate?

Q2 Define the term 'ventilation rate'.

Exam Questions

Q1 In a laboratory experiment, an animal was anaesthetised and dilute carbonic acid (carbon dioxide in solution) was added to the blood in the coronary artery.
Explain the effect you would expect this to have on the animal's breathing rate? [5 marks]

Q2 The ventilation centres in the medulla oblongata control the rate of breathing.

a) Which row of the table shows the effects of nervous impulses being sent from the inspiratory centre? [1 mark]

	Diaphragm	Intercostal muscles	Expiratory centre
A	Contracts	Relax	Inhibited
B	Relaxes	Relax	Activated
C	Contracts	Contract	Inhibited
D	Relaxes	Relax	Inhibited

b) Describe how stretch receptors in the lungs trigger exhalation following inhalation. [5 marks]

All this revision is putting me a bit out of puff...

Well, there are quite a few different steps that you have to remember here to fully understand how exercise affects breathing rate. Try to write down every step from when the carbon dioxide level in the blood increases until the inspiratory centre is no longer inhibited, to put it all together. Take a deep breath and off you go...

Variations in Heart Rate

As well as your breathing rate, your heart rate also increases when you exercise. It's time to meet (the very technical sounding) cardiovascular control centre...

The **Medulla Oblongata** Controls **Heart Rate**

1) Heart rate is controlled **unconsciously** by the **cardiovascular control centre** in the **medulla oblongata**.

2) The cardiovascular control centre controls the **rate** at which the **SAN fires** — the SAN generates **electrical impulses** that cause the atria to **contract**, which sets the **rhythm** of the heartbeat (see page 158).

3) Animals need to **alter** their **heart rate** to **respond** to **internal stimuli**, e.g. to prevent fainting due to low blood pressure or to make sure the heart rate is high enough to supply the body with enough oxygen.

4) **Chemical receptors** and **pressure receptors** detect **stimuli** in the blood:

   - There are **pressure receptors** called **baroreceptors** in the **aortic** and **carotid bodies**. They're stimulated by **high** and **low blood pressure**.

   - There are **chemoreceptors** in the **aortic** and **carotid bodies** and in the **medulla oblongata**. They **monitor** the **oxygen** level in the **blood** and also **carbon dioxide** and **pH** (which are indicators of O_2 level).

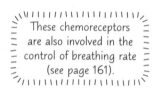
These chemoreceptors are also involved in the control of breathing rate (see page 161).

5) **Electrical impulses** from these receptors are sent to the **medulla oblongata** along **sensory** neurones.

6) The cardiovascular control centre **processes** the information and sends impulses to the SAN along **sympathetic** or **parasympathetic** neurones — these release different chemicals (called **neurotransmitters** — see page 182) onto the SAN, which determines whether it **speeds up** or **slows down** the heart rate.

   - The **sympathetic nervous system** gets the body ready for **action**. It's the **'flight or fight'** system — it helps to **increase the heart rate** during exercise.

   - The **parasympathetic nervous system** calms the body down. It's the **'rest and digest'** system — it helps to **decrease the heart rate** after exercise.

You can find out more about the nervous system on pages 174-183.

Stimuli Detected by **Receptors** Cause **Heart Rate** to **Change**

This table shows how the heart responds to different **stimuli**:

Stimulus	Receptor	Neurone and transmitter	Response
High blood pressure.	**Baroreceptors** detect **high** blood pressure.	Impulses are sent to the cardiovascular control centre, which sends impulses along **parasympathetic** neurones. These secrete **acetylcholine** (a neurotransmitter), which binds to receptors on the SAN.	The SAN fires impulses **less frequently** to **slow** heart rate and **reduce blood pressure** back to normal.
Low blood pressure.	**Baroreceptors** detect **low** blood pressure.	Impulses are sent to the cardiovascular control centre, which sends impulses along **sympathetic** neurones. These secrete **noradrenaline** (a neurotransmitter), which binds to receptors on the SAN.	The SAN fires impulses **more frequently** to **increase** heart rate and **increase blood pressure** back to normal
High blood O_2, **low** CO_2 or **high** pH levels.	**Chemoreceptors** detect chemical changes in the blood.	Impulses are sent to the cardiovascular control centre, which sends impulses along **parasympathetic** neurones. These secrete **acetylcholine**, which binds to receptors on the SAN.	The SAN fires impulses **less frequently** to **decrease** heart rate and return O_2, CO_2 and pH levels back to normal.
Low blood O_2, **high** CO_2 or **low** pH levels.	**Chemoreceptors** detect chemical changes in the blood.	Impulses are sent to the cardiovascular control centre, which sends impulses along **sympathetic** neurones. These secrete **noradrenaline**, which binds to receptors on the SAN.	The SAN fires impulses **more frequently** to **increase** heart rate and return O_2, CO_2 and pH levels back to normal.

The **last row** of the table explains why heart rate **increases** during exercise — during exercise, your **rate of respiration** increases, which results in an **increase** in the CO_2 level and a **reduction** in the **pH** and **oxygen levels** of the blood.

Variations in Heart Rate

Cardiac Output Increases with Exercise

1) Cardiac output is the **total volume** of blood pumped by a **ventricle** every **minute**.

2) The **equation** for working out cardiac output is:

Cardiac output (cm³ min⁻¹) = **heart rate** (beats per minute) × **stroke volume** (cm³)

3) **Stroke volume** is the volume of blood pumped by **one ventricle** each time it **contracts**.

4) Cardiac output increases during **exercise** because **heart rate** and **stroke volume** increase.

5) You can **rearrange** the equation above to find **stroke volume** or **heart rate** — for example:

6) You could be asked to use these equations in the exam:

$$\text{Stroke volume (cm}^3) = \frac{\text{cardiac output (cm}^3 \text{ min}^{-1})}{\text{heart rate (beats per minute)}}$$

Example:

At rest, a swimmer has a heart rate of 65 bpm and a stroke volume of 70 cm³.
After swimming 50 m, he has a heart rate of 120 bpm and a cardiac output of 10 800 cm³ min⁻¹.
What is the difference in cardiac output before and after his swim?

Answer:

Before swim:
heart rate = 65 bpm, stroke volume = 70 cm³
cardiac output = 65 × 70
= **4550 cm³ min⁻¹**

After swim:
cardiac output = 10 800 cm³ min⁻¹

Difference before and after swim:
10 800 – 4550 = **6250 cm³ min⁻¹**

What is his stroke volume after his swim?

Answer: cardiac output = 10 800 cm³ min⁻¹
heart rate = 120 bpm

$$\text{stroke volume} = \frac{10\ 800}{120} = \textbf{90 cm}^3$$

Practice Questions

Q1 Which type of receptors detect changes in blood pressure?

Q2 What effect do neurotransmitters released from parasympathetic neurones have on heart rate?

Q3 What neurotransmitter do sympathetic neurones release onto the SAN?

Q4 What is the definition of cardiac output?

Exam Question

Q1 Before a race a runner has a stroke volume of 72 cm³ and a cardiac output of 5420 cm³ min⁻¹.

   a) Calculate the runner's heart rate before the race.   [2 marks]

   b) Once the runner has started the race, explain how information about chemical changes
in his blood are relayed to his brain.   [3 marks]

   c) Explain how increased activity of sympathetic neurones affects the runner's heart rate
when he is running.   [3 marks]

Sympathetic neurones — enough to get your pulse racing...

*Imagine if you had to consciously make sure your heart was beating at the right speed and pumping enough blood
around your body all the time... You'd be so busy doing that, you wouldn't have enough time to do all the things you
love — like studying for your exams or reading all of these hilarious captions. I don't think I would cope...*

Investigating Ventilation

You need to know how to investigate the effects of exercise on all things to do with ventilation. And I'm not talking about the ventilation that Bruce Willis is fond of climbing through in films...

Tidal Volume is the Volume of Air in a Normal Breath

Here are some terms that you need to know about breathing:

1) **Tidal volume** — the **volume** of air in **each breath**, usually about **0.4 dm³**.
2) **Breathing rate** — **how many breaths** are taken, usually in a **minute**.
3) **Oxygen consumption** — the volume of **oxygen used** by the body, often expressed as a **rate**.
4) **Respiratory minute ventilation** — the **volume** of gas **breathed in or out** in a **minute**. Here's how it's calculated:

dm³ is short for decimetres cubed — it's the same as litres. 1 dm³ = 1000 cm³

> **respiratory minute ventilation = tidal volume × breathing rate** (breaths per minute)

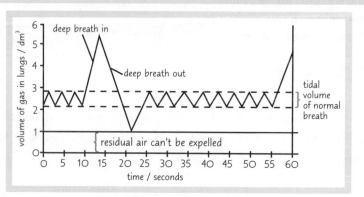

Respiratory minute ventilation can also be called ventilation rate (per minute).

Jane couldn't maintain her breathing rate when she saw all those TVs.

Spirometers Can be Used to Measure Ventilation

A spirometer is a machine that can give readings of **tidal volume** and allow measurement of a person's **breathing rate**, **oxygen consumption** and **respiratory minute ventilation**.

1) A spirometer has an **oxygen-filled** chamber with a **movable lid**.

2) A person breathes through a **tube** connected to the oxygen chamber.

3) As the person breathes **in** the lid of the chamber moves **down**. When they breathe **out** it moves **up**.

4) These movements are recorded by a **pen** attached to the lid of the chamber — this writes on a **rotating drum**, creating a **spirometer trace**.

5) The total volume of gas in the chamber **decreases** over time. This is because the air that's breathed out is a **mixture** of oxygen and carbon dioxide, but the carbon dioxide is absorbed by the **soda lime** in the tube. This means there's only **oxygen** in the chamber which the person inhales from — as this oxygen gets used up by **respiration**, the total volume **decreases**.

Spirometers Can be Used to Investigate the Effects of Exercise

Exercise causes an increase in **breathing rate** (see page 161) and **tidal volume**, as well as an increase in **oxygen consumption** and **respiratory minute ventilation**. A **spirometer** can be used to investigate the effect that **exercise** has on these things. For example:

1) A person breathes into a spirometer for **one minute** at **rest** and **recordings** are taken.

2) The person then **exercises**, e.g. runs on a treadmill, for **two minutes**. While the person is exercising, the **spirometer chamber** is refilled with **oxygen**.

3) Immediately after the person **stops exercising**, they breathe into the spirometer again and recordings are taken for **another minute**.

4) The recordings taken **before** and **after** exercise are then compared.

Investigating Ventilation

The trace for a **spirometer** may look **different** to the graph on the previous page (because it shows the volume of air in the spirometer, not in the lungs) but you use it in a **similar way**:

- **Breathing rate** (per minute) — count the **number of peaks** in the trace in a **minute**.
- **Tidal volume** — find the **average difference** in the **volume of gas** between each peak and trough on the trace.
- **Oxygen consumption** — find the **change** in **volume of gas** in the spirometer (read values from the troughs).

Example 1 shows the **effect** of **exercise** on breathing rate, tidal volume, oxygen consumption and respiratory minute ventilation:

EXAMPLE 1

A person with a body mass of **60 kg** used a **spirometer** to investigate the effects of exercise, using the method described on the previous page. The spirometer trace is shown in the **graphs**:

1) At **rest**, tidal volume is about **0.4 dm³**, and breathing rate is **12 breaths per minute**.

2) The rate of **oxygen consumption** at rest is about 0.6 dm³ per minute — to work this out you find the **difference** between the **lowest points** of the trace at the start and at the end of the minute. You could also find out the rate of oxygen consumption **per kg** of **body mass** by **dividing** your answer by 60 here (as the person weighs 60 kg).

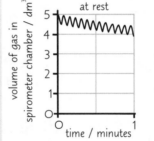 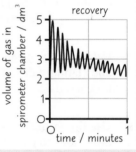

3) At rest, the **respiratory minute ventilation** is 0.4 dm³ × 12 = 4.8 dm³ min⁻¹ (using the formula on the previous page).

4) During **exercise**, the body needs **more oxygen** for muscle contraction and it needs to **remove more carbon dioxide** (see page 160). So breathing rate, tidal volume and rate of oxygen consumption will have all **increased**. During **recovery**, the body still needs to keep **breathing hard** (to get oxygen to remove any lactate that's built up), but eventually breathing rate, tidal volume, rate of oxygen consumption and respiratory minute ventilation return to **rest levels**.

Example 2 shows the **effect** of a **fitness training programme** on breathing rate and tidal volume:

EXAMPLE 2

A person's **breathing rate** and **tidal volume** were measured using a **spirometer** and the method described on the previous page. The results are shown in the **graphs** below. The **same test** was repeated three months later on the **same person**, after they'd gone through a **fitness training programme**. The spirometer results were plotted to **compare** the **effects** of training:

1) Training **decreased breathing rate** both at rest and during recovery because the lung muscles are **strengthened**, so **more air** is taken in with each breath, meaning **fewer breaths** are needed.

2) Training also **increased tidal volume**, again because muscles are strengthened, so more air is taken in with each breath.

3) During **recovery**, **breathing rate** and **tidal volume** **decreased faster** due to training because the muscles are strengthened, so the lungs can get oxygen and carbon dioxide supplies back to normal quicker.

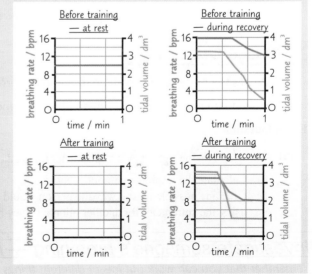

Investigating Ventilation

Analyse the Effect of Exercise on Tidal Volume using Student's t-Test

You can test whether **exercise** has a **significant** effect on **tidal volume at rest** by using **Student's t-test**.
You need **two sets of data** — the example below uses results from two groups of 8 people. One group received
twelve weeks of **high intensity training** (Set 1) and the other group **did not** undergo any training (Set 2). The
tidal volumes at rest of both groups were then **measured**.

Student's t-test is used to find out whether there is a
significant difference in the **means** of the two data sets.
The value obtained is compared to a **critical value**,
which helps you decide how **likely** it is that the results
or 'differences in the means' were due to **chance**.

$$t = \frac{\bar{x}_1 - \bar{x}_2}{\sqrt{(s_1^2 / n_1) + (s_2^2 / n_2)}}$$

$\bar{x}$ = mean
s = standard deviation
n = number of values in group
$_1$ or $_2$ = group being referred to

There is a different equation that you can use for paired data
(data that includes two measurements for each person,
e.g. before and after high intensity training).

To carry out the t-test, follow these steps:

1) **Identify the null hypothesis**.
   This is always that the **means**
   for the two sets of data are
   going to be **exactly the same**,
   i.e. there is no significant
   difference between them.

2) **Calculate the mean
   and standard deviation**
   for each data set.

3) **Use the formula** in the pink
   box above to calculate t.

4) **Calculate the degrees of
   freedom** by doing $(n_1 + n_2) - 2$.
   (Look at the key next to the
   formula above to help you here).

5) **Look up the values for t**
   in a table of **critical
   values**. If the value
   obtained from the t-test is **greater** than the **critical value** at a probability (or P
   value) of **5% or less** (≤ 0.05), then you can be **95% confident** that the difference
   is **significant** and not due to chance. So you'd **reject** the null hypothesis.

If the t value is smaller than the critical value at a P value of 0.05, it suggests there is no significant
difference between the two sets of data, so you would 'accept' (fail to reject) the null hypothesis.

Example

(1) **Null hypothesis** — there is no **significant difference**
between the mean tidal volumes at rest of the group
that received high intensity training and the group
that did no training.

(2) $\bar{x}_1 = 0.90$, $\bar{x}_2 = 0.55$ $s_1 = 0.14$, $s_2 = 0.07$

(3) $t = \dfrac{0.90 - 0.55}{\sqrt{(0.14^2 / 8) + (0.07^2 / 8)}}$

$t = 6.32$ (to 2 decimal places)
(If t is negative you can ignore the minus sign.)

| Tidal volume at end of test period (dm³) ||
Set 1	Set 2
1.15	0.65
0.80	0.47
0.72	0.52
0.96	0.50
0.85	0.58
0.92	0.57
0.78	0.49
1.02	0.62

(4) Degrees of freedom
$= (8 + 8) - 2 = 14$

(5) Critical value is 2.145.
The t value of 6.32 is greater —
this means that the mean tidal volume
at rest for the group that received high
intensity training was **significantly
lower** after 12 weeks than for the
group that did not receive training.

degrees of freedom	critical t values			
12	1.356	1.782	2.179	2.681
13	1.350	1.771	2.160	2.650
14	1.345	1.761	2.145	2.624
15	1.341	1.753	2.131	2.602
probability that result is due to chance only	0.2 (20%)	0.1 (10%)	0.05 (5%)	0.02 (2%)

You'll be given a table of critical values in the exam.

Fisher, Statistical tables for Biological,
Agricultural & Medical Research, 1st Ed.
© 1930 p46. Reprinted by permission of
Pearson Education Inc., New York, New York.

Student's t-test could
come up in any of your
A-level papers — it won't
necessarily be tested with
Topic 7 material.

Practice Questions

Q1 What's the purpose of soda lime in a spirometer?

Q2 How do you find the tidal volume from a spirometer trace?

Exam Question

Q1 The graph on the right shows a spirometer trace taken from a person at rest.

a) Calculate the respiratory minute ventilation. [3 marks]

b) Give one possible reason why the person would not be able to carry on
using the spirometer for another minute if they began exercising. [1 mark]

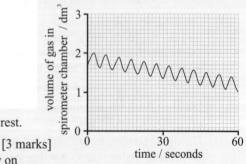

Investigate someone's breathing — make sure they've had a mint first...

Remember that you can work out lots of different things from a single spirometer trace — so always read the question in
your exam to make sure you don't do something silly like find the tidal volume instead of the breathing rate.

Homeostasis

Whilst you're pounding on the treadmill, behind the scenes your body is working to control your body temperature.

Homeostasis is the Maintenance of a Stable Internal Environment

1) Your **external environment** and **what you're doing** (e.g. exercising) can affect your **internal environment** — the blood and tissue fluid that surrounds your cells.

2) **Homeostasis** involves **control systems** that keep your **internal environment** within **narrow limits** — your internal environment is kept in a state of **dynamic equilibrium** (i.e. fluctuating around a normal level).

Homeostasis is particularly important during exercise because you respire more, so you use up more glucose, your body temperature increases and you sweat more.

3) **Keeping** your internal environment **constant** is vital for cells to **function normally** and to **stop** them being **damaged**. For example, if **body temperature** is **too high** (e.g. 40 °C) **enzymes** may become **denatured**. The enzyme's molecules **vibrate too much**, which **breaks** the **hydrogen bonds** that hold them in their **3D shape**. The **shape** of the enzyme's **active site** is **changed** and it **no longer works** as a **catalyst**. This means **metabolic reactions** are **less efficient**.

4) **Cells** need a constant **energy supply** to work so **blood glucose concentration** must be carefully **controlled**. The **concentration of glucose** in the blood is **normally** around **90 mg per 100 cm³** of blood — it's **monitored** by cells in the **pancreas**. Blood glucose concentration **falls** after **exercise**, as **more glucose** is used in **respiration** to **release energy**.

5) Water is **essential** to keep the body **functioning**, so the **amount** of water in the **blood** needs to be kept **constant**. Water is lost during the removal of waste products from the body (e.g. in urine). Water is also lost in **sweat**. The kidneys **regulate** the **water content** of the blood (and urine), so the body has just the **right amount** of water.

Homeostatic Systems Use Negative Feedback to Reverse a Change

1) Homeostatic systems involve **receptors**, a **communication system** and **effectors** (see p. 174).

2) Receptors detect when a level is **too high** or **too low**, and the information's communicated via the **nervous** system or the **hormonal** system to **effectors**.

3) The effectors respond to **counteract** the change — bringing the level **back** to **normal**. The mechanism that **restores** the level to **normal** is called a **negative feedback** mechanism.

4) Negative feedback **keeps** things around the **normal** level, e.g. body temperature is usually kept **within 0.5 °C above or below 37 °C**.

5) Negative feedback only works within **certain limits** though — if the change is **too big** then the **effectors** may **not** be able to **counteract** it, e.g. a huge drop in body temperature caused by prolonged exposure to cold weather may be too large to counteract.

Control of Body Temperature by Negative Feedback

receptors detect temperature's too hot

effectors respond to decrease the temperature

your internal environment stays around the normal level (37 °C)

receptors detect temperature's too cold

effectors respond to increase the temperature

body temperature

time

Positive Feedback Mechanisms Amplify a Change from the Normal Level

1) Some changes trigger a **positive feedback** mechanism, which **amplifies** the change.

2) The effectors respond to **further increase** the level **away** from the **normal** level.

3) Positive feedback is useful to **rapidly activate** something. e.g. a **blood clot** after an injury.

4) Positive feedback can also happen when a **homeostatic system breaks down**, e.g. if you're too cold for too long (hypothermia).

5) Positive feedback **isn't** involved in **homeostasis** because it **doesn't** keep your internal environment **stable**.

- **Platelets** become **activated** and release a **chemical** — this triggers **more platelets** to be activated, and so on.
- Platelets **very quickly** form a **blood clot** at the injury site.
- The process **ends** with **negative feedback**, when the body detects the **blood clot** has been **formed**.

Homeostasis

Many Mechanisms are Used to Change Body Temperature

Mechanisms to REDUCE body temperature:

Sweating — **more sweat** is secreted from **sweat glands** when the body's too hot. The water in sweat **evaporates** from the surface of the skin and **takes heat** from the body. The **skin** is **cooled**.

Hairs lie flat — mammals have a layer of **hair** that provides **insulation** by **trapping air** (air is a poor conductor of heat). When it's hot, **erector pili muscles relax** so the hairs lie flat. **Less air** is trapped, so the skin is **less insulated** and **heat** can be **lost** more easily.

Vasodilation — when it's hot, **arterioles** near the surface of the skin **dilate** (this is called **vasodilation**). **More blood** flows through the **capillaries** in the surface layers of the dermis. This means **more heat** is **lost** from the skin by **radiation** and the **temperature** is **lowered**.

Mechanisms to INCREASE body temperature:

Shivering — when it's cold, **muscles contract** in **spasms**. This makes the body **shiver** and **more heat** is **produced** from **increased respiration**.

Much less sweat — less sweat is secreted from sweat glands when it's cold, **reducing** the amount of **heat loss**.

Hairs stand up — **erector pili muscles contract** when it's cold, which makes the **hairs stand up**. This **traps more air** and so **prevents heat loss**.

Hormones — the body releases **adrenaline** and **thyroxine**. These **increase metabolism** and so **more heat is produced**.

Vasoconstriction — when it's cold, **arterioles** near the surface of the skin **constrict** (this is called **vasoconstriction**) so **less blood** flows through the **capillaries** in the surface layers of the dermis. This **reduces heat loss**.

epidermis, hair, DERMIS, sweat gland, erector pili muscle, capillary, arteriole

The Hypothalamus Controls Body Temperature

1) **Body temperature** in mammals is **maintained** at a **constant level** by a part of the **brain** called the **hypothalamus** (see page 186).

2) The hypothalamus **receives information** about **temperature** from **thermoreceptors** (temperature receptors).

3) Thermoreceptors send **impulses** along **sensory neurones** to the **hypothalamus**, which sends **impulses** along **motor neurones** to **effectors** (muscles and glands).

4) The effectors respond to **restore** the body temperature **back** to **normal**.

5) The control of body temperature is called **thermoregulation**. Here's how it all works:

thermoreceptors detect temperature is too high
hypothalamus sends signals to effectors
- vasodilation
- sweating
- hairs lie flat
- no shivering
- no adrenaline or thyroxine released

rise in body temperature

more heat's produced and conserved by the body → NORMAL BODY TEMPERATURE (37 °C) ← more heat's lost and less heat's produced by the body

- vasoconstriction
- much less sweating
- hairs stand upright
- shivering
- adrenaline and thyroxine released

hypothalamus sends signals to effectors
thermoreceptors detect temperature is too low
fall in body temperature

Remember — exercise increases body temperature.

Homeostasis

Hormones Can Affect Transcription Factors

1) In a cell there are **proteins** called **transcription factors** that **control** the **transcription** of genes.

2) Transcription factors **bind** to **DNA sites** near the **start** of genes and **increase** or **decrease** the **rate** of transcription. Factors that **increase** the rate are called **activators** and those that **decrease** the rate are **repressors**.

3) **Hormones** can affect the activity of transcription factors.

Some Hormones Work Inside Cells...

Some hormones (e.g. steroid and thyroid hormones) can **cross the cell membrane**, **enter the nucleus** and **bind** to transcription factors to alter gene transcription.

> **EXAMPLE — Hormonal regulation of body temperature**
>
> 1) At **normal** body temperature, the **thyroid hormone receptor** (a transcription factor) binds to DNA at the **start** of a gene.
>
> 2) This **decreases** the **transcription** of a gene coding for a **protein** that increases **metabolic rate**.
>
> 3) At **cold** temperatures **thyroxine** is released, which **binds** to the thyroid hormone receptor, causing it to act as an **activator**.
>
> 4) The **transcription rate increases**, producing **more protein**. The protein **increases the metabolic rate**, causing an increase in **body temperature**.

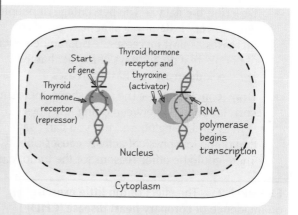

...and Some Hormones Work from the Cell Membrane

1) Some hormones (e.g. protein hormones) **can't cross the cell membrane**, but they can still affect the activity of transcription factors.

2) They bind to **receptors** in the **cell membrane**, which activate **messenger molecules** in the **cytoplasm** of the cell.

3) These messenger molecules activate **enzymes** called **protein kinases**, which trigger a **cascade** (a chain of reactions) inside the cell.

4) During the cascade, transcription factors can be **activated** — these then affect the transcription of genes in the cell **nucleus**.

> Protein hormones can't easily pass across the cell membrane because, unlike steroid and thyroid hormones, they aren't lipid-soluble.

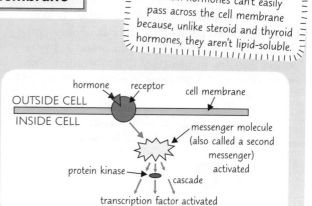

Practice Questions

Q1 What is homeostasis and why is it necessary?

Q2 Which part of the brain is responsible for maintaining a constant body temperature?

Q3 Describe how steroid hormones affect transcription factors.

Exam Questions

Q1 Describe what is meant by a positive feedback mechanism. [1 mark]

Q2 a) Describe how homeostasis reduces body temperature during exercise. [3 marks]
   b) Give two mechanisms that can reduce body temperature. [2 marks]
   c) Describe and explain what effect a very high body temperature has on metabolic reactions. [2 marks]

Homeostasis works like a teacher — everything always gets corrected...

The key to understanding homeostasis is to get your head around negative feedback. Basically, if one thing goes up, the body responds to bring it down — and vice versa. So sweat might be pongy, but you'd be a bit too hot without it.

Exercise and Health

I hope you didn't think you'd get through a lovely section like this without some data analysis to spice things up a bit.

Not Doing Enough Exercise can be Unhealthy...

In the exam you might have to analyse some **data** from a **study** looking at the effect of **too little exercise** on **health**. You need to be able to **describe** what the data shows and say if there's a **correlation** (see p. 206). Be careful what you **conclude** about the data because a correlation **doesn't** always mean that one thing **causes** another.

EXAMPLE 1 — The effect of too little exercise on obesity

As part of a national **survey** of Australian adults, data was collected about how much **physical activity** each participant did per week and their **body mass index (BMI)**. The **table** shows the **amount** of physical activity done each week compared to **BMI**.

> BMI can be used as an indicator of obesity — people who have a BMI of ≥ 30 kg m⁻² are classed as obese.

- **Describe the data** — The **percentage** of people who do **very little** physical activity per week **increases** as **BMI increases**. Also, the percentage of people that do ≥ **5 days** of physical activity per week **decreases** as **BMI increases**.

- **Draw conclusions** — The table shows there's a **correlation** (link) between doing less physical activity and being **obese**. But you **can't** say that doing less physical activity **causes** obesity.

BMI / kg m⁻²	Zero or one day of physical activity per week / %	Five or more days of physical activity per week / %
Underweight (<18.5)	15.2	44.3
Normal (18.5-24.9)	20.2	36.3
Overweight (25-29.9)	22.9	30.8
Obese (≥ 30)	34.2	22.8

There could be **other reasons** for the trend, e.g. people may do less physical activity **because** they're obese.

EXAMPLE 2 — The effect of too little exercise on incidence of coronary heart disease (CHD)

2678 men who had no existing **CHD** (a type of **cardiovascular disease**) and who were physically capable, were involved in a study looking at how **distance walked daily** affects the **risk** of developing CHD. The men were followed up over a 2-4 year period, and any **incidence** of CHD recorded. The men were aged **71-93 years** at the start of the follow-up period.

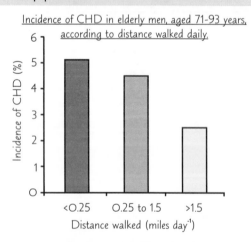

Incidence of CHD in elderly men, aged 71-93 years, according to distance walked daily.

EXAMPLE 3 — The effect of too little exercise on prevalence of Type 2 diabetes.

In the US, the results of a national survey of **68 500 adults** were used to investigate how **BMI** and **physical activity** are associated with the prevalence of **Type 2 diabetes**. As part of the survey, respondents were asked to **self-report** their **height** and **weight** and whether they did **at least 30 minutes** of moderate to vigorous **physical activity at least 3 times a week** (those who did were classed as **active**). Data was also collected about whether each respondent had ever been diagnosed with **diabetes**.

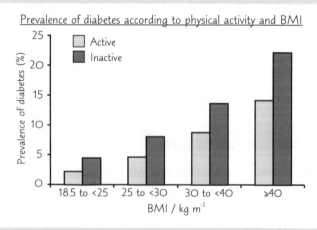

Prevalence of diabetes according to physical activity and BMI

- **Describe the data** — Men aged 71-93 who walked less each day had a **higher incidence** of CHD than men who walked more.

- **Draw conclusions** — There's a **correlation** between **increased incidence of CHD** and **decreased distance walked** each day in **elderly men**. However, the study **only** involved **elderly men** and only looked at **walking**, so you **can't say** that the same applies to **other age groups**, **women** or **other forms** of exercise.

- **Describe the data** — The data shows that diabetes is **more prevalent** in **inactive** than active people, **regardless of BMI**. The data also shows a **correlation** between **increasing BMI** and **increasing prevalence** of diabetes.

- **Draw conclusions** — Although the data clearly shows that **inactivity** is associated with an **increased prevalence** of diabetes, you **can't conclude** how **different levels** of physical activity affect the prevalence of diabetes. Also, there could be **other factors**, such as **diet**, influencing the results.

Exercise and Health

...But Doing **Too Much Exercise** can be **Unhealthy** Too

It's thought that **too much exercise** could cause some problems too, e.g. wear and tear of the joints and suppression of the immune system. So you might get asked to interpret **data** looking at the **effects** of **too much exercise** as well...

EXAMPLE 1 — The effect of **too much exercise** on **wear** and **tear** of **joints**

The number of **hospital admissions** for osteoarthritis of the **hip, knee** and **ankle joints** for **2049** former **male elite athletes** and **1403 healthy, fit controls** were compared by analysing **hospital records** from 1970 to 1990.

- <u>Describe the data</u> — The percentage of **male former elite athletes** admitted to hospital for **osteoarthritis** (wear and tear of the joints) is **more than twice** that of healthy men (5.9% compared to 2.6%). The table shows similar high percentages for different kinds of athletes, with **endurance athletes** being **worse affected** (6.8% admitted to hospital).

- <u>Draw conclusions</u> — The table shows a **correlation** between being an **elite male athlete** of any kind and having **osteoarthritis** of the hip, knee or ankle. But you can't say that doing a lot of exercise **causes** osteoarthritis — there may be **other reasons** for the trend, e.g. elite athletes may be more likely to injure themselves in competitions, which could lead to arthritis.

Group of men	% of men admitted to hospital for osteoarthritis of the hip, knee or ankle
Healthy men, fully fit for military service	2.6
Former elite athletes (all)	5.9
• Endurance athletes (e.g. long-distance runners)	6.8
• Mixed sports athletes (e.g. footballers)	5.0
• Power sports athletes (e.g. boxers)	6.6

Reproduced from Osteoarthritis of weight bearing joints of lower limbs in former elite male athletes. UM Kujala, J Kaprio, S Sarno, Volume 308, © 1994 with permission from BMJ Publishing Group Ltd.

EXAMPLE 2 — The effect of **too much exercise** on the **immune system**

The number of people showing **two or more** symptoms of **upper respiratory tract infection** was recorded for a group containing **32 elite** and **31 recreational triathletes** and **cyclists** during a **five-month** period in their training season. It was also recorded for **20 control** subjects during a five-month period.

- <u>Describe the data</u> — There was a **much higher** number of cases of respiratory illnesses in **elite athletes** (21) than in athletes (7) and sedentary controls (9) over the five-month period.

- <u>Draw conclusions</u> — There's a **correlation** between doing **a lot of exercise** (being an elite athlete) and getting **more** cases of **respiratory illnesses**. But there's also a **correlation** between doing **some exercise** (recreationally competitive athletes) and getting **fewer** cases of respiratory illnesses. You **can't** say doing a lot of exercise **causes** more respiratory illnesses — there could be **other reasons** for the trend, e.g. elite athletes might be exposed to lots of infections when competing a lot.

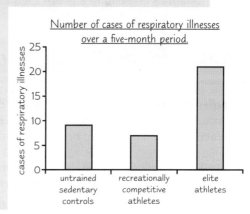

Number of cases of respiratory illnesses over a five-month period.

Practice Questions

Q1 What is a correlation?

Exam Question

Physical activity (hours/week)	≥3.5	1–3.5	<1
Relative risk of CHD	1.0	1.32	1.48

Q1 A study investigated the effects of physical activity on the risk of coronary heart disease (CHD) in 88 393 women. The results are shown in the table.
Analyse the data to make a conclusion about the effects of physical activity on risk of CHD. [2 marks]

Drawing conclusions — you'll need wax crayons and some paper...

These pages give you some examples to help you deal with what the examiners are sure to hurl at you — they really love throwing data around. There's some important advice here — it's easy to leap to a conclusion that isn't really justified. So make sure you know that just because things are correlated, it doesn't mean one causes the other.

Exercise and Health

Yoga on an exotic beach somewhere, that's my kind of exercise. Apparently not all sports are as calm or as stress-free. There are injuries galore...

Surgery can Help People with Injuries to Play Sports

Some injuries can cause **permanent damage** to the body, e.g. head or spinal injuries. But people can **recover** from some injuries if they're **treated correctly**. A lot of injuries happen when **playing sports** because the body's put under a lot of **stress** (fast running, hard tackles, etc.). Advances in **medical technology** can help people with an injury to **recover** and **participate in sports**. One advance you need to know about is **keyhole surgery**:

1) Keyhole surgery is a way of doing surgery **without** making a **large incision** (cut) in the skin.

2) Surgeons make a much **smaller incision** in the patient, and they insert a tiny **video camera** and **specialised medical instruments** through the incision into the body.

3) There are many **advantages** of keyhole surgery over regular surgery:

- Operations don't involve opening up the patient as much, so patients **lose less blood** and have **less scarring** of the skin.

- Patients are usually in **less pain** after their operation and they **recover more quickly**, because less damage is done to the body.

- This makes it **easier** for the patient to return to **normal activities** and their **hospital stay** is **shorter**.

Injuries aren't usually fixed by surgery alone — other treatments (e.g. physiotherapy, anti-inflammatory drugs) are needed too for a full recovery.

For example, damaged **cruciate ligaments** can be fixed by **keyhole surgery**:

1) A **common sports injury** is damage to the cruciate ligaments — **ligaments** found in the middle of your **knee**, connecting your **thigh bone** to your **lower leg bone**.

2) **Damaged** cruciate ligament can be **removed** and **replaced** with a **graft**. The graft is likely to be from a **tendon** in the patient's leg (or it may come from a **donor's** tendon instead).

After a slight mishap, Ruth was tragically left with her elbows grafted to her knees.

Prostheses can Replace Damaged Body Parts

Some people are **born without** a particular **body part**, e.g. without a leg. Other people suffer **injuries** that result in them **losing** or **badly damaging** a **body part**, e.g. tennis players can damage their knees so much that they can no longer play sports. Sometimes it's possible to **replace** damaged or missing body parts with an **artificial device** called a **prosthesis**:

1) Prostheses can be used to replace whole limbs (e.g. an artificial leg can replace a missing leg) or parts of limbs (e.g. artificial hip joints can replace damaged hip joints).

2) Some prostheses include electronic devices that operate the prosthesis by picking up information sent by the nervous system (e.g. artificial hand prostheses with an electronic device allow the user to move the fingers).

So prostheses make it possible for people with some **disabilities** to **participate** in **sport**, e.g. prosthetic 'legs' (called blades) allow people without legs to run. They also make it possible for people who have certain **injuries** to **play sport again**.

For example, damaged **knee joints** can be replaced by **prosthetic joints**:

1) A metal device is inserted into the knee to replace damaged cartilage and bone.

2) The knee joint and the ends of the leg bones are replaced to provide a smooth knee joint. Cushioning in the new joint helps to reduce the impact on the knee.

3) A knee joint replacement allows people with serious knee problems to move around and participate in low-impact sports, such as walking and swimming.

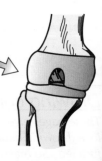

Exercise and Health

Some Athletes Use **Performance-Enhancing Drugs**

When involved in a very **competitive sport**, some people choose to take **performance-enhancing drugs**
— these are drugs that will **improve** a person's **performance**.
There are various kinds of performance-enhancing drugs that have different effects on the body, for example:

- Anabolic steroids — these drugs **increase strength**, **speed** and **stamina** by increasing muscle size and allowing athletes to train harder. They also **increase aggression**.
- Stimulants — these drugs **speed up reactions**, **reduce fatigue** and **increase aggression**.
- Narcotic analgesics — these drugs **reduce pain**, so **injuries don't affect performance**.

Performance-enhancing drugs are **banned** in most sports. Athletes can be **tested** for drugs at any time
and if they're **caught**, they can be **banned** from **competing** and stripped of any medals.

The **Use** of **Performance-Enhancing Drugs** is **Controversial**

Some people (**absolutists**) think that performance-enhancing drugs should be **banned** from all sports
— they think the use of drugs is **morally wrong** and that they should **never** be used. However, other
people (**rationalists**) think that the use of these drugs can be **justified** in certain **circumstances**.
You need to know both sides of the argument:

Arguments AGAINST using performance-enhancing drugs	Arguments FOR using performance-enhancing drugs
• Some performance-enhancing drugs are **illegal**. • Competitions become **unfair** if some people take drugs — people gain an advantage by taking drugs, not through training or hard work. • There are some **serious health risks** associated with the drugs used. Side effects include **high blood pressure** and **heart problems**. • Athletes may **not** be **fully informed** of the health risks of the drugs they take.	• It's up to each individual — athletes have the right to make their **own decision** about taking drugs and whether they're worth the risk or not. • Drug-free sport **isn't** really **fair** anyway — different athletes have access to different training facilities, coaches, equipment, etc. The use of performance-enhancing drugs might **overcome** these **inequalities**. • Athletes that want to compete at a **higher level** may only be able to by using performance-enhancing drugs.

Practice Questions

Q1 How is keyhole surgery performed?

Q2 What are performance-enhancing drugs?

Q3 Give three reasons why people may support the use of performance-enhancing drugs in sport.

Exam Questions

Q1 A cricketer suffers a knee injury during a game. When examined by doctors, he's told he may need surgery.
    a) Give three benefits of keyhole surgery compared to open surgery.   [3 marks]
    b) The damage to his knee may be so bad that it can't be repaired. How could a prosthesis help?   [2 marks]

Q2 Many sports organisations have banned the use of performance-enhancing drugs.
    Give two arguments in favour of such a ban.   [2 marks]

<u>Through the keyhole — who operates on a knee like this...</u>

*Wow, I didn't know sport could be so technical. Eeeee, if you hurt yourself when I were a lad, you'd be lucky to get
yourself a sticky plaster... Anyway, it seems the world of sport has come on a bit since then — and you need to know all
about the newfangled technology and drugs used these days, as well as arguments for and against them.*

Nervous and Hormonal Communication

Right, it's time to get your brain cells fired up and get your teeth stuck into a mammoth — a mammoth section, that i

Responding to their Environment Helps Organisms Survive

1) **Animals increase** their **chances** of **survival** by **responding** to **changes** in their **external environment**, e.g. by **avoiding harmful environments** such as places that are too hot or too cold.

2) They also **respond** to **changes** in their **internal environment** to make sure that the **conditions** are always **optimal** for their **metabolism** (all the chemical reactions that go on inside them).

3) **Plants** also **increase** their **chances** of **survival** by **responding** to **changes** in their **environment** (see p. 184).

4) Any **change** in the internal or external **environment** is called a **stimulus**.

Receptors Detect Stimuli and Effectors Produce a Response

1) **Receptors detect stimuli** — they can be **cells** or **proteins** on **cell surface membranes**. There are **loads** of **different types** of receptors that detect **different stimuli**.

2) **Effectors** are cells that bring about a **response** to a **stimulus**, to produce an **effect**. Effectors include **muscle cells** and cells found in **glands**, e.g. the **pancreas**.

3) Receptors **communicate** with effectors via the **nervous system** (see below) or the **hormonal system** (see the next page), or sometimes using **both**.

The Nervous System Sends Information as Electrical Impulses

1) The **nervous system** is made up of a **complex network** of cells called **neurones**. There are **three main types** of neurone:

- **Sensory neurones** transmit electrical impulses from **receptors** to the **central nervous system** (**CNS**) — the **brain** and **spinal cord**.
- **Motor neurones** transmit electrical impulses from the **CNS** to **effectors**.
- **Relay neurones** transmit electrical impulses **between** sensory neurones and motor neurones.

There's more about the different types of neurone on page 178.

2) A stimulus is detected by **receptor cells** and an **electrical impulse** is sent along a **sensory neurone**.

3) When an **electrical impulse** reaches the end of a neurone chemicals called **neurotransmitters** take the information across to the **next neurone**, which then sends an **electrical impulse** (see pages 182-183).

Electrical impulses are also called nerve impulses or action potentials — see p. 179.

4) The **CNS processes** the information and sends impulses along **motor neurones** to **effectors**.

5) You need to know how your **eyes** (and the eyes of other mammals) **respond** to **dim light** (to **help you see better**) or **bright light** (to **protect** them):

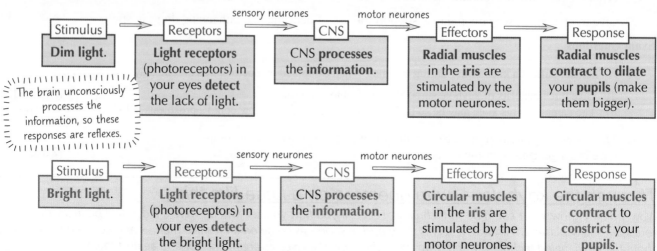

Stimulus		Receptors		CNS		Effectors		Response
Dim light.	→	**Light receptors (photoreceptors) in** your eyes **detect** the lack of light.	→	CNS **processes** the **information.**	→	**Radial muscles** in the **iris** are **stimulated** by the motor neurones.	→	**Radial muscles contract** to **dilate** your **pupils** (make them bigger).

sensory neurones ... *motor neurones*

The brain unconsciously processes the information, so these responses are reflexes.

Stimulus		Receptors		CNS		Effectors		Response
Bright light.	→	**Light receptors (photoreceptors) in** your eyes **detect** the bright light.	→	CNS **processes** the **information.**	→	**Circular muscles** in the **iris** are **stimulated** by the motor neurones.	→	**Circular muscles contract** to **constrict** your **pupils.**

sensory neurones ... *motor neurones*

Nervous and Hormonal Communication

The Hormonal System Sends Information as Chemical Signals

1) The **hormonal system** is made up of **glands** and **hormones**:

   - A **gland** is a group of cells that are specialised to **secrete** a useful substance, such as a **hormone**. E.g. the **pancreas** secretes **insulin**.
   - **Hormones** are 'chemical messengers'. Many hormones are **proteins** or **peptides**, e.g. **insulin**. Some hormones are **steroids**, e.g. **progesterone**.

2) **Hormones** are **secreted** when a **gland** is **stimulated**:

   - Glands can be **stimulated** by a **change** in **concentration** of a specific **substance** (sometimes **another hormone**).
   - They can also be **stimulated** by **electrical impulses**.

3) Hormones **diffuse directly into** the **blood**, then they're **taken** around the body by the **circulatory system**.

4) They **diffuse out** of the blood **all over** the **body** but each hormone will only **bind** to **specific receptors** for that hormone, found on the membranes of some cells (called **target cells**).

5) The hormones trigger a **response** in the **target cells** (the **effectors**).

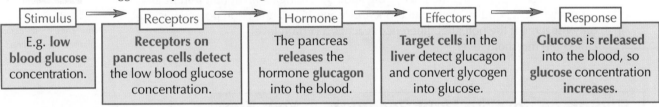

Stimulus		Receptors		Hormone		Effectors		Response
E.g. **low blood glucose** concentration.	→	**Receptors on pancreas cells detect** the low blood glucose concentration.	→	The pancreas **releases** the hormone **glucagon** into the blood.	→	**Target cells** in the **liver** detect glucagon and convert glycogen into glucose.	→	**Glucose is released** into the blood, so **glucose** concentration **increases**.

You Might Have to Compare Nervous and Hormonal Communication

Nervous Communication	Hormonal Communication
Uses electrical impulses.	Uses chemicals
Faster response — electrical impulses are really fast.	Slower response — hormones travel at the 'speed of blood'.
Localised response — neurones carry electrical impulses to specific cells.	Widespread response — target cells can be all over the body.
Short-lived response — neurotransmitters are removed quickly.	Long-lived response — hormones aren't broken down very quickly.

Practice Questions

Q1 Why do organisms respond to changes in their environment?

Q2 Give two types of effector.

Q3 What is a hormone?

Exam Questions

Q1 Describe and explain the roles of receptors and effectors in the human eye's response to bright light. [4 marks]

Q2 Give three ways in which nervous communication is different from hormonal communication. [3 marks]

Vacancy — talented gag writer required for boring Biology topics...

Actually, this stuff is really quite fascinating once you realise just how much your body can do without you even knowing. Just sit back and relax, let your nerves and hormones do the work... apart from the whole revision thing — your body can't do that without you knowing unfortunately. You best crack on and get your head around these pages.

The Nervous System — Receptors

So now you know why organisms respond it's time for the hugely thrilling details... First up — receptors.

Receptors are Specific to One Kind of Stimulus

1) Receptors are **specific** — they only **detect one particular stimulus**, e.g. light, pressure or glucose concentration

2) There are **many different types** of receptor that each detect a **different type of stimulus**.

3) Some receptors are **cells**, e.g. photoreceptors are receptor cells that connect to the nervous system. Some receptors are **proteins** on **cell surface membranes**, e.g. glucose receptors are proteins found in the cell membranes of some pancreatic cells.

4) When a nervous system receptor is in its **resting state** (not being stimulated), there's a **difference in charge** between the **inside** and the **outside** of the cell. This means there's a **voltage** across the membrane. The membrane is said to be **polarised**.

5) The **voltage** across the membrane is called the **potential difference**.

6) It is **generated** by **ion pumps** and **ion channels** (see page 178).

7) When a **stimulus** is detected, the **permeability** of the **cell membrane** to **ions changes** (ions are stopped from moving, or more move in and out of the cell). This **changes the potential difference**.

8) If the **change** in potential difference is **big enough** it'll trigger an **action potential** — an electrical impulse along a neurone (see page 179). An action potential is only triggered if the potential difference reaches a certain level called the **threshold** level.

Forget polarised membranes, it's all about polarised hair darling...

Photoreceptors are Light Receptors in Your Eye

1) **Light** enters the eye through the **pupil**. The **amount** of light that enters is **controlled** by the muscles of the **iris**.

2) Light rays are **focused** by the **lens** onto the **retina**, which lines the inside of the eye. The retina contains **photoreceptor cells** — these **detect light**.

3) The **fovea** is an area of the retina where there are **lots of photoreceptors**.

4) **Nerve impulses** from the photoreceptor cells are carried from the **retina** to the **brain** by the **optic nerve**, which is a bundle of **neurones**. Where the optic nerve leaves the eye is called the **blind spot** — there **aren't** any **photoreceptor cells**, so it's **not sensitive to light**.

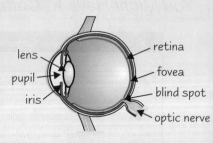

Photoreceptors Convert Light into an Electrical Impulse

1) **Light** enters the eye, hits the **photoreceptors** and is **absorbed** by **light-sensitive pigments**.

2) Light bleaches the pigments, causing a **chemical change**.

3) This triggers a **nerve impulse** along a **bipolar neurone**.

4) Bipolar neurones connect **photoreceptors** to the **optic nerve**, which takes impulses to the **brain**.

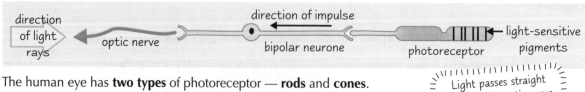

5) The human eye has **two types** of photoreceptor — **rods** and **cones**.

6) Rods are mainly found in the **peripheral** parts of the **retina**, and cones are found **packed together** in the **fovea**.

Light passes straight through the optic nerve and the bipolar neurone to the photoreceptor.

7) Rods only give information in **black and white** (monochromatic vision), but cones give information in **colour** (trichromatic vision). There are three types of cones — **red-sensitive**, **green-sensitive** and **blue-sensitive**. They're stimulated in **different proportions** so you see different colours.

The Nervous System — Receptors

Rod Cells Hyperpolarise when Stimulated by Light

Rods contain a light-sensitive pigment called **rhodopsin**.
Rhodopsin is made of **two chemicals** joined together — **retinal** and **opsin**.
When it's **dark**, your rods **aren't stimulated** — here's what happens:

1) **Sodium ions (Na⁺)** are **pumped out** of the cell using **active transport**.

2) But sodium ions **diffuse back in** to the cell through **open sodium channels**.

3) This makes the **inside** of the cell **only slightly negative** compared to the outside — the cell membrane is said to be **depolarised**.

4) This triggers the **release of neurotransmitters**.

5) But the neurotransmitters **inhibit the bipolar neurone** — the bipolar neurone **can't fire an action potential** so **no information** goes to the brain.

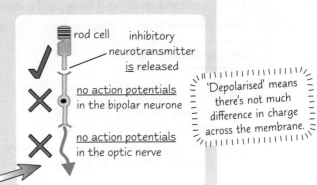

'Depolarised' means there's not much difference in charge across the membrane.

When it's **light**, your rod cells **are stimulated** — here's what happens:

Sodium channels are cation channels because they only let positively charged ions (cations) through.

1) **Light energy** causes rhodopsin to **break apart** into **retinal** and **opsin** — this process is called **bleaching**.

2) The bleaching of rhodopsin causes the **sodium ion channels to close**.

3) So **sodium ions** are actively transported **out** of the cell, but they **can't diffuse back in**.

4) This means **sodium ions build up** on the **outside** of the cell, making the **inside** of the membrane **much more negative** than the outside — the cell membrane is **hyperpolarised**.

5) When the rod cell is hyperpolarised it **stops releasing neurotransmitters**. This means there's **no inhibition** of the **bipolar neurone**.

6) Because the bipolar neurone is no longer inhibited, it **depolarises**. If the **change** in **potential difference** reaches the **threshold**, an **action potential** is transmitted to the **brain** via the **optic nerve**.

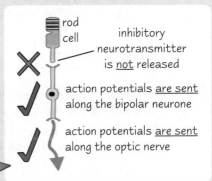

Practice Questions

Q1 How many types of stimuli does one type of receptor detect?

Q2 Name the bundle of neurones that links the eye to the brain.

Q3 What do photoreceptors convert light into?

Q4 When it's dark, is a bipolar neurone inhibited or uninhibited?

Exam Question

Q1 Which of the following best describes rhodopsin?

A A channel that controls the movement of sodium ions in and out of rod cells in the eye.

B A light-sensitive pigment that's broken apart by light energy when rod cells are stimulated.

C A type of neurone that connects photoreceptors to the optic nerve.

D A neurotransmitter released by rod cells when they are not being stimulated by light. [1 mark]

Rods — useful for both seeing and catching fish...

Wow, loads of stuff here, so cone-gratulations if you manage to remember it. In fact, get someone to test you, just to make sure it's well and truly fixed in that big grey blob you call your brain. Remember, receptors are really important because without them you wouldn't be able to see this book, and without this book revision would be way trickier.

The Nervous System — Neurones

Ah, on to the good stuff — how neurones carry info (in the form of action potentials) to other parts of the body...

You Need to **Learn** the **Structure** and **Function** of **Neurones**

1) All neurones have a **cell body** with a **nucleus** (plus **cytoplasm** and all the other **organelles** you usually get in a ce

2) The cell body has **extensions** that **connect** to **other neurones** — **dendrites** and **dendrons** carry nerve impulses **towards** the **cell body**, and **<u>axons</u>** carry nerve impulses **away** from the **cell body**.

3) The **three different types** of neurone have slightly **different structures** and **different functions**:

1 **Motor Neurones**

- **Many short dendrites** carry nerve impulses from the **central nervous system (CNS)** to the **cell body**.
- **One long axon** carries nerve impulses from the **cell body** to **effector cells**.

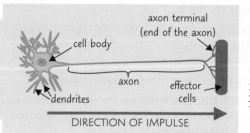

This is a non-myelinated motor neurone — see p. 181 for the structure of a myelinated one.

2 **Sensory Neurones**

- **One long dendron** carries nerve impulses from **receptor cells** to the **cell body**, which is located in the **middle** of the neurone.
- **One short axon** carries nerve impulses from the **cell body** to the CNS.

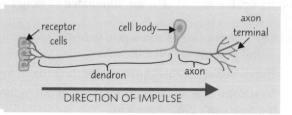

3 **Relay Neurones**

- **Many short dendrites** carry nerve impulses from **sensory neurones** to the **cell body**.
- **An axon** carries nerve impulses from the **cell body** to **motor neurones**.

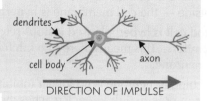

Relay neurones transmit action potentials through the CNS.

Neurone **Cell Membranes** are **Polarised** at **Rest**

1) In a neurone's **resting state** (when it's not being stimulated), the **outside** of the membrane is **positively charged** compared to the **inside**. This is because there are **more positive ions outside** the cell than inside.

2) So the membrane is **polarised** — there's a **difference in charge**.

3) The voltage across the membrane when it's at rest is called the **resting potential** — it's about **–70 mV**.

4) The resting potential is created and maintained by **sodium-potassium pumps** and **potassium ion channels** in a neurone's membrane:

'mV' stands for 'millivolts'. There are 1000 mV in 1 V.

Sodium-potassium pump
These pumps use **active transport** to move **three sodium ions (Na^+) out** of the neurone for every **two potassium ions (K^+) moved in**. ATP is needed to do this.

Potassium ion channel
These channels allow **facilitated diffusion of potassium ions (K^+) out** of the neurone, down their **concentration gradient**.

- The sodium-potassium pumps move **sodium ions out** of the neurone, but the membrane **isn't permeable** to **sodium ions**, so they **can't diffuse back in**. This creates a **sodium ion electrochemical gradient** (a **concentration gradient** of **ions**) because there are **more** positive sodium ions **outside** the cell than inside.

- The sodium-potassium pumps also move **potassium ions in** to the neurone, but the membrane **is permeable** to **potassium ions** so they **diffuse back out** through potassium ion channels.

- This makes the **outside** of the cell **positively charged** compared to the inside.

The Nervous System — Neurones

Neurone **Cell Membranes** Become **Depolarised** When They're **Stimulated**

A **stimulus** triggers other ion channels, called **sodium ion channels**, to **open**. If the stimulus is big enough, it'll trigger a **rapid change** in **potential difference**. The sequence of events that happen are known as an **action potential**:

① **Stimulus** — this **excites** the neurone cell membrane, causing **sodium ion channels** to **open**. The membrane becomes **more permeable** to sodium, so **sodium ions diffuse into** the neurone down the sodium ion electrochemical gradient. This makes the **inside** of the neurone **less negative**.

② **Depolarisation** — if the potential difference reaches the **threshold** (around –55 mV), **more sodium ion channels open**. **More sodium ions diffuse into** the neurone.

③ **Repolarisation** — at a potential difference of around **+30 mV** the **sodium ion channels close** and **potassium ion channels open**. The membrane is **more permeable** to potassium so **potassium ions diffuse out** of the neurone down the potassium ion concentration gradient. This starts to get the membrane **back** to its **resting potential**.

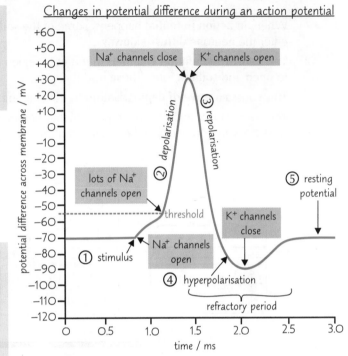

Changes in potential difference during an action potential

④ **Hyperpolarisation** — **potassium ion channels** are **slow to close** so there's a slight 'overshoot' where too many potassium ions diffuse out of the neurone. The potential difference becomes **more negative** than the **resting potential** (i.e. less than –70 mV).

The sodium and potassium channels are voltage-gated — they open at a certain voltage.

⑤ **Resting potential** — the ion channels are **reset**. The **sodium-potassium pump** returns the membrane to its **resting potential** and maintains it until the membrane's excited by another stimulus.

After an **action potential**, the neurone cell membrane **can't** be **excited** again straight away. This is because the ion channels are **recovering** and they **can't** be made to **open** — sodium ion channels are **closed** during repolarisation and **potassium ion channels** are **closed** during hyperpolarisation. This period of recovery is called the **refractory period**.

Practice Questions

Q1 Draw and label a motor neurone.

Q2 Name the pumps and channels that maintain a neurone's resting potential.

Exam Question

Q1 The graph shows an action potential across an axon membrane following the application of a stimulus.

a) Explain what causes the change in potential difference between point A and point B. [2 marks]

b) The same stimulus was applied consistently for over one hour. The next action potential fired at 4.5 ms. Calculate how many action potentials fired in one hour. Give your answer in standard form. [2 marks]

c) A stimulus was applied at 1.5 ms, but failed to produce an action potential. Explain why. [2 marks]

I'm feeling a bit depolarised after all that...

All this stuff about neurones can be a bit tricky to get your head around at first. Take your time and try scribbling it down a few times till it starts to make sense. Neurones work because there's an electrical charge across their membrane, which is set up by ion pumps and ion channels. It's a change in this charge that transmits an action potential.

The Nervous System — Neurones

Action potentials don't just sit there once they've been generated — they have to hotfoot it all the way down the neurone so the information can be passed on to the next cell...

The **Action Potential** Moves **Along** the **Neurone** as a **Wave** of **Depolarisation**

1) When an **action potential** happens, some of the **sodium ions** that enter the neurone **diffuse sideways**.
2) This causes **sodium ion channels** in the **next region** of the neurone to **open** and **sodium ions diffuse into** that part.
3) This causes a **wave of depolarisation** to travel along the neurone.
4) The **wave** moves **away** from the parts of the membrane in the **refractory period** because these parts **can't fire** an action potential.

This 'wave of depolarisation' had Pete deeply concerned.

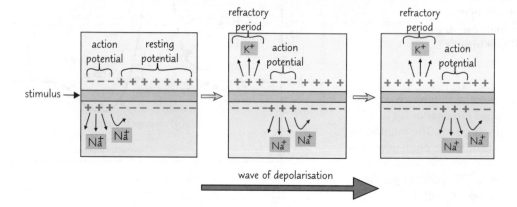

wave of depolarisation

It's like a Mexican wave travelling through a crowd — sodium ions rushing inwards causes a wave of activity along the membrane.

The **Refractory Period** Produces **Discrete Impulses**

1) During the **refractory period**, **ion channels** are **recovering** and **can't be opened**.
2) So the refractory period acts as a **time delay** between one action potential and the next. This makes sure that **action potentials don't overlap** but pass along as **discrete** (separate) **impulses**.
3) The refractory period also makes sure **action potentials** are **unidirectional** (they only travel in **one direction**).

A **Bigger Stimulus** Causes **More Frequent Impulses**

1) Once the threshold is reached, an action potential will **always fire** with the **same change in voltage**, no matter how big the stimulus is.
2) If **threshold isn't reached**, an action potential **won't fire**.
3) A **bigger stimulus** won't cause a bigger action potential, but it will cause them to fire **more frequently**.

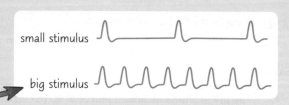

small stimulus

big stimulus

Preventing the **Movement** of **Sodium Ions** Stops **Action Potentials**

1) **Local anaesthetics** are **drugs** that **stop** you from **feeling pain** in a localised area of your body.
2) They work by **binding** to **sodium ion channels** in the membrane of neurones.
3) This **stops sodium ions** from **moving into** the neurones, so their membranes will **not depolarise**.
4) This **prevents action potentials** from being **conducted** along the neurones and **stops information about pain** reaching the **brain**.

The Nervous System — Neurones

Action Potentials Go Faster in Myelinated Neurones

1) Some neurones are **myelinated** — they have a **myelin sheath**.
2) The myelin sheath is an **electrical insulator**.
3) It's made of a type of cell called a **Schwann cell**.
4) Between the Schwann cells are tiny patches of **bare membrane** called the **nodes of Ranvier**.
   Sodium ion channels are **concentrated** at the nodes.

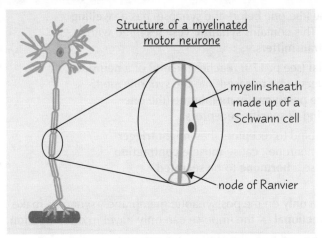

Structure of a myelinated motor neurone

myelin sheath made up of a Schwann cell

node of Ranvier

5) In a **myelinated** neurone, **depolarisation** only happens at the **nodes of Ranvier**
   (where sodium ions can get through the membrane).
6) The neurone's **cytoplasm conducts** enough electrical charge to **depolarise**
   the **next node**, so the impulse 'jumps' from node to node.
7) This is called **saltatory conduction** and it's **really fast**.
8) In a **non-myelinated** neurone, the impulse travels as a
   wave along the **whole length** of the **axon membrane**.
9) This is **slower** than saltatory conduction
   (although it's still pretty quick).
10) The **speed** at which an impulse **moves** along a **neurone**
    is known as the **conduction velocity**. A **high** conduction
    velocity means that the impulse is travelling **quickly**.

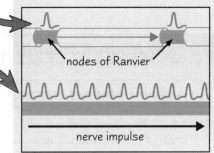

nodes of Ranvier

nerve impulse

Practice Questions

Q1 Briefly describe how an action potential moves along a neurone.

Q2 Give one function of the refractory period in nervous transmission.

Q3 How does a bigger stimulus affect the size of an action potential?

Q4 What is the function of Schwann cells on a neurone?

Q5 What are nodes of Ranvier?

Q6 Does a nerve impulse travel faster or slower along a non-myelinated neurone than a myelinated neurone?

Exam Question

Q1 Multiple sclerosis is a disease of the nervous system characterised by damage to the myelin sheaths
of neurones. Explain how this will affect the transmission of action potentials. [3 marks]

Never mind the ion channels, I need to recover after this lot...

*I'd expect animals like cheetahs, or even humans, to have super myelinated neurones so that nerve impulses are
conducted really fast. But no, apparently we've been outdone by shrimps. That's right, top of the leader board so far
are shrimps with their myelinated giant nerve fibre conducting impulses faster than 200 ms⁻¹. They must get a lot done.*

The Nervous System — Synapses

When an action potential arrives at the end of a neurone the information has to be passed on to the next cell — this could be another neurone, a muscle cell or a gland cell.

A **Synapse** is a **Junction** Between a **Neurone** and the **Next Cell**

1) A **synapse** is the junction between a **neurone** and another **neurone**, or between a **neurone** and an **effector cell**, e.g. a muscle or gland cell.

2) The **tiny gap** between the cells at a synapse is called the **synaptic cleft**.

3) The **presynaptic neurone** (the one before the synapse) has a **swelling** called a **synaptic knob**. This contains **synaptic vesicles** filled with **chemicals** called **neurotransmitters**.

4) When an **action potential** (see p. 179) reaches the end of a neurone it causes **neurotransmitters** to be **released** into the synaptic cleft. They **diffuse across** to the **postsynaptic membrane** (the one after the synapse) and **bind** to **specific receptors**.

5) When neurotransmitters bind to receptors they might **trigger** an **action potential** (in a neurone), cause **muscle contraction** (in a muscle cell), or cause a **hormone** to be **secreted** (from a gland cell).

6) Because the receptors are **only** on the postsynaptic membranes, synapses make sure **impulses** are **unidirectional** — the impulse can only travel in **one direction**.

7) Neurotransmitters are **removed** from the **cleft** so the **response** doesn't keep happening, e.g. they're taken back into the **presynaptic neurone** or they're **broken down** by **enzymes** (and the products are taken into the neurone).

8) There are many **different** neurotransmitters, e.g. **acetylcholine** and **dopamine**. **Acetylcholine** is involved in **muscle contraction** and the **control of heart rate** (see page 162).

Typical structure of a synapse

presynaptic membrane

postsynaptic membrane

synaptic knob

vesicle filled with neurotransmitters

synaptic cleft

receptors

Here's How **Neurotransmitters Transmit Nerve Impulses Between Neurones**

1 An **Action Potential** Triggers **Calcium Influx**

1) An action potential arrives at the **synaptic knob** of the **presynaptic neurone**.

2) The action potential stimulates **voltage-gated calcium ion channels** in the **presynaptic neurone** to **open**.

3) **Calcium ions diffuse into** the synaptic knob. (They're pumped out afterwards by active transport.)

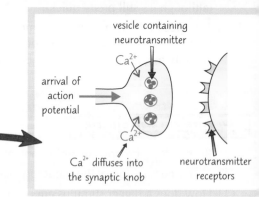

vesicle containing neurotransmitter

Ca^{2+}

arrival of action potential

Ca^{2+}

Ca^{2+} diffuses into the synaptic knob

neurotransmitter receptors

2 **Calcium Influx** Causes **Neurotransmitter Release**

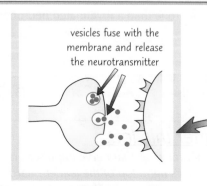

vesicles fuse with the membrane and release the neurotransmitter

1) The influx of **calcium ions** into the synaptic knob causes the **synaptic vesicles** to **move** to the **presynaptic membrane**. They then **fuse** with the presynaptic membrane.

2) The **vesicles release** the neurotransmitter into the **synaptic cleft** — this is called **exocytosis**.

Synaptic knobs contain lots of mitochondria — they make ATP, which is needed for active transport and the movement of vesicles.

The Nervous System — Synapses

3) The Neurotransmitter Triggers an Action Potential in the Postsynaptic Neurone

1) The neurotransmitter **diffuses** across the **synaptic cleft** and **binds** to specific **receptors** on the **postsynaptic membrane**.

2) This causes **sodium ion channels** in the **postsynaptic neurone** to **open**.

3) The **influx** of **sodium ions** into the postsynaptic membrane causes **depolarisation**. An **action potential** on the **postsynaptic membrane** is generated if the **threshold** is reached.

4) The **neurotransmitter** is **removed** from the **synaptic cleft** so the **response** doesn't keep happening.

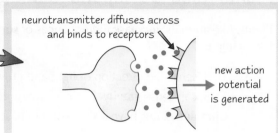

neurotransmitter diffuses across and binds to receptors

new action potential is generated

Synapses Play Vital Roles in the Nervous System

1) Synapses allow Information to be Dispersed or Amplified

1) When **one** neurone **connects** to **many** neurones information can be **dispersed** to **different parts** of the body. This is called **synaptic divergence**.

2) When **many** neurones **connect** to **one** neurone information can be **amplified** (made stronger). This is called **synaptic convergence**.

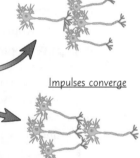

Impulses diverge

Impulses converge

2) Summation at Synapses Finely Tunes the Nervous Response

1) If a stimulus is **weak**, only a **small amount** of **neurotransmitter** will be released from a neurone into the synaptic cleft. This might not be enough to **excite** the postsynaptic membrane to the **threshold** level and stimulate an action potential.

2) **Summation** is where the effect of neurotransmitter released from **many neurones** (or **one** neurone that's stimulated **a lot** in a short period of time) is **added together**.

Practice Questions

Q1 What is a synapse?

Q2 What name is given to the tiny gap between the cells at a synapse?

Q3 How do synapses ensure that nerve impulses are unidirectional?

Q4 What is synaptic divergence?

Exam Questions

Q1 The diagram on the right shows a synapse. Name the parts labelled A-C.   [3 marks]

Q2 Describe the sequence of events from the arrival of an action potential at the presynaptic membrane of a synapse to the generation of a new action potential at the postsynaptic membrane.   [6 marks]

Synaptic knobs and clefts — will you stop giggling at the back...

Some more pretty tough pages here — aren't I kind to you. And lots more diagrams to have a go at drawing. Don't worry if you're not the world's best artist, just make sure you add labels to your drawings to explain what's happening. Then there are only two more pages of this section before you can put your feet up and have a break.

Responses in Plants

Plants also have ways of responding to stimuli — OK so they're not as quick as animals, but they're important all the same.

Plants Need to Respond to Stimuli Too

Plants, like animals, **increase** their chances of **survival** by **responding** to changes in their **environment**. For example:

- They sense the direction of **light** and **grow** towards it to **maximise** light absorption for **photosynthesis**.
- They can sense **gravity**, so their roots and shoots **grow** in the **right direction**.
- **Climbing** plants have a sense of **touch**, so they can find things to climb and **reach** the **sunlight**.

A Tropism is a Plant's Growth Response to an External Stimulus

1) A **tropism** is the **response** of a plant to a **directional stimulus** (a stimulus coming from a particular direction).
2) Plants respond to directional stimuli by **regulating** their **growth**.
3) A p<u>o</u>sitive tropism is growth **to<u>wards</u>** the stimulus.
4) A neg<u>a</u>tive tropism is growth **<u>away</u>** from the stimulus.

- **Phototropism** is the growth of a plant in response to **light**.
- **Shoots** are **positively phototropic** and grow **towards** light.
- **Roots** are **negatively phototropic** and grow **away** from light.

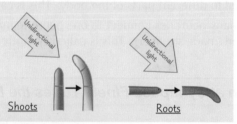

Shoots   Roots

- **Geotropism** is the growth of a plant in response to **gravity**.
- **Shoots** are **negatively geotropic** and grow **upwards**.
- **Roots** are **positively geotropic** and grow **downwards**.

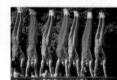

The men's gymnastics team were negatively geotropic.

Responses are Brought About by Growth Factors

1) Plants **don't** have a **nervous system** so they can't respond using neurones, and they **don't** have a **circulatory system** so they can't respond using hormones either.
2) Plants **respond** to stimuli using **growth factors** — these are chemicals that **speed up** or **slow down** plant **growth**.
3) Growth factors are **produced** in the **growing regions** of the plant (e.g. shoot tips, leaves) and they **move** to where they're needed in the **other parts** of the plant.
4) Growth factors called **auxins** stimulate the **growth** of shoots by **cell elongation** — this is where **cell walls** become **loose** and **stretchy**, so the cells get **longer**.
5) **High** concentrations of auxins **inhibit growth** in **roots** though.
6) There are many **other** plant growth factors such as:
   - **Gibberellins** — stimulate **flowering** and **seed germination**.
   - **Cytokinins** — stimulate **cell division** and **cell differentiation**.
   - **Ethene** — stimulates **fruit ripening** and **flowering**.
   - **Abscisic acid (ABA)** — involved in **leaf fall**.

Responses in Plants

Indoleacetic Acid (IAA) is an Important Auxin

1) **Indoleacetic acid (IAA)** is an important **auxin** that's produced in the **tips** of **shoots** in flowering plants. When it **enters** the **nucleus** of a cell, it's able to **regulate** the **transcription** of genes related to **cell elongation** and **growth**.

2) IAA is **moved** around the plant to **control tropisms** — it moves by **diffusion** and **active transport** over short distances, and via the **phloem** over longer distances.

3) This results in **different parts** of the plants having **different amounts** of IAA. The **uneven distribution** of IAA means there's **uneven growth** of the plant, e.g.

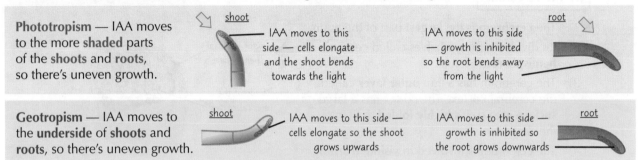

Phototropism — IAA moves to the more **shaded** parts of the **shoots** and **roots**, so there's uneven growth.

shoot
IAA moves to this side — cells elongate and the shoot bends towards the light

IAA moves to this side — growth is inhibited so the root bends away from the light
root

Geotropism — IAA moves to the **underside** of **shoots** and **roots**, so there's uneven growth.

shoot
IAA moves to this side — cells elongate so the shoot grows upwards

IAA moves to this side — growth is inhibited so the root grows downwards
root

Plants Detect Light Using Photoreceptors

1) Plants **detect light** using **photoreceptors** called **phytochromes**.

2) They're **found** in **many parts** of a plant including the **leaves**, **seeds**, **roots** and **stem**.

3) Phytochromes **control** a range of **responses**. For example, plants **flower** in **different seasons** depending on how much **daylight** there is at that time of year, e.g. some plants flower during **summer** when there are **long days**.

4) Phytochromes are **molecules** that **absorb light**. They exist in **two states** — the P_R state absorbs **red light** at a wavelength of **660 nm**, and the P_{FR} state absorbs **far-red light** at a wavelength of **730 nm**.

5) Phytochromes are **converted** from **one state** to **another** when **exposed** to **light**:

   - P_R is **quickly converted** into P_{FR} when it's exposed to **red light**.
   - P_{FR} is **quickly converted** into P_R when it's exposed to **far-red light**.
   - P_{FR} is **slowly converted** into P_R when it's in **darkness**.

   $$P_R \underset{\text{far-red light (fast)}}{\overset{\text{red light (fast)}}{\rightleftharpoons}} P_{FR}$$
   darkness (slow)

6) **Daylight** contains **more red light** than far-red light, so **more** P_R is converted into P_{FR} than P_{FR} is converted to P_R.

7) So the **amount** of P_R and P_{FR} **changes** depending on the **amount of light**, e.g. whether it's **day or night**, or **summer or winter**.

8) The **differing amounts** of P_R and P_{FR} **control** the **responses** to **light** by **regulating** the **transcription** of **genes** involved in these responses. E.g. flowering — in some plants, **high levels** of P_{FR} **stimulates flowering**. When **nights** are **short** in the summer, there's not much time for P_{FR} to be converted back into P_R, so P_{FR} **builds up** and genes involved in flowering are **transcribed**. This means the plants **flower** in **summer**.

Practice Questions

Q1 Why do plants need to respond to stimuli?

Q2 What is a tropism?

Exam Questions

Q1 Explain how the movement of IAA in a growing shoot enables the plant to grow towards the light. [4 marks]

Q2 Iris plants are stimulated to flower by high levels of P_{FR}.
   a) What is P_{FR}? [1 mark]
   b) What time of year would an iris would flower? Explain your answer. [4 marks]

Auxin Productions — do you have the growth factor — with Simon Trowel...

I never knew plants were so complicated — you'd never guess just by looking at one. I thought they just sort of sat there. Make sure you learn these pages and get your head around how plants detect and respond to light.

Brain Structure and Function

So... the brain... a big old squelchy mass that controls all the goings on in your body, from a sniffle to your heart rate. Without your brain you wouldn't be able to see, hear, think or learn — in fact, you wouldn't be much use at all...

Different Areas of the Brain control Different Functions

Your brain **controls** the rest of your body, but **different parts** control **different functions**.
You need to know the **location** and **function** of these **four** brain structures:

1. The cerebrum

1) The **cerebrum** is the **largest** part of the brain.
2) It's divided into **two halves** called **cerebral hemispheres**.
3) The cerebrum has a thin **outer layer** called the **cerebral cortex**. The cortex has a **large surface area** so it's **highly folded** to fit into the skull.
4) The cerebrum is involved in **vision, learning, thinking, emotions** and **movement**.
5) **Different parts** of the **cerebrum** are involved in **different functions**, e.g. the **back** of the cortex is involved in **vision** and the **front** is involved in **thinking**.

right cerebral hemisphere

left cerebral hemisphere

folds of the cerebral cortex

The diagram below shows the brain cut in half from front to back — you might get a diagram of the brain from a different angle in your exam.

2. The hypothalamus

1) The hypothalamus is found just **beneath** the **middle part** of the brain.
2) The hypothalamus automatically **maintains body temperature** at the normal level (**thermoregulation**) — see page 168.
3) The hypothalamus produces **hormones** that **control** the **pituitary gland** — a gland just below the hypothalamus.

FRONT

BACK

pituitary gland

3. The medulla oblongata

1) The **medulla oblongata** is at the **base** of the **brain**, at the top of the spinal cord.
2) It automatically controls **breathing rate** and **heart rate**.

4. The cerebellum

1) The **cerebellum** is **underneath** the **cerebrum** and it also has a **folded cortex**.
2) It's important for **coordinating movement** and **balance**.

Come on cerebellum, don't fail me now, it's going to really hurt.

Brain Structure and Function

Scanners are used to Visualise the Brain

1) To investigate the **structure** and **function** of the brain, and to **diagnose medical conditions**, you need to **look inside** the brain.

2) This can be done with **surgery**, but it's **pretty risky**.

3) The brain can be visualised without surgery using **scanners**.

4) You need to **know** about **four** different types of scanner:

Betty was none the wiser as Jane continued to look inside her brain...

1. Computed Tomography (CT) Scanners use Lots of X-rays

CT scanners use **radiation** (**X-rays**) to produce **cross-section images** of the brain. **Dense structures** in the brain **absorb more radiation** than less dense structures so show up as a **lighter colour** on the scan.

Computers can build up many 2D images to produce a 3D image of the brain.

Investigating brain structure and function

A CT scan shows the **major structures** in the brain — but it doesn't show the **functions** of these structures. However, if a CT scan shows a **diseased** or **damaged brain structure** and the patient has **lost some function**, the **function** of that part of the brain can be **worked out**. E.g. if an area of the brain is damaged and the patient can't see, then that area is involved in vision.

Medical diagnosis

CT scans can be used to **diagnose medical problems** because they show **damaged** or **diseased** areas of the brain, e.g. **bleeding** in the brain after a **stroke**:

* **Blood** has a **different density** from brain tissue so it shows up as a **lighter colour** on a CT scan.

* A scan will show the **extent** of the bleeding and its **location** in the brain.

* You can then work out **which blood vessels** have been damaged and what **brain functions** are likely to be **affected** by the bleeding.

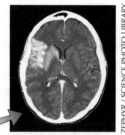

ZEPHYR / SCIENCE PHOTO LIBRARY

This CT scan looks up at the brain from below. The white area is heavy bleeding due to a blood vessel ruptured after a stroke.

CT scans are potentially dangerous because they use **X-rays** — X-rays can cause **mutations** in **DNA**, which may lead to **cancer**. The **risk** of developing cancer as a result of having a CT scan is **very low**.

2. Magnetic Resonance Imaging (MRI) Scanners use Magnetic Fields

MRI scanners use a **really strong magnetic field** and **radio waves** to produce **cross-section images** of the brain.

An MRI scanner costs a lot more than a CT scanner.

Investigating brain structure and function

Compared to CT scans, MRI gives **higher quality images** for soft tissue types (such as the brain), and better resolution between **tissue types** for an overall **better resolution** final picture. MRIs allow you to **clearly see** the **difference** between **normal** and **abnormal** (diseased or damaged) brain tissue. For example, a scan can show diseased tissue caused by multiple sclerosis (a disease of the central nervous system). However, as with CT scanning, brain **function** can only be worked out by looking at **damaged areas**.

Medical diagnosis

MRI scans can also be used to **diagnose medical problems** because they show **damaged** or **diseased** areas of the brain, e.g. a **brain tumour** (an abnormal mass of cells in the brain):

* **Tumour cells respond differently** to a **magnetic field** than healthy cells, so they show up as a **lighter colour** on an MRI scan.

* A scan will show the **exact size** of a tumour and its **location** in the brain. Doctors can then use this information to decide the most effective treatment.

* You can also work out what **brain functions** may be **affected** by the tumour.

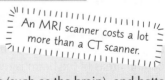

SIMON FRASER / SCIENCE PHOTO LIBRARY

This MRI scan looks down on the brain from above. The white area is a tumour.

Brain Structure and Function

3. *Functional Magnetic Resonance Imaging (fMRI) Scanners show Brain Activity*

fMRI scanners are **like MRI** scanners (see previous page), but they show **changes** in **brain activity** as they happen:

1) **More oxygenated blood** flows to **active areas** of the brain (to supply the neurones with oxygen and glucose).

2) Molecules in **oxygenated blood respond differently** to a **magnetic field** than those in **deoxygenated blood** — the signal returned to the scanner is **stronger** from the oxygenated blood, which allows **more active areas** of the brain to be **identified**.

Investigating brain structure and function

An fMRI scan gives a **detailed, high resolution** picture of the **brain's structure**, similar to an MRI scan — but they can also be used to research the **function** of the brain. If a function is **carried out** whilst **in the scanner**, the **part** of the brain that's involved with that function will be **more active**. E.g. a patient might be asked to **move** their **left hand** when in the fMRI scanner. The areas of the brain involved in moving the hand will **be highlighted** on the fMRI scan.

Medical diagnosis

fMRI scans show **damaged** or **diseased areas** of the brain and allow you to study conditions caused by **abnormal activity** in the brain (some conditions don't have an obvious structural cause). E.g. an fMRI scan can be taken of a patient's brain **before** and **during** a seizure. This can help to pinpoint which part of the brain's **not working properly** and find the **cause** of the seizure. Then the patient can receive the **most effective treatment** for the seizures.

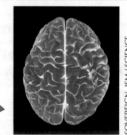

This fMRI scan looks down on the brain from above. The red area is active when the person moves their left hand. The right side's active because it controls the left side of your body.

4. *Positron Emission Tomography (PET) Scanners use Radioactive Material*

PET scanners can show how **active** different areas of the brain are.

1) A **radioactive tracer** is introduced into the body and is **absorbed** into the tissues.

2) The scanner detects the **radioactivity** of the tracer — building up a **map** of radioactivity in the body.

3) **Different tracers** can be used — e.g. radioactively labelled **glucose** can be used to look at **glucose metabolism**.

Investigating brain structure and function

PET scans, like fMRI scans, are **very detailed** and can be used to investigate both the **structure** and the **function** of the brain in **real time**.

This PET scan shows a normal brain (left) and one from a person with Alzheimer's (right) — you can see the reduction in function in the brain with Alzheimer's.

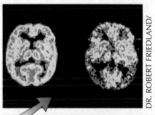

Medical diagnosis

PET scans can show if areas in the brain are **unusually inactive** or **active**, so they are particularly useful for studying disorders that change the brain's **activity**. E.g. in Alzheimer's disease, metabolism in certain areas of the brain is reduced — PET scans show this reduction when compared to a **normal brain**.

Practice Questions

Q1 Which part of the brain is involved in learning?

Q2 What type of scanner produces an image of the brain using X-rays?

Exam Questions

Q1 a) Give two roles of structure B. [2 marks]

b) What effect might damage to structure C have on the body? [1 mark]

Q2 A doctor recommends an MRI scan to investigate suspected bleeding in his patient's brain.

a) Give two pieces of information about the bleeding that the doctor could get from the MRI scan. [2 marks]

b) What kind of scans could be carried out to assess the patient's brain activity? [2 marks]

My PET scan came back — I've got a bad case of 'Whoseagoodboyitis'...

There are quite a few different ways of investigating brain structure and function, and they probably all seem quite similar. Try and write down the main points for each one so that you can easily see the differences between them.

Habituation

Animals need to be able to learn to respond to different stimuli in their environment if they are to survive. Habituation is all about differentiating between important and unimportant stimuli...

Habituation *is a type of* Learned Behaviour

1) Animals (including humans) **increase** their chance of **survival** by **responding** to **stimuli** (see page 174).

2) But if the stimulus is **unimportant** (if it's not threatening or rewarding), there's **no point** in **responding** to it.

3) If an unimportant stimulus is **repeated** over a period of **time**, an animal **learns** to **ignore it**.

4) This **reduced response** to an **unimportant stimulus** after **repeated** exposure **over time** is called **habituation**.

5) Habituation means animals **don't waste energy** responding to unimportant stimuli. It also means that they can spend more time doing other activities for their survival, such as feeding. E.g. **prairie dogs** use **alarm calls** to warn others of a predator but they've **habituated** to **humans** because we're **not** a **threat**. They **no longer** make alarm calls when they see humans, so they **don't waste time** or **energy**.

6) Animals still remain **alert** to **important stimuli** (stimuli which might **threaten** their **survival**). E.g. you can become **habituated** to the sound of traffic at night and get to sleep, but if you hear an **unfamiliar noise**, like a burglar, you'll **wake up**.

To **investigate habituation**, you can **measure** an animal's **response** to an **unimportant stimulus**. Here's an example with **snails**, but the principles are the **same** for any organism:

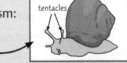

1) **Gently brush** something soft, like a blade of grass, across the **surface** of the snail's skin — close to its **tentacles**. The snail should **withdraw** them back into its head. ⟶

2) Using a stopwatch, **time** how **long** it takes for the snail to fully extend its tentacles again after you touched it.

3) Repeat this process at **regular intervals** and **record** the **time** it takes for the tentacles to fully extend every time you touch the snail.

If **habituation has taken place** the snail should **re-extend** it's tentacles **quicker** the **more** you **repeat** the **stimulus** (or it **might not withdraw** at all eventually). If habituation **hasn't occurred** the snail will take the **same length of time** to **re-extend** its tentacles each time. The snail should still **remain alert** to an **unfamiliar stimulus**, e.g. if you cast a **shadow** over the snail, it should still **withdraw** its tentacles or even its entire head.

Fewer Electrical Impulses *are Sent to* Effectors

Effectors that carry out the responses to different stimuli (e.g. **muscles**) are controlled by **nervous stimulation**. **Habituation** to a stimulus means **fewer electrical impulses** are sent to the effectors. Here's why:

1) **Repeated exposure** to a stimulus **decreases** the amount of **calcium ions** that enter the **presynaptic neurone**.

2) This decrease in the influx of calcium ions means that less **neurotransmitter** is released from **vesicles** into the **synaptic cleft**, so fewer neurotransmitters can bind to receptors in the postsynaptic membrane.

3) **Fewer sodium ion channels** on the **postsynaptic membrane** open — so there is a **reduced chance** of the **threshold** for an **action potential** being reached on the **postsynaptic membrane**.

4) As a result, fewer **signals** are sent to the **effector** to carry out the **response**.

See pages 182-183 for more on how synapses work.

Practice Questions

Q1 What is habituation?

Q2 Describe how you could demonstrate habituation in a snail.

Exam Question

Q1 A birdwatcher sat in his garden quietly for an hour each day. At first this scared the birds away, but over the next few weeks he saw more and more birds. The birdwatcher predicted that this was due to habituation.
a) Explain why the birds' behaviour could be described as habituation. [1 mark]
b) What is the advantage of habituation to birds in the wild? [1 mark]

I don't think I'd habituate to someone rubbing grass between my eyes...

Habituation is a relatively simple behaviour — it's basically just getting used to unimportant stimuli. Once you've got that, just make sure you know what's happening at the synapses and why it's a useful response for an animal to have.

Development of the Visual Cortex

Your brain continues to develop even after you're born — good job too, or you'd have trouble learning this stuff.

The **Visual Cortex** is Made Up of **Ocular Dominance Columns**

1) The **visual cortex** is an area of the **cerebral cortex** (see p. 186) at the **back** of your brain.

2) The role of the visual cortex is to **receive** and **process visual information**.

3) **Neurones** in the visual cortex **receive information** from **either** your **left** or **right eye**.

4) Neurones are **grouped together** in columns called **ocular dominance columns**. If they receive information from the **right eye** they're called **right** ocular dominance columns, and if they receive information from the **left eye** they're called **left** ocular dominance columns.

5) The columns are the **same size** and they're arranged in an **alternating pattern** (left, right, left, right) across the visual cortex.

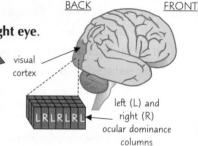

BACK   FRONT

visual
cortex

left (L) and
right (R)
ocular dominance
columns

Hubel and **Wiesel** Used **Animal Models** to Study the **Visual Cortex**

1) **Some animals** have fairly **similar brains** to **humans**. This means scientists can do **experiments** on these animals (that would be **unethical** to do **in humans**) to **investigate brain development**.

2) The **structure** of the **visual cortex** was **discovered** by two scientists called **Hubel** and **Wiesel**.

3) They used **animal models** to study the **electrical activity** of **neurones** in the visual cortex.

4) They found that the **left ocular dominance columns** were **stimulated** when an animal used its **left eye**, and the **right ocular dominance columns** were **stimulated** when it used its **right eye**.

5) Hubel and Wiesel (1963) investigated **how** the **visual cortex develops** by experimenting on very **young kittens**:

   • They **stitched shut one eye** of each kitten so they could only see out of their other eye.
   • The kittens were kept like this for **several months** before their eyes were **unstitched**.
   • Hubel and Wiesel found that the kitten's **eye** that had been **stitched up** was **blind**.
   • They also found that **ocular dominance columns** for the **stitched up eye** were a **lot smaller** than normal, and the ocular dominance columns for the **open eye** were a **lot bigger** than normal.
   • The ocular dominance columns for the **open eye** had **expanded** to **take over** the other columns that **weren't** being stimulated — when this happens, the **neurones** in the visual cortex are said to have **switched dominance**.

6) They then investigated if the **same thing** happened in an **adult cat's brain**.

   • They **stitched shut one eye** of each cat, who were kept like this for **several months**.
   • When their eyes were **unstitched**, Hubel and Wiesel found that these eyes **hadn't gone blind**.
   • The cats **fully recovered** their **vision** and their **ocular dominance columns** remained the **same**.

7) They **repeated** the experiments on **young** and **adult monkeys** and saw the **same results**.

8) Hubel and Wiesel's experiments showed that the **visual cortex only develops** into normal **left** and **right** ocular dominance columns if **both eyes** are **visually stimulated** in the **very early stages** of **life**.

Their Experiments Provide **Evidence** for a **Critical Period** in **Humans**

1) Hubel and Wiesel's experiments on cats show there's a **period** in **early life** when it's **critical** that a kitten is **exposed** to **visual stimuli** for its visual cortex to **develop properly**. This is called the **critical period**.

2) The **human visual cortex** is **similar** to a **cat's visual cortex** (the human visual cortex has **ocular dominance columns** too) so Hubel and Wiesel's experiments provide **evidence** for a **critical period** in **humans**.

3) Scientists have also **investigated visual development** in **humans**, e.g. by looking at **cataracts** in the **eye**:

   • A **cataract** makes the **lens** in the eye go **cloudy**, causing **blurry vision**.
   • If a **baby** has a **cataract**, it's **important** to **remove** the cataract within the **first few months** of the baby's life — otherwise their visual system **won't develop properly** and their vision will be **damaged for life**.
   • If an **adult** has a **cataract** then it's not so serious — when the cataract is **removed**, **normal vision** comes back **straight away**. This is because the visual system is **already developed** in an adult.

Development of the Visual Cortex

Visual Stimulation Organises the Neurones During the Critical Period

1) **Baby mammals** (including humans) are born with **lots** of neurones in their **visual cortex**.
These neurones need **visual stimulation** to become **properly organised**.

2) Proper organisation of the visual cortex involves the **elimination** of **unnecessary synapses**
to leave behind those that are needed in processing visual information.

> 1) During the critical period of development, synapses that **receive visual stimulation** and **pass nerve impulses** into the **visual cortex** are **retained**.
>
> 2) Synapses that **don't receive** any visual stimulation and **don't pass on** any nerve impulses to the visual cortex are **removed**.
>
> 3) This means that if the eyes are **not stimulated** with **visual information** during this **critical period** of development, the visual cortex will not **develop properly** as many of the synapses will be **destroyed**.

Using Animals in Medical Research Raises Ethical Issues

Hubel and Wiesel used **animals** in their experiments, which is **common** in **medical research**.
This raises some **ethical issues** — you need to **know** a range of **arguments** from **both sides**:

Arguments AGAINST using animals in medical research	Arguments FOR using animals in medical research
Animals are different from humans, so drugs tested on animals may have different effects in humans.	Animals are similar to humans, so research has led to loads of medical breakthroughs, e.g. antibiotics, insulin for diabetics and organ transplants.
Experiments can cause pain and distress to animals.	Animal experiments are only done when it's absolutely necessary and scientists follow strict rules, e.g. animals must be properly looked after, painkillers and anaesthetics must be used to minimise pain.
There are alternatives to using animals in research, e.g. using cultures of human cells or using computer models to predict the effects of experiments.	Using animals is currently the only way to study how a drug affects the whole body — cell cultures and computers aren't a true representation of how cells may react when surrounded by other body tissues. It's also the only way to study behaviour.
Some people think that animals have the right to not be experimented on, e.g. animal rights activists.	Other people think that humans have a greater right to life than animals because we have more complex brains, e.g. compared to rats, fish, fruit flies (which are commonly used in experiments).

Practice Questions

Q1 Where in the brain are ocular dominance columns found?
Q2 What kind of pattern are ocular dominance columns arranged in?
Q3 Describe one piece of evidence that suggests a critical 'window' exists for human visual system development.
Q4 Give two arguments against the use of animals in medical research.

Exam Question

Q1 Hubel and Wiesel conducted experiments on animals to investigate the structure and development of the visual cortex.
  a) i) Describe Hubel and Wiesel's experiment on kittens. [3 marks]
    ii) Explain what their experiment showed about how the visual cortex develops. [1 mark]
  b) Do their experiments give evidence for a critical period in the development of the human visual system? Explain your answer, with reference to what is meant by a critical period. [2 marks]
  c) Describe what happens during this critical period in the development of the visual system in cats and other mammals. [2 marks]
  d) Give two arguments for using animals in medical research. [2 marks]

Hubel and Wiesel — weren't they a '60s pop duo...

The experiments that Hubel and Wiesel did on cats and monkeys may have been a bit gross, but they did provide us with good knowledge of how the visual cortex develops. There's evidence to suggest a critical 'window' for other things too, like language development. Interesting stuff, so make sure you learn it and then you can impress everyone.

Studying Brain Development

Revising for your exams — one way to really nurture your brain. Go on, treat yourself...

You can Investigate the Role of **Nature and Nurture** in **Brain Development**

1) **Brain development** is how the brain **grows** and how **neurones connect together**.

2) Measures of brain development include the **size** of the brain, the **number of neurones** it has and the **level of brain function** (e.g. speech, intelligence) a person has.

3) Your brain develops the way it does because of both your **genes** (**nature**) and your **environment** (**nurture**) — your brain would **develop differently** if you had **different genes** or were brought up in a **different environment**.

4) **Scientists disagree** about whether nature or nurture **influences** brain development the **most** — this **argument** is called the **nature-nurture debate**.

> It's really hard to investigate the effects of nature and nurture because:
> • Genetic and environmental factors interact, so it's difficult to know which one is the main influence.
> • There are lots of different genes and lots of different environmental factors to investigate.
> • To do an accurate experiment, you need to cancel out one factor to be able to investigate the other. This is really difficult to do — you'd need to cut out all environmental influences to investigate the role of a genetics, and vice versa.

5) You need to know these **five methods** for **investigating** the effects of **nature** and **nurture** on **brain development**:

1. Animal Experiments

1) Scientists study the effects of **different environments** on the **brain development** of animals of the **same species**. Individuals of the same species will be genetically similar, so any differences in their brain development are **more likely** to be due to **nurture** than nature.

2) To study the effects of **different genes**, scientists can **genetically engineer** mice to **lack a particular gene** and then raise mice with and without the gene in **similar environments**.

3) Differences between the brain development of the genetically engineered mice and **normal mice** are **more likely** to be due to **nature** than nurture. For example, animal experiments have shown that:

> For example, animal experiments have shown that:
> • Rats raised in a stimulating environment have larger brains and get better scores on problem-solving tasks than rats raised in boring environments (e.g. in a bare, dark cage). This suggests nurture plays a big role in brain size and the development of problem-solving skills.
> • Rats reared in isolation have similar brain abnormalities to those found in schizophrenic patients, suggesting nurture plays a big role in brain development.

> Mice engineered to lack the Lgl1 gene develop enlarged brain regions and fluid builds up in their brains. This suggests that nature plays a big role in brain development.

2. Twin Studies

> Identical twins are genetically identical.

1) If **identical** twins are **raised separately** then they'll have **identical genes** but **different environments**.

2) Scientists can compare the brain development of **separated identical twins** — any **differences** between them **are due to nurture** not nature, and any **similarities** between them are due to **nature**.

3) For example:

> Identical twins have very similar IQ scores — suggesting nature plays a big role in intelligence.

4) Scientists can use this comparison to show the **relative contribution** of environmental and genetic factors to **brain development**.

5) However, even if they've been raised separately, twins will still have shared the **same environment** in the **womb** — so **environmental** and **genetic factors** are not **completely separated**.

6) Identical twins **raised together** are genetically identical and have **similar environments** — this means it's hard to tell if any **differences between them** are due to nature or nurture. So scientists compare them to **non-identical twins** (who are **genetically different** but have **similar environments**) — they act like a control to **cancel out** the **influence** of the **environment**. Any difference in brain development between identical and non-identical twins is **more likely** to be due to **nature** than nurture.

7) For example:

> • Stuttering of both twins is more common in identical twins than in non-identical twins. This suggests nature plays a big role in developing the speech area of the brain.
> • There's no difference in reading ability between pairs of identical and non-identical twins. This suggests nurture plays a big role in reading ability.

Studying Brain Development

3. Cross-Cultural Studies

1) Children brought up in **different cultures** have **different environmental influences**, e.g. beliefs and education.

2) Scientists can study the **effects** of a different upbringing on **brain development** by comparing **large groups** of children who are the **same age** but from **different cultures**.

3) Scientists look for **major differences** in **characteristics**. Any **differences** in brain development between different cultures are **more likely** to be due to **nurture** than nature. Any **similarities** in brain development between different cultures are **more likely** to be due to **nature** than nurture. For example:

> The **mapping abilities** (e.g. perspective drawing) of young children are **well-developed across cultures**.
> This suggests that **nature** plays a big role in **mapping abilities**.

4. Newborn Studies

> The brain of a newborn baby has been affected a bit by the environment in the womb.

1) The brain of a newborn baby **hasn't** really been **affected** by the **environment**.

2) Scientists study the brains of newborn babies to see what **functions** they're **born with** and **how developed different parts** of the brain are — what they're born with is **more likely** to be due to **nature** than nurture. For example, newborn studies have shown that:

- Babies are **born** with a number of **abilities**, e.g. they can **cry**, **feed** and **recognise** a **human face**. This suggests that **nature** plays a big role in controlling these abilities.
- Newborn babies **don't** have the ability to **speak**, suggesting that **nurture** plays a big role in the ability to **speak**.

5. Brain Damage Studies

1) **Damage** to an adult's brain can lead to the **loss** of **brain function**, e.g. a stroke may cause loss of vision.

2) If an **adult's brain** is damaged, it can't repair itself so well because it's **already fully developed**. But a **child's brain** is **still developing** — so scientists can **study** the effects of **brain damage** on their development.

3) Scientists **compare** the development of a chosen **function** in children **with** and **without** brain damage.

4) If the **characteristic still develops** in children who have brain damage, then brain development is **more likely** to be due to **nurture** than nature for that characteristic.

5) If it **doesn't develop** in children who have brain damage, then brain development is **more likely** to be due to **nature** than nurture for that characteristic (because nurture isn't having an effect). For example:

- Children aged 1-3 who were **born** with **damage** to the area of the brain associated with **language**, show a **delay** in the major language milestones (e.g. understanding words, producing sentences) when compared to children born without brain damage.
- But by **age 5**, their **language skills** are the **same** as children with no brain damage. If a young child's brain is damaged, they can **still develop language** — this suggests that **nurture** plays a big role in **language development**.

Practice Questions

Q1 Explain why it is difficult to determine whether a characteristic is influenced more by nature or nurture.

Q2 Describe how genetic engineering can be used to study the nature vs. nurture debate.

Exam Question

Q1 A scientist carries out a series of studies on newborn babies to find out how brain development is affected by nature.
   a) Explain what is meant by 'nature'.   [1 mark]
   b) What is the advantage of using newborn babies to study the effects of nature on brain development?   [2 marks]
   c) Give two other types of study that a scientist could carry out to directly research the effect of
      nature and nurture on brain development in humans.   [2 marks]

You say nature and I say nurture — let's call the whole thing off...

Whether a brain function is influenced by nature or nurture is pretty important — if it's heavily influenced by nurture then you can figure out how to improve that brain function by changing an organism's environment. Clever stuff.

Drugs and Disease

Before you get stuck into these pages, have another read over the stuff about synaptic transmission on pages 182-18.
— it'll really help you to understand what's coming up next...

Imbalances in Some Neurotransmitters can Contribute to Disorders

Neurotransmitters are **chemicals** that **transmit** nerve impulses across **synapses** (see page 182).
Some **disorders** are **linked** to an **imbalance** of specific, **naturally occurring** neurotransmitters in the brain.
Here are two examples you need to know:

Parkinson's Disease

1) Parkinson's disease is a **brain disorder** that affects the **motor skills** (the movement) of people.

2) In Parkinson's disease the **neurones** in the **parts** of the **brain** that **control movement** are **destroyed**.

3) These **normally produce** the neurotransmitter **dopamine**, so **losing them** causes a **lack of dopamine**.

4) This means that **less** dopamine is released into the **synaptic clefts**, so less dopamine is available to bind to the **receptors** on the **postsynaptic membranes**.

5) Fewer **sodium ion channels** on the postsynaptic membrane **open**, so the postsynaptic cell is less likely to **depolarise**.

6) This means **fewer action potentials** are produced, leading to **symptoms** like **tremors** (shaking) and **slow movement**.

7) Scientists know that the **symptoms** are **caused by** a **lack of dopamine** so they've **developed drugs** (e.g. **L-dopa**, see below) to **increase** the level of **dopamine** in the brain.

Depression

1) Scientists think there's a **link** between a **low level** of the neurotransmitter **serotonin** and **depression**.

2) Serotonin transmits **nerve impulses** across synapses in the **parts** of the **brain** that **control mood**.

3) Scientists know that **depression** is **linked** to a **low level** of **serotonin** so they've **developed drugs** (antidepressants) to **increase** the level of **serotonin** in the brain.

4) Some drugs that are used to **treat** depression (called selective serotonin reuptake inhibitors — SSRIs) increase serotonin levels by **preventing** **its reuptake** at synapses.

Some Drugs Work by Affecting Synaptic Transmission

L-dopa

1) L-dopa is a drug that's used to **treat** the **symptoms** of **Parkinson's disease**.

2) Its **structure** is very **similar** to **dopamine**.

3) When L-dopa is given, it's **absorbed** into the **brain** and **converted** into **dopamine** by the enzyme **dopa-decarboxylase** (**dopamine can't be given** to treat Parkinson's disease because it **can't enter** the **brain**). This **increases** the level of **dopamine** in the brain.

4) A higher level of dopamine means that **more nerve impulses** are **transmitted** across synapses in the **parts** of the **brain** that **control movement**.

5) This gives sufferers of Parkinson's disease **more control** over their **movement**.

MDMA (Ecstasy)

1) MDMA **increases** the level of **serotonin** in the brain.

2) Usually, serotonin is **taken back** into a **presynaptic neurone** after triggering an action potential, to be **used again**.

3) MDMA **increases** the level of **serotonin** by **inhibiting** the **reuptake** of serotonin into **presynaptic neurones** — it binds to and **blocks** the **reuptake proteins** on the presynaptic membrane.

4) MDMA also **triggers** the **release** of serotonin **from presynaptic neurones**.

5) This means that serotonin levels **stay high** in the synapse and cause **depolarisation** of the **postsynaptic** neurones in **parts** of the **brain** that **control mood**.

6) So the **effect** of MDMA is **mood elevation**.

All Eric needed was
a hat and a mobile
phone to increase his
serotonin level.

Drugs and Disease

Info *from* **Genome Sequencing Projects** *is Being Used to Create* **New Drugs**...

1) The **H**uman **G**enome **P**roject (**HGP**) was a 13 year long project that **identified** all of the **genes** found in **human DNA** (the human genome).

2) The **information obtained** from the HGP is **stored** in **databases**.

3) Scientists use the databases to **identify genes**, and so **proteins**, that are **involved** in **disease**.

4) Scientists are using this information to create **new drugs** that **target** the **identified proteins**, e.g. scientists have identified an **enzyme** that **helps cancer cells** to **spread** around the body — a **drug** that **inhibits** this **enzyme** is being developed.

5) The HGP has also highlighted **common genetic variations** between people.

6) It's known that **some** of these **variations** make **some drugs less effective**, e.g. some asthma drugs are less effective for people with a particular mutation.

7) Drug companies can use this knowledge to design **new drugs** that **are tailored** to people with these **variations** — these are called **personalised medicines**.

8) Doctors can also **personalise** a patient's **treatment** by using their **genetic information** to predict how well they will **respond** to different drugs and only prescribe the ones that will be **most effective**.

...*but this Raises* **Social**, **Moral** *and* **Ethical Issues**

1) Creating drugs for specific genetic variations will **increase research costs** for drugs companies. These new drugs will be **more expensive**, which could lead to a **two-tier health service** — only **wealthier** people could **afford** these new drugs.

2) Some people might be **refused** an **expensive drug** because their genetic make-up indicates that it **won't be that effective** for them — it may be the **only drug available** though.

3) The **information** held within a person's genome could be **used by others**, e.g. employers or insurance companies, to **unfairly discriminate** against them. For example, if a person is **unlikely** to respond to any **drug treatments** for a certain disease an **insurance company** might **increase** their **life insurance premium**.

4) Revealing that a drug might not work for a person could be **psychologically damaging** to them, e.g. it could be their **only hope** to treat a disease.

Practice Questions

Q1 Name a disorder that's linked to a low level of serotonin.

Q2 Describe one way that MDMA increases the level of serotonin in the brain.

Q3 What is the Human Genome Project?

Exam Questions

Q1 Parkinson's disease affects around 127 000 people in the UK.
a) Explain the role of dopamine in controlling movement. [1 mark]
b)* Describe and explain the effects that Parkinson's disease has on the brain. [6 marks]
c) Name a drug that is used to treat Parkinson's disease and explain how it works. [4 marks]

Q2 Describe how the results from the Human Genome Project are being used to create new drugs. [5 marks]

Q3 Give three ethical issues surrounding the development of personalised medicines. [3 marks]

* You will be assessed on the quality of your written response in this question.

The Minnesota Donkey and Mule Association — a different kind of MDMA...

It's not just drugs that increase your serotonin level — chocolate does too, which is a great excuse to gobble some down... More to the point though, make sure you learn the specific drugs and diseases mentioned here. You also need to know how information from the Human Genome Project can be used, and the issues that this project raises.

Producing Drugs Using GMOs

Unsavoury characters in dark alleyways aren't the only things that produce drugs on demand...

Drugs can be Produced Using Genetically Modified Organisms

Genetically modified organisms (GMOs) are organisms that have had their **DNA altered**.
Microorganisms, **plants** and **animals** can all be **genetically modified** to **produce proteins** which are **used as drugs**:

1. Genetically Modified Microorganisms

Here's how microorganisms are genetically engineered to produce drugs:

Only drugs that are proteins can be produced by genetically modified organisms.

1) The **gene** for the protein (drug) is **isolated** using enzymes called **restriction enzymes**.
2) The **gene** is **copied** using **PCR** (see page 132).
3) **Copies** are **inserted** into **plasmids** (small circular molecules of DNA).
4) The **plasmids** are **transferred** into **microorganisms**.
5) The **modified microorganisms** are **grown** in large containers so that they **divide** and produce **lots** of the **useful protein**, from the inserted gene.
6) The **protein** can then be **purified** and **used** as a drug.

Plasmids are a type of vector — vectors carry genes into an organism.

Lots of drugs are produced from **genetically modified bacteria**, for example **human insulin** (used to treat **Type 1 diabetes**) and **human blood clotting factors** (used to treat **haemophilia**).

2. Genetically Modified Plants

Here's how plants are genetically engineered to produce drugs:

1) The **gene** for the protein (drug) is **inserted** into a **bacterium** (see above).
2) The **bacterium infects** a **plant cell**.
3) The **bacterium inserts** the **gene** into the **plant cell DNA** — the **plant cell** is now **genetically modified**.
4) The **plant cell** is **grown** into an **adult plant** — the **whole plant** contains a **copy** of the **gene** in **every cell**.
5) The **protein** produced from the gene can be **purified** from the **plant tissues**, or the **protein** (drug) could be **delivered** by **eating** the **plant**.

The bacterium is used as a vector to carry the gene into the plant.

Malcolm had unwittingly eaten the VIAGRA® plant.

Some drugs have been produced from genetically **modified** plants, for example **human insulin** and a **cholera vaccine**.

3. Genetically Modified Animals

Here's how animals are genetically engineered to produce drugs:

1) The **gene** for the protein (drug) is **injected** into the **nucleus** of a **fertilised animal egg cell**.
2) The **egg cell** is then **implanted** into an **adult animal** — it grows into a **whole animal** that contains a **copy** of the **gene** in **every cell**.
3) The **protein** produced from the gene is normally **purified** from the **milk** of the animal.

Various animals have been **modified** with **human genes** to produce drugs, for example **human antithrombin** (used to treat people with a **blood clotting disorder**) has been produced from **genetically modified goats**.

Producing Drugs Using GMOs

197

There are **Benefits** and **Risks** Associated with Using **GMOs**

1) As well as producing drugs, GMOs are used in **agriculture** and the **food industry**. For example, genes for **herbicide resistance** can be inserted into **agricultural crops**. Herbicides can then be applied which will **kill weeds** but **not** the **herbicide-resistant crops** — the **genetically modified crop** will **thrive** without the weeds and this results in a **high yield**.

2) You need to know the **benefits** and **risks** associated with the **use** of GMOs:

Benefits

1) Agricultural **crops** can be modified so that they give **higher yields** or are **more nutritious**. This means these plants can be used to **reduce** the risk of **famine** and **malnutrition**.

2) Crops can also be modified to have **pest resistance**, so that **fewer pesticides** are **needed**. This **reduces costs** (making **food cheaper**) and **reduces** any **environmental problems** associated with using pesticides.

3) Industrial processes often use **enzymes**. These enzymes can be produced from genetically modified organisms in **large quantities** for less money, which **reduces costs**.

4) Some **disorders** can now be **treated** with **human proteins** from genetically engineered organisms instead of with **animal proteins**. Human proteins are **safer** and **more effective**. For example, **Type 1 diabetes** used to be treated with **cow insulin** but some people had an **allergic reaction** to it. **Human insulin**, produced from genetically modified **bacteria**, is more effective and **doesn't cause** an **allergic reaction** in humans.

5) **Vaccines** produced in plant tissues **don't need** to be **refrigerated**. This could make vaccines **available** to **more people**, e.g. in areas where **refrigeration** (usually needed for storing vaccines) **isn't available**.

6) **Producing drugs** using **plants** and **animals** would be **very cheap** because once the plants or animals are genetically modified they can be reproduced using **conventional farming methods**. This could make some drugs **affordable** for **more people**, especially those in poor countries.

Risks

1) Some people are **concerned** about the **transmission** of genetic material. For example, if **herbicide-resistant** crops **interbreed** with **wild plants** it could create '**superweeds**' — weeds that are **resistant** to **herbicides**, and if **drug crops** interbreed with other crops people might end up **eating drugs they don't need** (which could be harmful).

2) Some people are worried about the **long-term impacts** of using GMOs. There may be **unforeseen consequences**.

3) Some people think it's **wrong** to **genetically modify animals** purely for **human benefit**.

Practice Questions

Q1 What is a genetically modified organism?
Q2 Describe how a genetically modified plant is created.
Q3 Describe how a genetically modified animal is created.

Exam Questions

Q1 Describe how the bacterium *E. coli* is genetically modified to produce human insulin. [4 marks]

Q2 Discuss the benefits and risks associated with growing a plant that has been genetically modified to produce a hepatitis B vaccine and to be resistant to herbicides. [4 marks]

Milking a goat to get drugs — who'd have thought that was possible...

We use organisms for lots of things, including food and drugs, but some people think that genetically modifying them is going a bit too far. Whatever you think about GMOs, remember to learn the arguments both for and against them — that way you can scoop up loads of marks if this sort of question comes up in your exams...

TOPIC 8B — THE BRAIN, BEHAVIOUR AND DISEASE

Planning an Experiment

As well as doing practical work in class, you can get asked about it in your exams too. Harsh I know.
You need to be able to plan the perfect experiment and suggest improvements to ones other people have planned.

Before You Start *Planning,* Be Clear *on What You're Trying to* Find Out

Like all scientists, you should start off by making a **prediction** or **hypothesis** — a **specific testable statement**, based on theory, about what will happen in the experiment. You then need to **plan** a good experiment that will provide **evidence to support the prediction** — or help **disprove it**.

A *Good Experiment* Gives *Results* that are:

1) **Precise** — precise results **don't vary** much **from the mean**. Precision is **reduced** by **random error**.

2) **Repeatable and reproducible** — repeatable means if the **same person** repeats the experiment using the same methods and equipment, they will get the same results. Reproducible means if **someone different** does the experiment, using a slightly different method or piece of equipment, the results will be the same. Repeatable and reproducible results give **reliable** data.

3) **Valid** — valid results **answer the original question**. To get valid results you need to **control all the variables** to make sure you're only testing the thing you want to.

4) **Accurate** — accurate results are **really close** to the **true answer**.

You need to be able to **design** a good experiment. Here are some things you'll need to consider:

1) **Only one variable should be changed** — Variables are **quantities** that have the **potential to change**, e.g. pH. In an experiment you usually **change one variable** and **measure its effect** on another variable.
   - The variable that you **change** is called the **independent variable**.
   - The variable that you **measure** is called the **dependent variable**.

2) **All the other variables should be controlled** — When you're investigating a variable you need to keep everything else that could affect it **constant**. This means you can be sure that **only** your **independent** variable is **affecting** the thing you're measuring (the dependent variable).

3) **Negative controls should be used** — Negative controls are used to **check** that only the independent variable is affecting the dependent variable. Negative controls **aren't expected** to have **any effect** on the experiment.

4) **The experiment should be repeated at least three times and a mean should be calculated** — This reduces the effect of **random error** on your experiment, which makes your results **more precise**. Doing repeats and getting similar results each time also shows that your data is **repeatable** and makes it more likely to be **reproducible**.

> **EXAMPLE:** Investigating the effect of **antibiotic concentration** on **bacterial growth**.
>
> 1) Antibiotic concentration is the **independent** variable.
> 2) The diameter of the clear zone is the **dependent** variable.
> 3) The type of antibiotic, strain of bacteria, growth medium and incubation time and temperature should all **stay the same** (and the details should be recorded to allow someone else to reproduce the experiment).
> 4) The experiment should be **repeated** at least **three times** at each antibiotic concentration used.
> 5) A **negative control**, containing everything used **except the antibiotic**, should be set up for each concentration of antibiotic tested. No inhibition of bacterial growth should be seen with these controls.

Select Appropriate *Apparatus, Equipment and* Techniques

1) When you're **planning** an experiment you need to decide what it is you're going to **measure** and **how often** you're going to take measurements. E.g. if you're investigating the **rate of respiration**, you could either measure the volume of **oxygen used** over time or the volume of **carbon dioxide produced** over time. You could take measurements at, e.g. 30 second intervals or 60 second intervals.

2) Then you need to choose the most **appropriate** apparatus, equipment and techniques for the experiment and explain why you'd use them. E.g.

   - The measuring apparatus you use has to be sensitive enough to measure the changes you're looking for. For example, if you need to measure small changes in pH, a pH meter (which can measure pH to several decimal places) would be more sensitive than indicator paper.

   - The technique you use has to be the most appropriate one for your experiment. E.g. if you're growing a culture of microorganisms, you need to use aseptic techniques to prevent contamination (see page 98).

Planning an Experiment

You Need to Know How to Use Apparatus and Techniques Correctly

Examiners could ask you about a **whole range** of different apparatus and techniques. Make sure you know how to use all the instruments and equipment you've come across in class and can carry out all the techniques too. Here are some **examples** of equipment you should be able to use:

- **Measuring cylinders** and **graduated pipettes** — These have a **scale** so you can measure specific **volumes**. Whichever one you use, make sure you read the volume from the **bottom** of the **meniscus** when it's at **eye level**.

- **Water baths** — Make sure you **allow time** for water baths to **heat up** before starting your experiment. Don't forget that your **solutions** will need **time** to get to the **same temperature** as the water before you start the experiment too. Also, remember to **check** the **temperature** of the water bath with a **thermometer** during the investigation to make sure it **doesn't change**.

- **Data logger** — Decide **what** you are **measuring** and what **type** of **data logger** you will need, e.g. temperature, pH. Connect an **external sensor** to the data logger if you need to. Decide **how often** you want the data logger to take readings depending on the **length** of the **process** that you are measuring.

The meniscus is the curved upper surface of the liquid inside the pipette.

Read volume from here — at the bottom of the meniscus.

For some experiments you need several solutions of **different**, **known concentrations**. These can be prepared using a **serial dilution** technique — this gives solutions that differ in concentration by a chosen **scale factor**. Here's an example:

This is how you'd make **six serial dilutions** of a vitamin C solution (see page 21), starting with an initial vitamin C concentration of **60 mg cm^{-3}** and **diluting** each solution by a **scale factor** of **2**.

1) Line up six **test tubes** in a rack.

2) Add **10 cm^3** of the initial **60 mg cm^{-3} vitamin C solution** to the first test tube and **5 cm^3 of distilled water** to the other five test tubes.

3) Then, using a pipette, draw **5 cm^3** of the solution from the **first** test tube, add it to the distilled water in the **second** test tube and **mix** the solution **thoroughly**. You now have **10 cm^3** of solution that's **half as concentrated** as the solution in the first test tube (it's **30 mg cm^{-3}**).

4) Repeat this process **four more times** to create solutions of **15 mg cm^{-3}**, **7.5 mg cm^{-3}**, **3.75 mg cm^{-3}** and **1.875 mg cm^{-3}**.

transfer 5cm^3, then mix

concentration (mg cm^{-3})
30   15   7.5   3.75   1.875

10 cm^3 of 60 mg cm^{-3} vitamin C solution

5 cm^3 of distilled water

Make sure you know how to do **all** the **practical investigations** described in this book. You should be able to **apply** the techniques described to **different** or **unfamiliar contexts**. For example, **serial dilutions** can be used to make up **vitamin C solutions** of different concentrations (as described above). You could also use serial dilutions when investigating the effect of **substrate concentration** on **enzyme activity**, to prepare solutions of varying substrate concentration.

You don't have to dilute solutions by a scale factor of 2. E.g. to dilute by a factor of 10, take 1 cm^3 from your original sample and add it to 9 cm^3 of water.

Risk Assessments Help You to Work Safely

1) When you're planning an experiment, you need to carry out a **risk assessment**. To do this, you need to identify:
   - All the **dangers** in the experiment, e.g. any hazardous chemicals, microorganisms or naked flames.
   - **Who** is at **risk** from these dangers.
   - What can be done to **reduce** the **risk**, such as wearing goggles or gloves or working in a fume cupboard.

2) You should also make sure you **dispose of waste materials safely**. E.g. **agar plates** that have been used to grow **microbes** should be **sterilised** before disposal to prevent potentially harmful bacteria spreading.

3) You also need to consider any **ethical issues** in your experiment. For example, if you're using **living animals** (e.g. insects) you must treat them with **respect**. This means **handling them carefully** and keeping them away from **harmful chemicals**, **extreme heat sources** and other things that might cause them **physical discomfort**.

Planning an Experiment

Record Your Data in a Table

It's a good idea to draw a table to **record** the **results** of your experiment in.

1) When you draw a table, make sure you **include** enough **rows** and **columns** to **record all of the data** you need to. You might also need to include a column for **processing** your data (e.g. working out an average).

2) Make sure each **column** has a **heading** so you know what's going to be recorded where.

3) The **units** should be in the **column** heading, not the table itself.

Farm	Length of hedgerows (km)	Number of species
1	49	21
2	90	28
3	155	30

data   heading   units   column

row

Watch Out for Anomalous Results

Doing repeats makes it easier to spot anomalous results.

When you look at all the **data** in your **table**, you may notice that you have a result that **doesn't seem to fit in** with the rest at all. These results are called **anomalous results**. You should **investigate** anomalous results — if you can work out what happened (e.g. you measured something totally wrong) you can **ignore** them when **processing** your results.

If you **don't control** all the **variables** in an experiment, you **increase** the **possibility** of getting an **anomalous result**. In this case, you **won't** be able to draw **valid conclusions** from the results shown.

You Might be Asked to Devise an Investigation in Your Exams

If you have to **devise** (or design) an investigation in your **exam**, you need to think about **everything** you have learnt about on pages 198-200. Here are some of the things that you should **make sure** you've mentioned:

- What the **dependent** and **independent variables** will be.
- What **variables** need to be **controlled** and **why** they need to be controlled (plus **how** it could be done). As with a lab experiment, in a **study** involving **human participants** you need to **control any variables** you're **not investigating** (e.g. participants' age, sex, etc.) because these could effect the **validity** of the results.
- What should be used as a **negative control** or **placebo**.
- What should be done to make the results more **reliable**, e.g. use a **large sample size** if samples are needed (see p. 17).
- Which **apparatus** and **techniques** will be most appropriate, e.g. will a microscope be needed to observe the results?
- How the results should be **measured** and **recorded**, including any **units** that should be used.
- Any **safety** or **ethical issues** the investigation might raise, e.g. how any animals will be used and how to ensure they will be treated with respect.

A placebo is like a negative control for drug trials on humans. It's an inactive substance that looks exactly like the drug being tested. People aren't told if they are taking the placebo or the real drug in the trial.

In his investigation into the knitability of sheep's wool, Farmer Knott was already regretting the size of his sample.

Examiners also love getting you to **suggest improvements** to **methods** or the **design** of an **investigation** — e.g. how an investigation could be changed to make the results more **reliable** or a conclusion more **valid** (see p. 206). You need to think about **everything** you've learnt on the past few pages when criticising other people's experiments too.

Exam Question

*Q1 It has been suggested that fish oil can act as an anticoagulant in the blood, reducing its clotting ability.

Devise an investigation that would give valid results to show whether fish oil affects the clotting ability of the blood.

[6 marks]

* You will be assessed on the quality of your written response in this question.

My best apparatus is the pommel horse...

It's not really, I just like the word pommel. Scientists are rightfully fussy about methods and equipment — I mean if you're going to bother doing an experiment, you should at least make sure it's going to give you results you can trust.

Processing and Presenting Data

Processing data means taking raw data and doing some calculations with it, to make it more useful.

Processing the Data Helps You to Interpret it

You Need to be Able to Calculate Percentages and Percentage Change...

Calculating **percentages** helps you to **compare amounts** from **samples** of **different sizes**.
To give the amount **X** as a percentage of sample **Y**, you need to **divide X by Y**, then **multiply by 100**.

E.g. a tissue sample containing **50** cells is viewed under the microscope. **22** are undergoing mitosis.
What percentage of the cells are undergoing mitosis? Answer: $22/50 \times 100 = \textbf{44\%}$

Calculating **percentage change** helps to **quantify** how much something has changed, e.g. the percentage change in the growth rate of pea plants when a fertiliser is added. To **calculate** it you use this equation:

$$\text{Percentage change} = \frac{\text{final value} - \text{original value}}{\text{original value}} \times 100$$

A **positive** value shows an **increase** and a **negative** value shows a **decrease**.

E.g. a cyclist's tidal volume before a race was **0.5 dm³**.
During the race it reached **1.2 dm³**.
Calculate the percentage change.

$$\text{Percentage change} = \frac{1.2 - 0.5}{0.5} \times 100 = \textbf{140\%}$$

So the cyclist's tidal volume was **140% higher** during the race.

After a particularly frivolous Christmas, Santa's waist measurement had seen a positive percentage change.

...as Well as Ratios

1) Ratios can be used to **compare** lots of different types of quantities. E.g. an organism with a **surface area to volume ratio** of 2 : 1 would theoretically have a surface area **twice as large** as its volume.

2) Ratios are usually most useful in their **simplest** (smallest) **form**. To simplify a ratio, **divide each side** by the **same number**. It's in its simplest form when there's nothing left you can divide by. E.g. to get a ratio of 75 : 35 in its simplest form, divide both sides by 5. You get 15 : 7.

3) To get a ratio of **X : Y** in the form **X : 1, divide both sides by Y**. E.g. to get 28 : 34 into the ratio of X : 1, divide both sides by 34. You get 0.82 : 1.

Averages and the Range Can be Used to Summarise Your Data

1) When you've done **repeats** of an experiment you should always calculate a **mean** (a type of average). To do this **add together** all the data values and **divide** by the **total** number of values in the sample.

Test tube	Repeat (g) 1	Repeat (g) 2	Repeat (g) 3	Mean (g)	Range (g)
A	28	37	32	$(28 + 37 + 32) \div 3 = 32.3$	$37 - 28 = 9$
B	47	51	60	$(47 + 51 + 60) \div 3 = 52.7$	$60 - 47 = 13$

2) You might also need to calculate the **range** (how **spread out** the data is). To do this find the **largest** data value and **subtract** the **smallest** data value from it.

Like the mean, the **median** and **mode** are both types of average.
- To calculate the **median**, put all your data in **numerical order**. The median is the **middle value** in this list. If you have an **even number** of values, the median is **halfway** between the middle two values.
- To calculate the **mode**, count **how many times** each value comes up. The mode is the number that appears **most often**. A set of data might not have a mode — or it might have more than one.

Processing and Presenting Data

The *Standard Deviation* Tells You About *Variation Within a Sample*

1) The **standard deviation** tells you how much the **values** in a **single sample vary**.
   It's a measure of the **spread** of **values** about the **mean**.

2) Sometimes you'll see the mean written as, e.g. **9 ± 3**. This means that the **mean** is **9** and
   the **standard deviation** is **3**, so most of the **values** are spread between **6 to 12**.

3) A **large standard deviation** means the values in the sample **vary a lot**. A **small standard
   deviation** tells you that most of the sample data is around the mean value, so **varies little**.

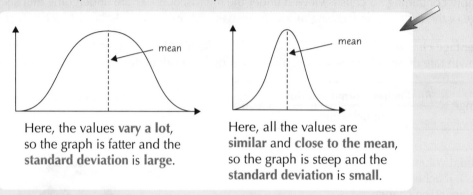

Here, the values **vary a lot**,
so the graph is fatter and the
standard deviation is **large**.

Here, all the values are
similar and **close to the mean**,
so the graph is steep and the
standard deviation is **small**.

Standard deviation can be more useful than the **range** because it tells you how **values** are spread about the **mean**
rather than just the **total spread** of data. A **small standard deviation** means the repeated results are all **similar** and
close to the mean, i.e. **precise**.

You Need to be Able to Calculate the *Standard Deviation*

This is the **formula** for finding the standard deviation of a group of values:

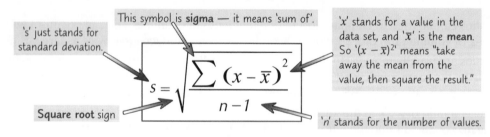

This symbol is **sigma** — it means 'sum of'.

's' just stands for
standard deviation.

Square root sign

'x' stands for a value in the
data set, and *'x̄'* is the **mean**.
So *'(x − x̄)²'* means "take
away the mean from the
value, then square the result."

'n' stands for the number of values.

$$ s = \sqrt{\frac{\sum (x - \bar{x})^2}{n-1}} $$

Example:

The table shows the height of four different trees in a forest.
To find the **standard deviation**:

Tree	Height (m)
A	22
B	27
C	26
D	29

1 Write out the **equation**. $s = \sqrt{\dfrac{\sum (x - \bar{x})^2}{n-1}}$

2 Work out the **mean** height of the trees, $\bar{x}$. $(22 + 27 + 26 + 29) \div 4 = \mathbf{26}$

3 Work out $(x - \bar{x})^2$ for each value of x.
   For each tree height in the table, you need to
   take away the mean, then square the answer.

A: $(22 - 26)^2 = (-4)^2 = \mathbf{16}$ B: $(27 - 26)^2 = 1^2 = \mathbf{1}$
C: $(26 - 26)^2 = 0^2 = \mathbf{0}$ D: $(29 - 26)^2 = 3^2 = \mathbf{9}$

4 Add up all these numbers to find $\sum(x - \bar{x})^2$. $16 + 1 + 0 + 9 = \mathbf{26}$

5 Divide this number by the number of values minus one,
   $(n - 1)$, then take the square root to get the answer.

$26 \div 3 = 8.66...$

$\sqrt{8.66...} = \mathbf{2.9 \text{ to 2 s.f.}}$

Processing and Presenting Data

You Can Use the *Standard Deviation* to Draw *Error Bars*

1) **Standard deviations** can be **plotted** on a graph or chart of **mean values** using **error bars**. For example:

2) Error bars extend **one standard deviation above** and **one standard deviation below** the mean (so the total **length** of an error bar is **twice the standard deviation**).

3) The **longer** the **bar**, the **larger** the **standard deviation** and the **more spread out** the sample data is from the mean.

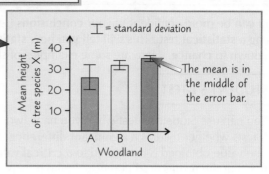

The mean is in the middle of the error bar.

Watch Out For *Significant Figures*...

1) The **first significant figure** of a number is the **first digit** that **isn't a zero**. The second, third and fourth significant figures follow on immediately after the first (even if they're zeros).

2) When you're processing your data you may well want to round any **really long numbers** to a certain number of **significant figures**. E.g. **0.6878976** rounds to **0.69** to **2 s.f.**.

3) When you're doing **calculations** using measurements given to a certain number of significant figures, you should give your **answer** to the **lowest number** of significant figures that was used in the calculation. For example:

$$1.2 \div 1.85 = 0.648648648... \quad = 0.65$$

2 s.f.   3 s.f.   Answer should be rounded to 2 s.f.   Round the last digit up to 5.

> When rounding a number, if the next digit after the last significant figure you're using is less than five, you should round it down and if it's 5 or more you should round it up.

4) This is because the **fewer digits** a measurement has, the less **accurate** it is. Your answer can only be as accurate as the **least accurate measurement** in the calculation.

...and *Standard Form*

1) When you're processing data you might also want to change **very big** or **very small numbers** that have **lots of zeros** into something more manageable — this is called **standard form**.

E.g. 1 000 000 can be written 1×10^6 and 0.017 can be written 1.7×10^{-2}.

2) To do this you just need to **move the decimal point** left or right. The number of places the decimal point moves is then represented by a **power of 10** — this is positive for big numbers, and negative for numbers smaller than one. For example:

$16\,500 = 1.65 \times 10^4$ The decimal point has moved **four places** to the **left**, so the power of 10 is **+4**.

$0.000362 = 3.62 \times 10^{-4}$ The decimal point has moved **four places** to the **right**, so the power of 10 is **−4**.

Make Sure You can *Convert Between Units*

When processing data, you'll quite often have to **convert** between **units**, e.g. seconds and minutes. Make sure you can convert between common units of time, volume and length.

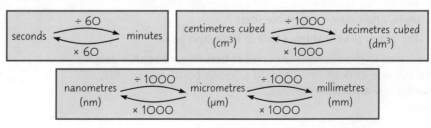

Processing and Presenting Data

Statistical Tests Are Used to *Analyse Data Mathematically*

You can be more confident in your **conclusions** (see page 206) if they're based on results that have been analysed using a **statistical test**. This will tell you how **statistically significant** your results are — and how likely they are to be down to **chance**. Here are some examples of statistical tests you need to be able to carry out and interpret...

STUDENT'S T-TEST

You can use Student's t-test when you have two sets of **data** that you want to **compare**. It tests whether there is a **significant difference** in the **means** of the two data sets. The value obtained is compared to a **critical value**, which helps you decide how likely it is that the results or 'differences in the means' were **due to chance**. If the value obtained from the t-test is **greater than** the critical value at a **probability (P value) of 5% or less** (≤ 0.05), then you can be 95% confident that the difference is significant and not due to chance. This is called a **95% confidence limit** — which is good enough for most biologists to **reject** the **null hypothesis**. A null hypothesis is a special type of hypothesis used with statistical tests. It states that there's **no significant difference** between the things you're measuring. Student's t-test is covered in more detail on page 166.

You need to be familiar with the symbols < (less than), > (more than), << (much less than) and >> (much greater than).

If the result of your statistical test is greater than the critical value at a P value of less than 2% (or 1%) you can be even more confident that the difference is significant.

CHI-SQUARED TEST

You can use the Chi-squared test when you have **categorical** (grouped) **data** and you want to compare whether your **observed results** are **statistically different** from your **expected results**. You compare your result to a **critical value** — if it's **larger** than or **equal** to the critical value at **P = 0.05**, you can be **95% certain** the difference is significant. There's loads more on the Chi-squared test on pages 52-53.

A CORRELATION COEFFICIENT, e.g. Pearson's correlation coefficient (*r*)

Pearson's correlation coefficient allows you to work out the **degree** to which **two** sets of **continuous data** (see below) are **correlated**. There's more on correlation on page 206. The result is a value between 1 and –1 (a value of 1 indicates a **perfect positive correlation**, 0 means there is **no correlation** and –1 is a **perfect negative correlation**). You can compare your result to a critical value to find out whether or not the correlation is **significant**.

Use a Suitable **Graph** or **Chart** to **Present** Your **Data**

Graphs and charts are a great way of **presenting data** — they can make results much **easier to interpret**.

1) When you have **qualitative** data (non-numerical data, e.g. blood group) or **discrete** data (numerical data that can only take certain values in a range, e.g. shoe size) you can use **bar charts** or **pie charts**.

2) When you have **continuous** data (data that can take any value in a range, e.g. height or weight) you can use **histograms** or **line graphs**.

3) When you want to show how **two variables** are **related** (or **correlated**, see page 206) you can use a **scatter graph**.

Whatever type of graph you use, you should make sure that:

- The **dependent variable** goes on the **y-axis** (the vertical axis) and the **independent** on the **x-axis** (the horizontal axis).

- You always **label** the **axes**, include the quantity and **units**, and choose a **sensible scale**.

- The graph covers **at least half** of the **graph paper**.

If you need to draw a **line** (or curve) **of best fit** on a **scatter graph**, draw the line through or as near to as many points as possible, **ignoring** any **anomalous** results.

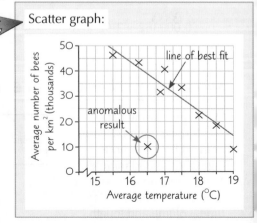

Scatter graph:

Processing and Presenting Data

Data can be Presented on a Logarithmic Scale

1) Sometimes experiments will produce results that have a really **wide range of values** — for example, the number of bacterial cells in a culture could range from 1 to 100 000 in a matter of hours.

2) Trying to **present** such a wide range of values can be **tricky** — for example, if you wanted to plot the results on a **graph**, the **scale** on one of your axes would have to be **really small** to fit on all your results.

3) To get around this problem, **logarithms** are used. The $\log_{10}$ of a number tells you how many times **10 has been multiplied by 10** to give you that number — e.g. the $\log_{10}$ of **10 000** is **4** because $10 \times 10 \times 10 \times 10 = 10\ 000$.

4) Data can be presented on a **logarithmic scale**, where each **large increment** is **10 times greater** than the one before. However, the **smaller increments** are **not evenly spaced** (they gradually get **closer together**) so you have to be careful when interpreting data that's presented on a logarithmic scale.

EXAMPLE

The graph on the right shows the growth of a bacterial culture over time. The graph is drawn with a logarithmic scale.

Estimate how many bacteria per cm^3 were in the culture after **4 hours**.

> The large square between 100 and 1000 is divided into nine sections, so the scale must be going up by 100 bacteria for each section.

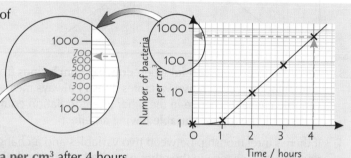

So there were approximately **650 bacteria per cm^3** after 4 hours.

Find the Rate By Finding the Gradient

Rate is a **measure** of how much something is **changing over time**. Calculating a rate can be useful when analysing your data, e.g. you might want to the find the **rate of a reaction**. Rates are easy to work out from a graph:

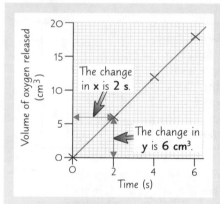

For a **linear** graph you can calculate the **rate** by finding the **gradient of the line**: $\Rightarrow$ $\text{Gradient} = \dfrac{\text{Change in Y}}{\text{Change in X}}$

So in this **example**: $\text{rate} = \dfrac{6\ cm^3}{2\ s} = \textbf{3 cm}^3\ \textbf{s}^{-1}$ — $cm^3\ s^{-1}$ means the same as cm^3/s (centimetres^3 per second)

The **equation** of a **straight line** can always be written in the form $y = mx + c$, where **m** is the **gradient** and **c** is the **y-intercept** (this is the **value of y** when the line crosses the **y-axis**). In this example, the equation of the line is $y = 3x + 0$ (or just $y = 3x$). Knowing the equation of the line allows you to estimate results not plotted on the graph. E.g. in this case, when x (the time) is **20 s**, y (the volume of oxygen released) will be $3x = 3 \times 20 = \textbf{60 cm}^3$.

For a **curved** (non-linear) graph you can find the **rate** by drawing a **tangent**:

1) Position a ruler on the graph at the **point** where you want to know the **rate**.

2) **Angle** the **ruler** so there is **equal space** between the **ruler** and the **curve** on **either** side of the point.

3) **Draw** a **line** along the ruler to make the tangent.

   Extend the line right across the graph — it'll help to make your gradient calculation easier as you'll have **more points** to choose from.

4) **Calculate** the **gradient** of the **tangent** to find the **rate**.

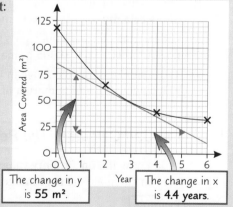

> Gradient = 55 m² ÷ 4.4 years = **12.5 m² year⁻¹**

The change in y is 55 m². | Year | The change in x is 4.4 years.

Significant figures — a result of far too many cream cakes...

Lots of maths to get your head around on these few pages, but stay calm and take your time with it all. You'll be fine.

Drawing Conclusions and Evaluating

There's no point in getting all those lovely results and just leaving it at that. You need to draw some conclusions...

You Need to be Able to **Draw Conclusions** From **Data**

1) Conclusions need to be **valid**. A conclusion can only be considered as valid if it answers the original question (see page 198) and is based on **repeatable** and **reproducible** (reliable) results.

2) You can often draw conclusions by looking at the relationship (**correlation**) between two variables:

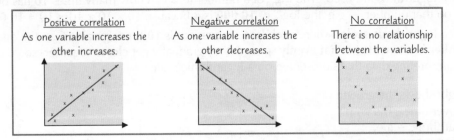

3) You have to be very **careful** when **drawing conclusions** from data like this because a **correlation** between two variables **doesn't** always mean that a **change** in one variable **causes** a **change** in the other (the correlation could be due to **chance** or there could be a **third variable** having an effect).

Despite all his colourful drawing equipment, Jack still struggled to draw conclusions.

4) If there's a relationship between two variables and a change in one variable **does** cause a change in the other it's called a **causal relationship**.

5) It can be **concluded** that a **correlation** is a **causal relationship** if every other variable that could possibly affect the result is **controlled**.

In reality this is very hard to do — correlations are generally accepted to be causal relationships if lots of studies have found the same thing, and scientists have figured out exactly how one factor causes the other.

6) When you're making a conclusion you **can't** make broad **generalisations** from data — you have to be very **specific**. You can only **conclude** what the results show and **no more**.

> **Example**
>
> The graph shows the results from a study into the **abundance of plant species A** and **distance** from a **footpath**. The only **conclusion** you can draw is that there's a **positive correlation** between abundance of plant species A and distance from the footpath (as the **distance** from the footpath **increases**, the **abundance** of plant species A also **increases**). It **wouldn't be valid** to conclude that this is true for **any other plant species**, or that it would be true near to **any other footpath** — the **results** could be **completely different**.
>
>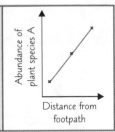

Uncertainty is the Amount of *Error* Your *Measurements* Might Have

1) The results you get from an experiment won't be completely perfect — there'll always be a **degree of uncertainty** in your measurements due to limits in the **sensitivity** of the apparatus you're using.

2) For example, an electronic mass balance might measure to the **nearest 0.01 g**, but the real mass could be up to **0.005 g smaller or larger**. It has an **uncertainty value** of **± 0.005 g**.

3) The ± sign tells you the **range** in which the **true value** lies (to within a certain probability). The range is called the **margin of error**.

You Can *Calculate* The *Percentage Error* of Your *Measurements*

If you know the **uncertainty value** of your measurements, you can calculate the **percentage error** using this formula: $\text{percentage error} = \dfrac{\text{uncertainty}}{\text{reading}} \times 100$

Example

50 cm³ of HCl is measured with an uncertainty value of ± 0.05 cm³.

percentage error = $\dfrac{0.05}{50} \times 100 = \mathbf{0.1\%}$

PRACTICAL SKILLS

Drawing Conclusions and Evaluating

You Can Minimise the Errors in Your Measurements

1) One obvious way to **reduce errors** in your measurements is to buy the most **sensitive equipment** available. In real life there's not much you can do about this one — you're stuck with whatever your school or college has got. But there are other ways to **lower the uncertainty** in experiments.

2) For example, you can plan your experiment so you **measure** a **greater amount** of something:

> If you use a **500 cm³** cylinder that goes up in **5 cm³** increments, each reading has an uncertainty of ± 2.5 cm³.
>
> So using a 500 cm³ cylinder to measure **100 cm³** of liquid will give you a percentage error of:
>
> But if you measure **200 cm³** in the same cylinder, the percentage error is:
>
> $$\frac{2.5}{100} \times 100 = \textbf{2.5\%}$$
>
> $$\frac{2.5}{200} \times 100 = \textbf{1.25\%}$$
>
> Hey presto — you've just **halved** the uncertainty.

You Also Need to Be Able to Evaluate Methods and Results

1) In the exams, you might get asked to **evaluate** experimental results or methods. Here are some things to think about:

- **Repeatability**: Did you take enough repeat readings of the measurements? Would you do more repeats if you were to do the experiment again? Do you think you'd get similar data if you did the experiment again?
- **Reproducibility**: Have you compared your results with other people's results? Were your results similar? Could other scientists gain data showing the same relationships that are shown in your data?
- **Validity**: Does your data answer the question you set out to investigate? Were all the variables controlled?

2) Make sure you **evaluate** your **method**. Is there anything you could have done to make your results more **precise** or **accurate**? Were there any **limitations** in your method, e.g. should you have taken measurements more **frequently**? Were there any **sources** of **error** in your experiment? Could you have used more sensitive **apparatus** or **equipment**? Think about how you could **refine** and **improve** your experiment if you did it again.

3) Once you've thought about these points you can decide how much **confidence** you have in your **conclusion**. For example, if your results are **repeatable**, **reproducible** (i.e. reliable) and **valid** and they back up your conclusion then you can have a **high degree** of **confidence** in your conclusion.

Solving Problems in a Practical Context

In the exams, you'll get plenty of questions set in a 'practical context'. As well as answering questions about the methods used or the conclusions drawn, you'll need to be able to **apply** your **scientific knowledge** to **solve problems** set in these contexts. For example:

☐ Sponge soaked in IAA and glucose
■ Sponge soaked in water and glucose

Q1 An experiment was carried out to investigate the role of IAA in shoot growth. The experimental set up is shown in the diagram on the right.

Four shoots were then placed in the dark (experiment 1) and the other four shoots were exposed to a light source directed from the right (experiment 2). After two days, the amount of growth (in mm) and direction of growth was recorded. The results are shown in the table.

a) Explain the results seen for shoot C. [3 marks]

A   B   C   D   ← Shoot minus the tip

	Growth / mm			
	Shoot A	Shoot B	Shoot C	Shoot D
Experiment 1 (dark)	6, right	6, left	6, straight	1, straight
Experiment 2 (light)	8, right	8, right	8, right	3, straight

You should remember from page 185 that **IAA** stimulates **cell elongation** in a shoot. In experiment 1, equal amounts of IAA diffuse down **both** sides of shoot C, making the cells elongate at the **same rate**, so the shoot grows **straight up**. In experiment 2, IAA moved to the **shaded** (left-hand side) of shoot C, so the shoot grew to the **right** — towards the **light**.

Correlation Street — my favourite programme...

Don't ever, ever assume that correlation means cause. There, I've told you again. No excuses now. A good evaluation is a sign that you really understand what makes a good experiment, so make sure your evaluation-writing-skills are top notch.

How to Do Well in Your Exams

The reason for learning all the lovely facts and diagrams in this book is so that you can ace your exams and get yourself an A-level in Biology. So, now it's a good idea to find out exactly what you'll be in for exam-wise...

Make Sure You Know the **Structure** of Your **Exams**

It seems obvious, but if you know exactly what will be **covered** in each of the exams, how much **time** you'll have to do them and how they'll be **structured**, you can be better prepared. So let's take a look at the ins and outs of all the exams you'll be facing for **A-level Biology**...

Paper	Total marks	Time	Topics assessed
1	100	2 hours	1, 2, 3, 4, 5, 6
2	100	2 hours	1, 2, 3, 4, 7, 8
3	100	2 hours	1 to 8

All this exam info is only relevant if you're taking the A-level in Biology. If you're taking the AS-level, you'll be sitting a completely different set of papers, which are structured in a different way.

1) As you can see from the table, **Papers 1 and 2** both test you on all the **Year 1 topics (1 to 4)**. **Paper 1** also tests you on the Year 2 **topics 5 and 6**. **Paper 2** tests you on the Year 2 **topics 7 and 8**.

2) **Paper 3** tests you on **all 8 topics** — the material from **both years** of your course.

3) **All three papers** will contain questions which test that you understand how to **design** and **carry out** a **valid experiment**. This is covered in the **Practical Skills** section of this book (pages 198-207). All three papers will also include **calculation questions**, which test your **mathematical skills**.

4) **Papers 1 and 2** will contain some **multiple choice questions**. The rest of the questions will be a mixture of **short answer** and **extended writing** questions. There's more on extended writing questions below.

5) **Paper 3** will contain a mixture of **short answer** and **extended writing** questions, as well as some **synoptic** questions — to answer these, you'll need to draw on your knowledge of **at least two different topics**.

6) **Eight weeks before the Paper 3** exam Edexcel will publish a **scientific article** on their website, which you'll be given to read. You'll then be told to answer questions in **part of the paper** using the **information in the article** and your **own scientific knowledge**. Make sure you've **fully familiarised** yourself with the article before the start of your Paper 3 exam.

Julie had heard of multiple choice, but this just took the biscuit...

All of Your Exams Will Contain **Extended Writing** Questions

1) In each of your three papers there will be **one** or **more extended writing** questions.

2) These questions are usually worth **6** or **9 marks** and will require a **long answer**.

3) The questions are shown with an **asterisk** (*) next to their number.

4) You'll be awarded marks for both the **content** of your answer, and its **structure**. So your answer needs to:

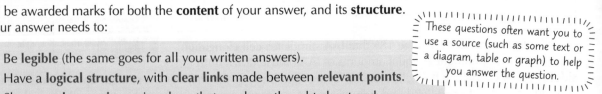

These questions often want you to use a source (such as some text or a diagram, table or graph) to help you answer the question.

- Be **legible** (the same goes for all your written answers).

- Have a **logical structure**, with **clear links** made between **relevant points**.

- Show **good reasoning** — i.e. show that you have thought about and understood the question, and can justify your answer with scientific evidence.

5) You can gain **practice** at extended writing questions by doing the exam questions marked with an asterisk in this book.

How to Do Well in Your Exams

Command Words Tell You *What You Need to do* in a Question

Command words are just the bits of a question that tell you **what to do**. You'll find answering exam questions much easier if you understand exactly what they mean, so here's a brief summary table of the **most common** ones:

Command word:	What to do:
Give / Name / State	Give a brief one or two word answer, or a short sentence.
Explain	Give reasons for something.
Describe	Write about what something's like, e.g. describe the process of glycolysis.
Calculate	Work out the solution to a mathematical problem.
Comment on	Make a judgement about something from information or data that's been provided.
Compare and contrast	Give the similarities and differences between two or more things.
Discuss	Write about different issues, problems or arguments relating to a particular subject.
Evaluate	Bring together different evidence or opposing arguments, before coming up with an overall judgement or conclusion.

Not all questions will have command words.

Always *Show Your Working* for *Calculation Questions*

Even though you're taking an A-level in Biology, there will be some **maths** to do in these papers that's set in a **biological context**. Here are some **tips** for answering calculation questions:

1) Whenever you answer a calculation question, remember to **write down** your **working**. If there's more than one mark available, you may be able to **pick up a mark** for **evidence** of the **correct calculation**, even if your **final answer** is **wrong**.

2) If the answer to a particular calculation has **units** (e.g. cm^3, kg) you **must write them down**.

3) You can use a **scientific calculator**, so make sure you **take one into the exam** with you.

4) Use a **ruler** to help you **read values** off a graph scale **accurately**.

Time Management is *Important*

1) For **all three papers** you get **just over a minute per mark**. So if you get stuck on a short question, it's sometimes worth moving on to another one and then coming back to it if you have time. Bear in mind that you might want to spend a **bit longer** than a minute per mark on the **extended writing questions** and on the questions related to the **scientific article** in Paper 3.

2) If you've got any time left once you've finished the paper, hold off on celebrating and have a **look back through** the questions. You can use the time to **go back** to any questions you've **skipped**, **check your answers** to **calculation questions** and to make sure you haven't **accidentally missed** any questions out.

You might think you need your head examined for picking A-level Biology...

...because there's a lot to learn and three big exams to do. But let me just stop you right there... Instead of worrying, just work through this book, including having a go at all of the questions and you'll be well and truly prepped for the exams. Then re-read these pages to make sure you know what's coming. After that, all there is to say is... good luck.

Answers

Topic 1A — The Circulatory System

Page 5 — Water and Transport

1 In a water molecule, the shared electrons are pulled closer to the oxygen atom than the hydrogen atoms, making the molecule dipolar *[1 mark]*. This makes water a good solvent for other ionic substances, which allows it to transport them *[1 mark]*. Water is also cohesive due to its dipolar nature, which helps water to flow, allowing it to transport substances *[1 mark]*.

Page 7 — The Heart and Blood Vessels

1 C *[1 mark]*

2 The valves only open one way and whether they open or close depends on the relative pressure of the heart chambers *[1 mark]*. If the pressure is greater behind a valve (i.e. there's lots of blood in the chamber behind it), it's forced open, to let the blood travel in the right direction *[1 mark]*. Once the blood's gone through the valve, the pressure is greater in front of the valve, which forces it shut, preventing blood from flowing back into the chamber *[1 mark]*.

Here you need to explain how valves function in relation to blood flow, rather than just in relation to relative pressures.

3 Their walls are only one cell thick to allow efficient diffusion of substances (e.g. glucose and oxygen) *[1 mark]*. Capillaries form networks called capillary beds, which provide a large surface area for exchange *[1 mark]*.

Page 9 — Cardiac Cycle

1 a) 0.2 - 0.4 seconds *[1 mark]*
The AV valves are shut when the pressure is higher in the ventricles than in the atria.

  b) 0.3 - 0.4 seconds *[1 mark]*
When the ventricles relax the volume of the chamber increases and the pressure falls. The pressure in the left ventricle was 16.5 kPa at 0.3 seconds and it decreased to 7.0 kPa at 0.4 seconds, so it must have started to relax somewhere between these two times.

  c) 16.5 − 0.5 = 16 *[1 mark]*
$(16 \div 0.5) \times 100$ *[1 mark]* = 3200% *[1 mark]*
In this question you need to calculate the percentage increase from 0.5 kPa (blood pressure at 0.0 s) to 16.5 kPa (blood pressure at 0.3 s). To do this you find the difference between the two blood pressures (16 kPa), divide this by the starting blood pressure (0.5 kPa), and multiply the whole thing by 100.

Page 11 — Investigating Heart Rate

1 a) The graph shows a positive correlation between caffeine concentration and *Daphnia* heart rate/as caffeine concentration increases, *Daphnia* heart rate increases *[1 mark]*.

  b) Any two from: e.g. the temperature of the caffeine solutions/ *Daphnia* *[1 mark]*. / The amount of light the *Daphnia* are exposed to *[1 mark]*. / The volume of caffeine solution used *[1 mark]*.

  c) E.g. invertebrates are considered to be simpler than vertebrates *[1 mark]*. / They're more distantly related to humans than other vertebrates *[1 mark]*. / They have less sophisticated nervous systems than vertebrates, so may feel less/no pain *[1 mark]*.

Topic 1B — Lifestyle and Disease

Page 15 — Cardiovascular Disease

1 E.g. people may overestimate the risk because they may have known someone who smoked and died from CVD, and therefore think that if you smoke you will die of CVD *[1 mark]*. Also, there are often articles in the media that highlight the link between smoking and CVD and constant exposure to information like this can make people worry that they'll get CVD *[1 mark]*.

2 a) thrombin *[1 mark]*
  b) Fibrin, red blood cells and platelets *[1 mark]*.
  c) calcium ions *[1 mark]*
  d) Their blood clotting mechanism will be impaired/their blood won't clot as fast as the blood of people without the disorder because less prothrombin is available to be converted to thrombin *[1 mark]*. This means that less fibrinogen will be converted to fibrin, which in turn reduces blood clot formation *[1 mark]*.

3 An atheroma plaque may break through the endothelium (inner lining) of the artery, leaving a rough surface *[1 mark]*. This damage could cause a blood clot (thrombus) to form over the area *[1 mark]*. If the blood clot completely blocks a coronary artery, it will restrict blood flow to part of the heart muscle *[1 mark]*, cutting off its oxygen supply and causing a heart attack *[1 mark]*.

4 ***5-6 marks:***
The answer explains fully at least three ways in which smoking increases the risk of developing CVD.
The answer has a clear and logical structure and ideas are well-linked. The information given is relevant and detailed.
3-4 marks:
The answer attempts to explain more than one way in which smoking increases the risk of CVD.
The answer has some structure and attempts to link ideas. Most of the information given is relevant and there is some detail involved.
1-2 marks:
The answer mentions at least one factor involved in smoking that increase the risk of developing CVD, but there is little or no attempt made to explain them.
The answer has very little clear structure and ideas are not well-linked. The information given is basic and lacking in detail. It may not all be relevant.
0 marks:
No relevant information is given.
Here are some points your answer may include:
Carbon monoxide in cigarette smoke combines with haemoglobin, which reduces the amount of oxygen transported in the blood. This reduces the amount of oxygen available to body tissues. If the heart muscle/brain doesn't receive enough oxygen it can cause a heart attack/stroke. Nicotine in cigarette smoke makes platelets sticky. This increases the chance of blood clots forming, which increases the risk of CVD. Smoking also decreases the amount of antioxidants in the blood. Fewer antioxidants means cell damage in the artery walls is more likely and this can lead to atheroma formation, which increases the risk of CVD.

Page 17 — Interpreting Data on Risk Factors

1 a) A large sample size was used *[1 mark]*.
The sample included many countries *[1 mark]*.

  b) E.g. the study could take into account other variables, such as diet, smoking and physical activity which could have affected the results *[1 mark]*. The study could be repeated by other scientists to see if they produce the same results *[1 mark]*.

Page 19 — Treatment of CVD

1 a) E.g. the number of prescriptions of each type of treatment have increased *[1 mark]*. The numbers of prescriptions of platelet inhibitory drugs have increased gradually, whereas the number of prescriptions of antihypertensive drugs and statins have increased more rapidly *[1 mark]*.

  b) Platelet inhibitory drugs. A benefit of this treatment is that they can be used to treat people who already have blood clots or CVD *[1 mark]*. However, there is a risk of side effects occurring, such as rashes/diarrhoea/nausea/liver function problems/excessive bleeding *[1 mark]*.

Prescriptions in 2006: 42 000
Prescriptions in 2011: 62 000
Increase of 62 000 – 42 000 = 20 000
Percentage increase = (20 000 ÷ 42 000) × 100 = **48%** *[1 mark]*
Statins work by reducing the amount of LDL cholesterol produced inside the liver, which reduces blood cholesterol *[1 mark]*. This reduces atheroma formation, which reduces the risk of CVD *[1 mark]*.
The GP could prescribe antihypertensive drugs to reduce his patient's blood pressure *[1 mark]*. Lower blood pressure would reduce the risk of damage occurring to the artery walls, reducing the risk of atheroma/clot formation and CHD *[1 mark]*.
Antihypertensive drugs can cause side effects, e.g. palpitations/abnormal heart rhythms/fainting/headaches/drowsiness/allergic reactions/depression *[1 mark]*.

pic 1C — Diet and Health

e 21 — Diet and Energy

0.2 mg cm⁻³ *[1 mark]*
Any three from: e.g. volume of DCPIP *[1 mark]* / concentration of DCPIP *[1 mark]* / time taken to shake the vitamin C and DCPIP solution *[1 mark]* / temperature *[1 mark]*.
i) Energy input – energy output = energy budget,
    2000 – (1200 + (2 × 513) + (2 × 328)) = **–882** *[1 mark]*.
ii) The woman's energy output is greater than her energy input, so she will lose weight *[1 mark]*.
The woman would become (severely) underweight *[1 mark]*.

e 23 — Carbohydrates

[1 mark for correct structure of maltose, 1 mark for showing water molecule.]
A molecule of water reacts with the glycosidic bond to split the glucose molecules apart / a hydrolysis reaction splits the glucose molecules apart *[1 mark]*.
Amylose is a long, unbranched chain, which forms a coiled shape making it compact so good for storage *[1 mark]*. Amylopectin is a long, branched chain, which allows stored energy to be released quickly, as the enzymes that break it down can reach the glycosidic bonds easily *[1 mark]*. Starch is insoluble in water, which makes it good for storage, as water doesn't enter cells by osmosis *[1 mark]*.

e 26 — Lipids and Cardiovascular Disease

E.g.

[1 mark]
ester bonds *[1 mark]*
Saturated lipids don't have any double bonds between their carbon atoms *[1 mark]*. Unsaturated lipids have one or more double bonds between their carbon atoms *[1 mark]*.

3 a) High density lipoproteins/HDLs are mainly protein, whereas low density lipoproteins/LDLs are mainly lipid *[1 mark]*. High density lipoproteins/HDLs transport cholesterol from body tissues to the liver, whereas low density lipoproteins/LDLs transport cholesterol from the liver to the blood *[1 mark]*. High density lipoproteins/HDLs reduce the total blood cholesterol level when it's too high, while low density lipoproteins/LDLs increase the total blood cholesterol level when it's too low *[1 mark]*.
   b) Having a high low density lipoprotein/LDL level has been linked to an increased risk of CVD (cardiovascular disease) *[1 mark]*.

Page 27 — Reducing Risk Factors of CVD

1 a) waist-to-hip ratio = waist (cm) ÷ hips (cm)
      = 76 cm ÷ 95 cm
      = **0.8** *[1 mark]*
   b) BMI = body mass (kg) ÷ height² (m²)
      body mass (kg) = BMI × height² (m²)
                     = 18.9 × 1.68²
                     = 18.9 × 2.82
                     = **53.3 kg**
      [2 marks for correct answer, otherwise 1 mark for correct working.]
      You need to rearrange the BMI formula to be able to find out the person's body mass.

Topic 2A — Gas Exchange, Cell Membranes and Transport

Page 29 — Gas Exchange

1 E.g. lungs contain many alveoli giving a large surface area *[1 mark]*. The alveolar epithelium and capillary endothelium are each only one cell thick, so there is a short diffusion pathway *[1 mark]*. Each alveolus has a good blood supply, which constantly removes oxygen and delivers carbon dioxide, maintaining a high concentration gradient of each gas *[1 mark]*. Concentration gradients are also maintained by breathing in and out, which refreshes the oxygen supply and removes carbon dioxide *[1 mark]*.
2 The patient would have a reduced number of alveoli in their lungs, so the surface area available for gas exchange would be decreased *[1 mark]*. This would decrease the rate of diffusion of oxygen and carbon dioxide *[1 mark]*.

Page 31 — Cell Membranes and Osmosis

1 B *[1 mark]*
2 a) The concentration of water molecules in the sucrose solution was higher than the concentration of water molecules in the potato *[1 mark]*. Water moves by osmosis from a higher concentration of water molecules to a lower concentration of water molecules *[1 mark]*. So water moved into the potato, increasing its mass *[1 mark]*.
   b) The concentration of water molecules in the potato and the concentration of water molecules in the sucrose solution were the same *[1 mark]*.
   c) – 0.4 g *[1 mark]*. The difference in concentration of water molecules between the solution and the potato is the same as with the 1% solution, so the mass difference should be about the same, but negative / mass should be lost not gained *[1 mark]*.
      A 5% sucrose solution has a lower concentration of water molecules than the potato. This means that water will move out of the potato into the sucrose solution, decreasing the mass of the potato.

Answers

Page 33 — Transport Across the Cell Membrane

1   Facilitated diffusion involves channel proteins, which transport charged molecules across the membrane *[1 mark]* and carrier proteins, which transport large molecules across the membrane *[1 mark]*. Both types of protein transport molecules down a concentration gradient *[1 mark]*.
2   Endocytosis takes in substances from outside the cell *[1 mark]* via vesicles formed from the cell membrane *[1 mark]*. Exocytosis secretes substances from the cell *[1 mark]* via vesicles made from the Golgi apparatus *[1 mark]*.
    Make sure you don't get these two processes mixed up — try to remember endo for 'in' and exo for 'out'.

Page 35 — Investigating Cell Membrane Structure

1 a) Cut five equal-sized pieces of beetroot and rinse them to remove any pigment released during cutting *[1 mark]*. Make up five test tubes with alcohol concentrations 0, 25, 50, 75 and 100% *[1 mark]*. Place a piece of beetroot in each test tube for the same length of time *[1 mark]*. Remove the piece of beetroot from each tube and use a colorimeter to measure how much light is absorbed by each of the remaining solutions *[1 mark]*.
  b) As the concentration of alcohol increased the absorbance also increased *[1 mark]*. This means that more pigment was released by the beetroot as the alcohol concentration increased, which suggests that the cell membrane became more permeable *[1 mark]*.
  c) E.g. alcohol dissolves the lipids in the cell membranes, so the membrane loses its structure *[1 mark]*.

Topic 2B — Proteins and Genetics

Page 37 — Protein Structure

1   More than two amino acids *[1 mark]* join together in a chain via condensation reactions *[1 mark]*. Each reaction forms a peptide bond and releases a molecule of water *[1 mark]*.

Page 41 — Enzymes

1 a) Gradient = 40 cm³ ÷ 3 s *[1 mark]* = **13.3 cm³ s⁻¹** *[1 mark]*
    [Accept between 10 cm³ s⁻¹ and 20 cm³ s⁻¹.]
  b) Increasing the enzyme concentration leads to a higher initial rate of reaction *[1 mark]* because more enzyme active sites are available to collide with the substrate and form enzyme-substrate complexes *[1 mark]*.
  c) The experiment should have also been carried out with a tube where no enzyme was added *[1 mark]*. This ensures that only the independent variable (enzyme concentration) is affecting the dependent variable (volume of product released) *[1 mark]*.
  d) The enzyme and substrate could be mixed together in a cuvette and then placed in a colorimeter, which measures the absorbance of the solution *[1 mark]*. The absorbance could be recorded every 10 seconds for 1 minute and plotted on an absorbance against time graph *[1 mark]*.

Page 43 — DNA and RNA Basics

1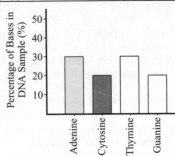

[1 mark for a bar drawn for thymine at 30%.
1 mark for a bar drawn for guanine at 20%]
Remember, thanks to complementary base pairing, there are always equal amounts of adenine and thymine in a DNA sample and equal amounts of cytosine and guanine. Double-check your answer by making sure the percentages of all four bases add up to 100%.

2 a) Mononucleotides are joined between the phosphate group of one mononucleotide and the deoxyribose sugar of the next *[1 mark]* in a condensation reaction *[1 mark]*.
  b) Two polynucleotide strands join through hydrogen bonding between the base pairs *[1 mark]*. Base pairing is complementary (e.g. A always pairs with T and C always pairs with G) *[1 mark]*. The two antiparallel polynucleotide strands twist to form a DNA double helix *[1 mark]*.

Page 45 — The Genetic Code and Protein Synthesis

1   C *[1 mark]*
2 a) 4 *[1 mark]*
  b) GUG = valine
      UGU = cysteine
      CGC = arginine
      GCA = alanine
      Correct sequence = **valine, cysteine, arginine, alanine**.
      [2 marks for all 4 amino acids in the correct order. 1 mark for a minimum of 3 correct amino acids in the correct order.]
3 a) The mRNA sequence is 18 mononucleotides long and the protein produced is 6 amino acids long *[1 mark]*. 18 ÷ 6 = 3, suggesting three mononucleotides code for a single amino acid *[1 mark]*.
  b) E.g. The sequence produced began leucine-cysteine-glycine. This would only be produced if the code is non-overlapping, e.g. UUGUGUGGG = UUG-UGU-GGG = leucine-cysteine-glycine *[1 mark]*.
      If the code was overlapping, the triplets would be, e.g. UUG-UGU-GUG-UGU, which would give a sequence starting leucine-cysteine-valine-cysteine. Also, this part of the DNA sequence produces 6 amino acids. This is only correct if the code is non-overlapping — the sequence of amino acids would be longer if the code overlapped [1 mark].

Page 47 — Transcription and Translation

1 a) CGCUUCAGGUAC *[1 mark]*
  b) GCGAAGUCCAUG *[1 mark]*
2   The drug binds to DNA, preventing RNA polymerase from binding, so transcription can't take place and no mRNA can be made *[1 mark]*. This means there's no mRNA for translation and so protein synthesis is inhibited *[1 mark]*.
3   (10 × 3 =) 30 mononucleotides long *[1 mark]*. Each amino acid is coded for by three mononucleotides (a codon), so the mRNA length in mononucleotides is the number of amino acids multiplied by three *[1 mark]*.

opic 2C — Inheritance

age 49 — Replication of DNA

a) Any five from: e.g. DNA helicase breaks the hydrogen bonds between the two DNA strands and the DNA helix unwinds *[1 mark]*. / Each strand acts as a template for a new strand *[1 mark]*. / Individual free DNA nucleotides join up along the template strand by complementary base pairing *[1 mark]*. / DNA polymerase joins the individual nucleotides together, so that the sugar-phosphate backbone forms *[1 mark]*. / Hydrogen bonds then form between the bases on each strand *[1 mark]*. / Two identical DNA molecules are produced *[1 mark]*. / Each of the new molecules contains a single strand from the original DNA molecule and a single new strand *[1 mark]*.
[Maximum of 5 marks available.]

b) Two samples of bacteria were grown — one in a nutrient broth containing light nitrogen, and one in a broth with heavy nitrogen *[1 mark]*. As the bacteria reproduced, they took up nitrogen to help make nucleotides for new DNA *[1 mark]*. A sample of DNA was taken from each batch of bacteria, and spun in a centrifuge. The DNA from the heavy nitrogen bacteria settled lower down the centrifuge tube than the DNA from the light nitrogen bacteria *[1 mark]*. Then the bacteria grown in the heavy nitrogen broth were taken out and put in a broth containing only light nitrogen. The bacteria were left for one round of DNA replication, and then another DNA sample was taken out and spun in the centrifuge *[1 mark]*.

c) The DNA spun in the centrifuge after one round of DNA replication in a light nitrogen broth, settled out in the middle, showing that the DNA molecules contained a mixture of heavy and light nitrogen. This showed that the bacterial DNA had replicated semi-conservatively in the light nitrogen *[1 mark]*. If the bacterial DNA had replicated conservatively, the DNA would have settled into two bands with the light new strands at the top and the heavy original strands at the bottom *[1 mark]*.

age 51 — Genes and Inheritance

a) genotype — Yy *[1 mark]*, phenotype — yellow *[1 mark]*.

b) E.g.

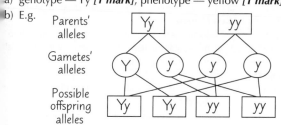

Parents' alleles
Gametes' alleles
Possible offspring alleles

[1 mark for parents' alleles correct, 1 mark for gametes' alleles correct, 1 mark for possible offspring alleles correct.]

c) 1:1 *[1 mark]*

ge 53 — The Chi-Squared Test

a) That there is no significant difference between the observed and expected results *[1 mark]*.

b)

Phenotype	Ratio	Expected result (E)	Observed result (O)	O − E	(O − E)^2	$\frac{(O - E)^2}{E}$
Tall	3	39	43	4	16	0.41
Dwarf	1	13	9	−4	16	1.23

$$\chi^2 = \Sigma \frac{(O - E)^2}{E} = 1.64$$

The chi-squared value is smaller than the critical value (1.64 < 3.84) so the difference between the observed and expected results is not significant. This means that the null hypothesis can't be rejected, so the results from this experiment support the scientist's theory.
[1 mark for correct calculation of expected results, 1 mark for correct calculation of (O − E)^2 ÷ E, 1 mark for correct calculation of χ^2, 1 mark for correct conclusion.]

Page 55 — Cystic Fibrosis

1 a) Emma is homozygous for the CF allele *[1 mark]*. Martha/James is a carrier *[1 mark]*.

b) E.g.

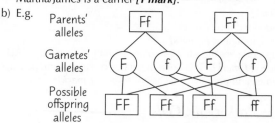

Parents' alleles
Gametes' alleles
Possible offspring alleles

1 in 4/25%
[1 mark for parents' and gametes' alleles correct, 1 mark for possible offspring alleles correct, 1 mark for correct final answer.]

c) **5-6 marks:**
The answer provides a detailed explanation of the ways in which the digestive system is affected by cystic fibrosis. The answer has a clear and logical structure and ideas are well-linked. The information given is relevant and detailed.
3-4 marks:
The answer explains some ways in which the digestive system is affected by cystic fibrosis.
The answer has some structure and attempts to link ideas. Most of the information given is relevant and there is some detail involved.
1-2 marks:
One or two points are given relating to how the digestive system is affected, but there is little or no explanation.
The answer has very little clear structure and ideas are not well-linked. The information given is basic and lacking in detail. It may not all be relevant.
0 marks:
No relevant information is given.
Here are some points your answer may include:
Cystic fibrosis leads to the production of abnormally thick and sticky mucus. The thick mucus can block the tubes connecting the pancreas to the small intestine, preventing digestive enzymes from reaching the small intestine. The mucus can also cause cysts/growths to form in the pancreas, which inhibits the production of digestive enzymes. These both reduce the ability of someone with cystic fibrosis to digest food and so fewer nutrients can be absorbed. The mucus lining the small intestine is very thick, which inhibits the absorption of nutrients.

Page 57 — Genetic Screening

1 C *[1 mark]*

2 a) To see if they're a carrier, because if they are, it will affect the chance of any of their children having the disorder *[1 mark]*. Testing means that they can make informed decisions on whether to have children *[1 mark]* or whether to have prenatal testing if the mother is already pregnant *[1 mark]*.

b) i) Screening embryos produced by IVF for genetic disorders before they're implanted into the uterus *[1 mark]*.

ii) E.g. it reduces the chance of having a baby with a genetic disorder as only 'healthy' embryos will be implanted *[1 mark]*. / Because it's performed before implantation, it avoids any issues about abortion raised by prenatal testing *[1 mark]*.

iii) E.g. it can be used to find out about other characteristics, leading to concerns about designer babies *[1 mark]*. Decisions could be made based on incorrect information (false positives and false negatives) *[1 mark]*.

Answers

Topic 3A — Cells

Page 60 — Eukaryotic Cells and Organelles

1   C *[1 mark]*
2 a) i) mitochondrion *[1 mark]*
    ii) Golgi apparatus *[1 mark]*
  b) Mitochondria are the site of aerobic respiration / are where ATP is produced *[1 mark]*. The Golgi apparatus processes and packages new lipids and proteins / makes lysosomes *[1 mark]*.

Page 61 — Prokaryotic Cells

1   C *[1 mark]*
2   Prokaryotic cells have a long coiled-up strand of circular DNA *[1 mark]*. They can also have small loops of DNA called plasmids *[1 mark]*.

Page 63 — Looking at Cells and Organelles

1   Magnification = image size ÷ object size
                = 80 mm ÷ 0.5 mm *[1 mark]*
                = **× 160** *[1 mark]*
  Always remember to convert everything to the same units first — the insect is 0.5 mm long, so the length of the image needs to be changed from 8 cm to 80 mm.
2   Image size = magnification × object size
             = 100 × 0.059 mm *[1 mark]*
             = **5.9 mm** *[1 mark]*
  Hint: To convert 59 μm into mm, divide by 1000.
3 a) mitochondrion and nucleus *[1 mark]*
  b) All of the organelles in the table would be visible *[1 mark]*.
4 a) 10 ÷ 6.5 = **1.5 μm** *[2 marks for the correct answer or 1 mark for the correct calculation.]*
  b) 14 × 1.5 = **21 μm** *[1 mark for multiplying 14 by answer to part a), 1 mark for an answer of 21 or 22 μm.]*

Page 65 — Cell Organisation

1   It's best described as an organ *[1 mark]* as it is made of many tissues working together to perform a particular function *[1 mark]*.
2   A *[1 mark]*
3   Similar cells are organised into tissues to carry out a particular function (e.g. squamous epithelium in the alveoli is made up of a single layer of flat cells) *[1 mark]*. Different tissues that work together to perform a particular function are organised into organs (e.g. the lungs are made of squamous epithelium tissue, fibrous connective tissue and endothelium tissue) *[1 mark]*. Organs work together to form organ systems with a particular function (e.g. the lungs are part of the respiratory system) *[1 mark]*.

Page 67 — The Cell Cycle and Mitosis

1 a) A — Metaphase *[1 mark]*, B — Telophase *[1 mark]*, C — Anaphase *[1 mark]*.
  b) X — Chromosome/Chromatid *[1 mark]*, Y — Centromere *[1 mark]*, Z — Spindle fibre *[1 mark]*.
2   32 ÷ 42 = **0.76** *[2 marks for the correct answer or 1 mark for the correct calculation.]*

Topic 3B — Reproduction and Inheritance

Page 69 — Gametes and Fertilisation

1   Sperm have flagella/tails, which allow them to swim/move towards the egg cell *[1 mark]*. They contain lots of mitochondria to provide the energy needed for swimming/movement *[1 mark]*. The acrosome in the sperm head contains digestive enzymes that break down the egg cell's zona pellucida, enabling the sperm to penetrate the egg *[1 mark]*.

2   Following the acrosome reaction, the sperm head fuses with the cell membrane of the egg cell *[1 mark]*. This triggers the cortical reaction, where the contents of the cortical granules are released from the egg cell *[1 mark]*. The chemicals from the cortical granules make the zona pellucida thick and impenetrable to other sperm *[1 mark]*. The sperm nucleus enters the egg cell and fuses with the egg cell nucleus — this is fertilisation *[1 mark]*.
This question asks you to describe the events that occur after the acrosome reaction, so you won't get any marks for describing the acrosome reaction or anything before it, e.g. the sperm swimming towards the egg cell in the oviduct.

Page 71 — Meiosis and Inheritance

1 a) It means the genes are both on the same chromosome *[1 mark]*.
  b) The closer together the loci of two genes, the more likely it is that they will stay linked *[1 mark]*. This is because crossing over is less likely to split them up *[1 mark]*.
2 a) Before the first division of meiosis, homologous pairs of chromosomes come together and pair up *[1 mark]*.
    The chromatids twist around each other and bits of the chromatid break off and rejoin onto the other chromatid *[1 mark]*.
    The chromatids now contain different combinations of alleles, so each of the four daughter cells will contain chromatids with different combinations of alleles *[1 mark]*.
  b) Independent assortment means the chromosome pairs can split up in any way *[1 mark]*. So, the cells produced can contain any combination of maternal and paternal chromosomes with different alleles *[1 mark]*.

Topic 3C — Differentiation and Variation

Page 73 — Cell Differentiation and Gene Expression

1 a) Totipotent stem cells can produce all cell types, including all the specialised cells in an organism and extraembryonic cells *[1 mark]*. Pluripotent stem cells have the ability to produce all the specialised cells in an organism, but not extraembryonic cells *[1 mark]*. This is because the genes for extraembryonic cells have become inactivated *[1 mark]*.
Be careful not to get totipotent and pluripotent mixed up. It might help you to think of totipotent as totally potent — they can produce absolutely every cell type needed for an organism to develop.
  b) **5-6 marks:**
The answer fully describes all of the steps involved in the production of specialised cells.
The answer has a clear and logical structure and ideas are well-linked. The information given is relevant and detailed.
3-4 marks:
The answer describes most of the steps involved in the production of specialised cells.
The answer has some structure and attempts to link ideas. Most of the information given is relevant and there is some detail involved.
1-2 marks:
The answer outlines one or two of the steps involved in the production of specialised cells.
The answer has very little clear structure and ideas are not well-linked. The information given is basic and lacking in detail. It may not all be relevant.
0 marks:
No relevant information is given.
Here are some points your answer may include:
All stem cells contain the same genes, but not all of them are expressed/active. Under the right conditions, some genes are activated and others are inactivated. mRNA is only transcribed from the active genes. mRNA from the active genes is translated into proteins. These proteins modify the cell by changing the cell structure and controlling the cell's processes. The changes cause the cell to become specialised, and they're hard to reverse.

Answers

ge 75 — Stem Cells in Medicine

a) Any one from: e.g. stem cells could be used to save lives *[1 mark]*. / Stem cells could be used to improve a person's quality of life *[1 mark]*. / Accept a description of stem cells being used to cure a specific disease *[1 mark]*.

b) i) E.g. embryonic stem cells can develop into all types of specialised cells *[1 mark]*, whereas adult stem cells can only develop into a limited range of cells *[1 mark]*.

   ii) Some people believe that fertilised embryos have a right to life from the moment of fertilisation *[1 mark]*. Some people believe it is wrong to destroy (viable) embryos *[1 mark]*.

ge 77 — Variation

a) Histones are proteins that DNA wraps around to form chromatin, which makes up chromosomes *[1 mark]*.

b) Histone modifications can affect how condensed the chromatin associated with the histones is/ how accessible the DNA is *[1 mark]*. This affects whether the proteins/enzymes needed for transcription are able to bind to the DNA and transcribe the genes *[1 mark]*.

opic 4A — Biodiversity

ge 80 — Biodiversity and Endemism

a) The number of different species *[1 mark]* and the number of individuals/population size of each species *[1 mark]*.

b) N = 35 + 25 + 34 + 12 + 26 = 132
   N (N − 1) = 132 (132 − 1) = 17292
   Σ n (n − 1) = 35 (35 − 1) + 25 (25 − 1) + 34 (34 − 1) + 12 (12 − 1) + 26 (26 − 1) = 3694
   Use of N (N − 1) ÷ Σ n (n − 1) to calculate diversity index of 17292 ÷ 3694 = **4.68**
   [3 marks for correct answer, otherwise 1 mark for N (N − 1) = 17292 and 1 mark for Σ n (n − 1) = 3694.]
   It's always best if you put your working — even if the answer isn't quite right you could get marks for correct working.

c) The diversity of bumblebee species is greater at site 2 *[1 mark]*. This suggests there's a link between enhanced field margins and an increased diversity of bumblebee species *[1 mark]*.

ge 83 — Adaptation and Evolution

a) E.g. the new species could not breed with each other *[1 mark]*.

b) Different populations of flies were physically/geographically isolated and experienced different selection pressures (different food) *[1 mark]*. This led to changes in allele frequencies between the populations *[1 mark]*, which made them reproductively isolated/unable to interbreed and produce fertile offspring, and eventually resulted in speciation *[1 mark]*.
   The brown owls may be better camouflaged/blend in with the landscape better than the grey owls when there's no snow cover, making them less likely to be eaten by predators *[1 mark]*. The decrease in the amount of snowfall puts a selection pressure on the grey owls *[1 mark]* making them less likely to survive *[1 mark]*. This leads to fewer owls in the population and reduces the competition for resources *[1 mark]*. The brown owls are more likely to survive, reproduce and pass on the allele for darker/ brown colouring to their offspring, increasing the frequency of the allele for darker/brown colouring in the population *[1 mark]*.
   Snow makes everything white, so lighter coloured owls blend in better when there's snow around. They stick out more when there's no snow though.

Page 85 — The Hardy-Weinberg Principle

1 q = 0.23
   p + q = 1
   so p = 1 − 0.23 = 0.77
   The frequency of the heterozygous genotype = 2pq
   = 2(0.77 × 0.23) = **0.35** *[1 mark]*

2 a) Frequency of genotype TT = p^2 = 0.14
   So the frequency of the dominant allele = p = $\sqrt{0.14}$ = 0.37
   The frequency of the recessive allele = q
   q = 1 − p
   q = 1 − 0.37 = **0.63** *[1 mark]*

   b) Frequency of homozygous recessive genotype tt = q^2 = 0.63^2 = **0.40** *[1 mark. Allow 1 mark for evidence of correct calculation using incorrect answer to part a).]*

   c) Those that don't have a cleft chin are homozygous recessive tt = 40%, so the percentage that do have a cleft chin, Tt or TT, is 100% − 40% = **60%** *[1 mark]*.
   There are other ways of calculating this answer, e.g. working out the value of 2pq and adding it to p^2. It doesn't matter which way you do it as long as you get the right answer.

Page 87 — Classification

1 a)

Domain	Kingdom	Phylum	Class	Order	Family	Genus	Species
Eukaryota	Animalia	Chordata	Actinopterygii	Salmoniformes	Salmonidae	Salmo	trutta

   [1 mark for 4 or more answers correct.
   2 marks for all 7 answers correct.]

   b) They are unable to reproduce to give fertile offspring *[1 mark]*. Although brook trout and brown trout do sometimes mate to produce offspring, those offspring are infertile.

Page 89 — Conservation of Biodiversity

1 E.g. it might be difficult to recreate the exact conditions of the lizard's environment in captivity, so they may have problems breeding *[1 mark]*. Some people think it's cruel to keep animals in captivity, even if it's done to prevent them becoming extinct *[1 mark]*. The reintroduced lizards could bring new diseases to the habitat, harming any organisms that are already there *[1 mark]*. Because they were born in captivity, any reintroduced lizards may not exhibit all their natural behaviours in the wild (e.g. they may have problems finding food or communicating with other members of their species) *[1 mark]*.

Topic 4B — Resources from Plants

Page 91 — Plant Cell Structure

1 D *[1 mark]*
2 a) chloroplast *[1 mark]*
   b) It is the site where photosynthesis takes place *[1 mark]*.

Page 93 — Plant Stems

1 a) X — sclerenchyma fibres *[1 mark]*, Y — xylem vessels *[1 mark]*
   b) The function of sclerenchyma fibres (X) is to provide support *[1 mark]*. The function of xylem vessels (Y) is to transport water and mineral ions up the plant, and provide support *[1 mark]*. *[Accept correct function of phloem tissue if identified incorrectly in part a).]*

Page 95 — Starch, Cellulose and Plant Fibres

1 a) The cell wall contains cellulose microfibrils in a net-like arrangement *[1 mark]*. The strength of the microfibrils and their arrangement in the cell wall makes plant fibres strong *[1 mark]*.
   b) Secondary thickening is the production of another cell wall between the normal cell wall and the cell membrane *[1 mark]*. The secondary cell wall is thicker and usually has more lignin than the normal cell wall, which gives plant fibres lots of strength *[1 mark]*.

Answers

2 a) E.g. for each of the four different types of plant fibre the students could have attached the fibre to a clamp stand at one end and hung a weight from the other end *[1 mark]*. Weights could then have been added one at a time to each of the fibres until they broke and the mass taken to break each fibre recorded *[1 mark]*. In order to reduce the effect of random error and make their results more precise they could have repeated the experiment at least three times and calculated the mean for each type of fibre *[1 mark]*.

b) Any two from: e.g. they should have ensured that all the fibres tested were of the same length *[1 mark]*. / They should have kept the temperature the same *[1 mark]*. / They should have kept the humidity of the environment constant *[1 mark]*.

c) Fibre B would be most suitable because it has the highest tensile strength/can hold the most weight without breaking *[1 mark]*.

Page 97 — Sustainability and Plant Minerals

1   1 — Nutrient broth containing all essential nutrients except magnesium ions.
     2 — Nutrient broth containing all essential nutrients except nitrate ions.
     [1 mark for both specific mineral deficient broths.]
     3 — Nutrient broth containing all essential nutrients.
     4 — Broth lacking all essential nutrients.
     [1 mark for both control broths.]

Page 99 — Drugs from Plants and Drug Testing

1   **5-6 marks:**
The answer gives a full description of a valid investigation, which is fully supported by scientific knowledge.
The answer has a clear and logical structure and ideas are well-linked. The information given is relevant and detailed.
3-4 marks:
The answer gives some description of a valid investigation, which is sometimes supported by scientific knowledge.
The answer has some structure and attempts to link ideas. Most of the information given is relevant and there is some detail involved.
1-2 marks:
The answer attempts to describe an investigation.
The answer has very little clear structure and ideas are not well-linked. The information given is basic and lacking in detail. It may not all be relevant.
0 marks:
No relevant information is given.
Here are some points your answer may include:
A sample of bacterial species X should be spread onto an agar plate. A disc of absorbent paper should be dipped into an extract of the plant, an equally-sized disc should be dipped in mouthwash Y and another equally-sized disc should be dipped in ethanol (to act as a control). The control is used to show that it's the plant extract or mouthwash (independent variables) inhibiting the growth of bacteria (the dependent variable). The discs should then be placed on the plate, widely spaced apart. The plate should then have a lid lightly taped on, be inverted and incubated at about 25 °C for 24-48 hours to allow the bacteria to grow. The clear zones around each disc should then be measured by measuring the diameter/calculating the area. The procedure should be repeated another two times and a mean of the results calculated to increase the reliability of the results. Throughout the experiment, variables such as the incubation temperature, the composition of the agar etc. should all be kept the same to ensure that the results are valid. Aseptic techniques should be used throughout the experiment to prevent contamination of microbial cultures.

Topic 5A — Ecosystems and Photosynthesis

Page 102 — Factors Affecting Abundance and Distribution

1   In the first three years, the population of prey increases (from 5000 to 30 000) and the population of predators increases slightly later (in the first five years, from 4000 to 11 000) *[1 mark]*. This is because there's more food available for the predators once the prey population has increased *[1 mark]*. The prey population then falls after year three (to 3000 just before year 10), because lots are being eaten by the large population of predators *[1 mark]*. Shortly after the prey population falls, the predator population also falls (back to 4000 by just after year 10) because there's less food available *[1 mark]*.

2 a) A niche is the role of a species within its habitat *[1 mark]*. It includes both its biotic and abiotic interactions *[1 mark]*.

b) The lizards feed on the same insects, so the amount of food available to both species is reduced *[1 mark]*. This means there will be fewer of each species in the area/there will be a lower abundance of each species than if there was only one lizard species *[1 mark]*.

Page 105 — Investigating Populations and Abiotic Factors

1 a) Several frame quadrats would be placed on the ground at random locations within the field to avoid bias *[1 mark]*. The percentage of each frame quadrat that's covered by daffodils would be recorded *[1 mark]*. The percentage cover for the whole field could then be estimated by averaging the data collected in all of the frame quadrats *[1 mark]*.

b) Any two from: e.g. temperature could be measured using a thermometer *[1 mark]*. / Rainfall could be measured using a rain gauge *[1 mark]*. / Humidity could be measured using an electronic hygrometer *[1 mark]*.

Page 107 — Succession

1 a) Primary succession *[1 mark]* because there is no soil or organic matter *[1 mark]*.

b) When the grass dies, microorganisms decompose the dead organic material, forming a soil *[1 mark]*. The formation of soil helps to retain water and makes the conditions less hostile, which allows larger plants, like shrubs, to move in *[1 mark]*.

2 a) **5-6 marks:**
The answer fully describes all of the stages and processes involved in secondary succession that would occur in the field. The answer has a clear and logical structure and ideas are well-linked. The information given is relevant and detailed.
3-4 marks:
The answer describes most of the stages and processes involved in secondary succession that would occur in the field.
The answer has some structure and attempts to link ideas. Most of the information given is relevant and there is some detail involved.
1-2 marks:
The answer outlines one or two of the stages and/or processes involved in secondary succession that would occur in the field. The answer has very little clear structure and ideas are not well-linked. The information given is basic and lacking in detail. It may not all be relevant.
0 marks:
No relevant information is given.

Answers

Here are some points your answer may include:
This is an example of secondary succession, because there is already a soil layer present in the field. The first species to grow will be the pioneer species, which in this case will be larger plants, e.g. shrubs. These will then be replaced with other large plants, e.g. small trees. At each stage, different plants and animals that are better adapted for the improved conditions will move in, out-compete the species already there, and become the dominant species. During the process of succession, the abiotic factors also change, such as when organisms die and decompose causing the soil layer to get deeper. As succession goes on, the ecosystem becomes more complex, so biodiversity (the variety of living organisms) increases. Eventually large trees will grow, forming the climax community, which is the final stage.

b) Ploughing destroys any plants that were growing *[1 mark]*, so larger plants may start to grow, but they won't have long enough to establish themselves before the field is ploughed again *[1 mark]*.

Page 109 — Photosynthesis and Energy Supply

a) They absorb the light energy needed for photosynthesis *[1 mark]*.
b) Any three from: e.g. it's surrounded by a chloroplast envelope, which keeps the reactants for photosynthesis close to their reaction sites *[1 mark]*. / The thylakoids have a large surface area to allow as much light energy as possible to be absorbed *[1 mark]*. / Lots of ATP synthase molecules are present in the thylakoid membranes to produce ATP (in the light-dependent reaction) *[1 mark]*. / The stroma contains all the enzymes, sugars and organic acids for the light-independent reaction to take place *[1 mark]*.

Page 113 — Photosynthesis Reactions

a) Any five points from: e.g. ribulose bisphosphate/RuBP and carbon dioxide/CO_2 join together to form an unstable 6-carbon compound *[1 mark]*. This reaction is catalysed by the enzyme RUBISCO *[1 mark]*. The compound breaks down into two molecules of a 3-carbon compound called glycerate 3-phosphate/GP *[1 mark]*. Two molecules of glycerate 3-phosphate are then converted into two molecules of glyceraldehyde 3-phosphate/GALP *[1 mark]*. The energy for this reaction comes from ATP *[1 mark]* and the H^+ ions come from reduced NADP *[1 mark]*.
b) Ribulose bisphosphate is regenerated from glyceraldehyde 3-phosphate/GALP *[1 mark]*. ATP provides the energy to do this *[1 mark]*.
This question is only worth two marks so only the main facts are needed, without the detail of the number of molecules.
c) No glycerate 3-phosphate/GP would be produced *[1 mark]*, so no glyceraldehyde 3-phosphate/GALP would be produced *[1 mark]*. This means there would be no glucose produced *[1 mark]*.

Page 115 — Energy Transfer and Productivity

a) Because not all of the energy available from the grass is taken in by the Arctic hare *[1 mark]*. Some parts of the grass aren't eaten, so the energy isn't taken in *[1 mark]*, and some parts of the grass are indigestible, so they'll pass through the hares and come out as waste *[1 mark]*. Some energy is lost to the environment when the Arctic hare uses energy from respiration for things like movement or body heat *[1 mark]*.
b) (137 ÷ 2345) × 100 = **5.8%** *[1 mark]*

Topic 5B — Climate Change and Evolution

Page 117 — Introduction to Climate Change

1   The diagram shows that the thickness of the pine tree rings fluctuated, but there was a trend of increasingly thicker rings from 1909 to 2009 *[1 mark]*. The thickness of each tree ring depends on the climate when the ring was formed *[1 mark]*. Warmer climates tend to give thicker rings than colder climates *[1 mark]*. This suggests that the climate where the pine tree lived became warmer over the last century, which is evidence of climate change *[1 mark]*.

2   Peat bogs can preserve pollen and are formed in layers *[1 mark]*. Pollen in different layers can be used to identify plant species in different time periods, with pollen in deeper layers being older *[1 mark]*. Scientists know the climate that different plant species live in now *[1 mark]*. When they find preserved pollen from similar plants, they know that the climate must have been similar when that pollen was produced *[1 mark]*.

Page 119 — Causes of Climate Change

1   The average global temperature fluctuated between 1970 and 2006, but the general trend was a steady increase from around 13.9 °C to around 14.5°C *[1 mark]*. The atmospheric CO_2 concentration also showed a trend of increasing from around 325 ppm in 1970 to around 380 ppm in 2006 *[1 mark]* so there's a positive correlation between temperature and CO_2 concentration *[1 mark]*. The increasing CO_2 concentration could be linked to the increasing temperature but you can't conclude that it's a causal relationship because other factors may have been involved *[1 mark]*.
You usually have to quote figures from graphs and tables in your answer to get full marks.

Page 121 — Effects of Climate Change

1 a) An increase in temperature causes an increase in enzyme activity *[1 mark]*, which speeds up metabolic reactions *[1 mark]*. Increasing the rate of metabolic reactions in a potato tuber moth will increase its rate of growth *[1 mark]*, so it will progress through its life cycle faster *[1 mark]*.
b) The range of the potato tuber moth may expand northwards into the rest of Europe *[1 mark]* because rising temperatures due to global warming may make the climate in northern Europe more suitable for the moth than it was previously *[1 mark]*.

Page 123 — Investigating the Effects of Climate Change

1 a) E.g.

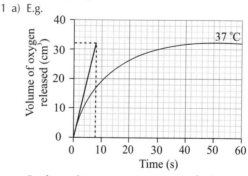

Gradient of tangent = 32 ÷ 8 = **4 cm³ s⁻¹**
[2 marks for correct answer, 1 marks for correct working. Accept answers in the range of 3.75 to 4.25 cm³ s⁻¹.]
b) $Q_{10} = \dfrac{\text{rate at 37 °C}}{\text{rate at 27 °C}} = \dfrac{4}{2.3} = \mathbf{1.7}$ (1 d.p.)
[1 mark. Accept incorrect answer from part a) ÷ 2.3]

Answers

2 Some seedlings (of the same variety and age) could be planted in soil trays, and the height of each seedling measured *[1 mark]*. The trays could then be placed in incubators at different temperatures *[1 mark]*. All other variables, e.g. the water content of the soil/the light intensity/the CO_2 concentration, would need to be kept the same for each tray as these all affect growth *[1 mark]*. After a period of incubation, the change in height of each seedling could be recorded and then the average growth rate for each tray calculated to get more reliable results *[1 mark]*.

Page 125 — Reducing Climate Change

1 **9-7 marks:**
The answer shows good biological knowledge of the carbon cycle and presents a clear, balanced argument or conclusion about the likely effectiveness of biofuels as an alternative to fossil fuels supported by evidence.
The answer has a clear and logical structure and ideas are well-linked.
6-4 marks:
The answer demonstrates biological knowledge of the carbon cycle and presents some supported arguments about the likely effectiveness of biofuels or attempts a conclusion.
The answer has some structure and attempts to link ideas.
3-1 marks:
The answer shows limited biological knowledge of the carbon cycle and any arguments about the likely effectiveness of biofuels are basic and unsupported.
The answer has very little structure and ideas are not well-linked.
0 marks:
No relevant information is given.
Here are some points your answer may include:
Biofuels are fuels produced from biomass / material that is or was recently living. Biofuels are burnt to release energy, which releases CO_2 into the atmosphere. There's no net increase in atmospheric CO_2 concentration though because the amount of CO_2 produced is the same as the amount of CO_2 taken in when the material was growing. Using biofuels as an alternative to fossil fuels stops the increase in atmospheric CO_2 concentration caused by burning fossil fuels. As well as providing us with a more sustainable fuel source, biofuels can benefit farmers because some governments fund the farming of crops for biofuels.
In addition, the price of biofuels is usually lower than oil-based fuels so it is likely to encourage drivers to use biofuels, reducing the demand for fossil fuels. However, using farmland to grow crops for biofuels will reduce the amount of land available to grow food crops, possibly causing food shortages. Also, to create enough space to grow crops for biofuels, forests have to be cleared which reduces the amount of CO_2 absorbed by plants through photosynthesis. In conclusion, using biofuels as an alternative to fossil fuels may be an effective strategy because it meets the human need for a fuel source without increasing atmospheric CO_2 concentrations. However, it will need careful management to ensure that food sources aren't compromised and deforestation is minimised.
It doesn't matter whether you conclude that biofuels are likely to be an effective alternative to fossil fuels or not, as long as your conclusion is supported with scientific evidence.

Page 127 — Evolution, Natural Selection and Speciation

1 a) B *[1 mark]*
   b) Some of the finches from the original species may have been isolated from the other finches, on an island that may have contained larger, tougher seeds *[1 mark]*. Random genetic mutations may have led to some members of this isolated population having larger beaks, which enabled them to feed on the larger, tougher seeds *[1 mark]*. These individuals would have been more likely to survive, reproduce and pass on their alleles, including the allele for larger beak size *[1 mark]*. Over time a greater proportion of the population would have inherited the allele for larger beak size *[1 mark]*. Over many generations the population on this island would have become genetically distinct from the original population, and the two populations would be unable to interbreed to produce fertile offspring *[1 mark]*.
   c) Any two from: e.g. seasonal changes (become sexually active at different times) *[1 mark]* / mechanical changes (changes to genitalia) *[1 mark]* / behavioural changes (changes in behaviour that prevent mating) *[1 mark]*.

Page 129 — Evidence for Evolution

1 Genomics uses DNA technology to determine the base sequence of an organism's genome/entire set of DNA, which enables scientists to make comparisons between organisms' DNA *[1 mark]*. Evolution is caused by gradual changes in the base sequence of organisms' DNA *[1 mark]* so organisms that diverged away from each other more recently should have more similar DNA *[1 mark]*, as less time has passed for changes in the DNA sequence to occur, which is exactly what scientists have found *[1 mark]*.

2 Before scientists can get their work published it must undergo peer review, which is when other scientists who work in that area read and review the work *[1 mark]*. The peer reviewer checks that the work is valid and supports the conclusion *[1 mark]*. Scientific journals also allow other scientists to repeat experiment and see if they get the same results using the same methods *[1 mark]*. If the results are replicated over and over again, the scientific community can be pretty confident that the evidence collected is reliable *[1 mark]*.

Topic 6A — Forensics

Page 131 — Microbial Decomposition and Time of Death

1 E.g. it was probably 4 to 6 hours ago *[1 mark]*.
Plus, any three from:
This is because a dead human body loses heat at a rate of approximately 1.5-2.0 °C per hour, which suggests the time of death was around 4 to 5 hours ago *[1 mark]*. / Rigor mortis has only recently started as it's limited to the upper parts of the body, which suggests that the time of death was around 4 to 6 hours ago *[1 mark]*. / There's a lack of visible decomposition, which suggests that the time of death was only a few hours ago *[1 mark]* / Blowfly larvae hatch from eggs approximately 24 hours after being laid, so no blowfly larvae on the body suggests that the time of death was less than 24 hours ago *[1 mark]*.
[Maximum of 4 marks available.]

age 135 — DNA Profiling

a) A sample of DNA is obtained, e.g. from a person's blood/saliva, and PCR is used to amplify specific regions of the DNA *[1 mark]*. A fluorescent tag is added to all the DNA fragments so they can be seen under UV light *[1 mark]*. Gel electrophoresis is used to separate the DNA fragments according to their length *[1 mark]*.

b) DNA profile 1 is most likely to be from the child's father because five out of six of the bands on his DNA profile match that of the child's, compared to only one on profile 2 *[1 mark]*.

c) E.g. it can be used to link a person to a crime scene (forensic science). / It can be used to prevent inbreeding between animals or plants *[1 mark]*.
Any three from: The DNA sample from the hair is mixed with free nucleotides, primers and DNA polymerase *[1 mark]*. / The mixture is heated to 95 °C to break the hydrogen bonds, then cooled to between 50-65 °C to allow the primers to bind/anneal to the DNA *[1 mark]*. / The mixture is then heated to 72 °C so that DNA polymerase can work *[1 mark]*. / The amount of DNA is doubled during one cycle, so the cycle would be repeated over and over to produce lots of copies *[1 mark]*.

opic 6B — Microorganisms and Immunity

age 138 — Bacterial and Viral Infections

a) i) C *[1 mark]*
   ii) A *[1 mark]*
   Remember, RNA is needed for protein production so it is present in bacteria along with DNA.

b) Any three from: e.g. TB has a cell wall whereas HIV has a capsid/protein coat. / TB has ribosomes/a cytoplasm and HIV doesn't. / HIV has an envelope/attachment proteins and TB doesn't.
[Maximum of 3 marks available, 1 mark for each difference.]
Initial infection by HIV may lead to severe flu-like symptoms, while HIV is replicating rapidly *[1 mark]*. After this follows a latency period, in which HIV replication drops to a lower level and the infected person won't experience symptoms *[1 mark]*. A person with HIV is classed as having AIDS when symptoms of their failing immune system start to appear or their T-helper cell count drops below a certain level *[1 mark]*. The initial symptoms of AIDS include minor infections of mucous membranes/recurring respiratory infections caused by a lower than normal number of T helper cells *[1 mark]*. As AIDS progresses the number of T helper cells decreases further and patients become susceptible to more serious infections, including chronic diarrhoea/serious bacterial infections/TB *[1 mark]*. During the late stages of AIDS, patients have a very low number of T helper cells and suffer from a range of serious infections that could kill them, such as toxoplasmosis/candidiasis *[1 mark]*.

age 140 — Infection and the Non-Specific mmune Response

a) Immune system cells recognise foreign antigens on the surface of a pathogen and release molecules that trigger inflammation *[1 mark]*.

b) The molecules released by immune system cells cause vasodilation (widening of the blood vessels) around the site of infection, increasing the blood flow to it *[1 mark]*. The molecules also increase the permeability of the blood vessels *[1 mark]*. The increased blood flow brings many more immune system cells to the site of infection *[1 mark]* and the increased permeability allows those cells to move out of the blood vessels and into the infected tissue *[1 mark]*.
When a phagocyte recognises the antigens on a pathogen, it engulfs the pathogen *[1 mark]*. The pathogen becomes contained in a phagocytic vacuole. A lysosome fuses with the phagocytic vacuole *[1 mark]* and digestive enzymes/lysozymes from the lysosome break down the pathogen *[1 mark]*.

Page 143 — The Specific Immune Response

1 a) T cells are activated when receptors on the surface of the T cells bind to complementary antigens *[1 mark]* presented to them by antigen-presenting cells (such as macrophages) *[1 mark]*.
   b) C *[1 mark]*

2 Antibodies agglutinate pathogens, so that phagocytes can get rid of a lot of the pathogens at once *[1 mark]*. Antibodies neutralise toxins produced by pathogens *[1 mark]*. Antibodies bind to pathogens to prevent them from binding to and infecting human cells *[1 mark]*.
There are three marks available for this question so you need to think of three different functions.

3 Genes contain sections called introns that don't code for amino acids and sections called exons that do code for amino acids *[1 mark]*. During transcription the introns and exons are both copied into mRNA *[1 mark]*. The introns are then removed and the exons are joined together forming mRNA strands by a process called splicing *[1 mark]*. Sometimes certain exons can be removed as well (alternative splicing), to form different mRNA strands *[1 mark]*. This means more than one amino acid sequence and so more than one protein can be produced from one gene *[1 mark]*.

Page 145 — Developing Immunity

1 **5-6 marks:**
The answer fully and accurately explains the changes in antibody concentration shown by the graph in relation to the primary and secondary immune responses.
The answer has a clear and logical structure. The information given is relevant and detailed and ideas are well-linked.
3-4 marks:
The answer makes some attempt to explain the changes in antibody concentration shown by the graph and makes some links to the primary and secondary immune responses.
The answer has some structure and attempts to link ideas. Most of the information given is relevant and there is some detail involved.
1-2 marks:
A brief reference is made to either the primary or secondary immune response. Some attempt may be made to link this to a change in antibody concentration shown by the graph.
The answer has very little clear structure and ideas are not well-linked. The information given is basic and lacking in detail. It may not all be relevant.
0 marks:
No relevant information is given.
Here are some points your answer may include:
Before the person is exposed to the antigen there are none of the right/complementary antibodies in their bloodstream. This is because the T and B cells haven't come into contact with the antigen. Shortly after the person is exposed to the antigen the concentration of the right/complementary antibody begins to rise. This is the primary response and it's slow because there aren't many B cells that can make the antibody needed to bind to the antigen. The concentration of antibody peaks at about 20 days after the first exposure and then it begins to fall. It begins to fall because the person's immune system is starting to overcome the infection. When the person is exposed to the same pathogen again at 60 days, the secondary response happens. The concentration of antibody rises quickly from the moment of the second exposure to a peak at about 7 days after the second exposure. This is because B memory cells that were created after the first exposure quickly divide into plasma cells. They produce the right/complementary antibody to the antigen almost immediately. T memory cells also recognise the antigen and divide into the correct type of T cells to kill the cell carrying the antigen.

Answers

2   E.g. HIV kills the immune systems cells that it infects *[1 mark]*, which reduces the overall number of immune system cells in the body, so there is less chance that HIV will be detected *[1 mark]*. / HIV forms new strains by varying the structure of its antigens/ undergoes antigenic variation *[1 mark]*, which means the antibodies produced for one strain of HIV won't recognise new strains (that have different antigens), so the immune system has to produce a primary response against each new strain *[1 mark]*. / HIV disrupts antigen presentation in infected cells *[1 mark]*, which prevents immune system cells recognising and killing the infected cells *[1 mark]*.
[Maximum of 2 marks available, 1 mark for an evasion mechanism and 1 mark for the accompanying explanation.]

Page 147 — Antibiotics

1 a) The bacteria to be tested are spread onto the agar plate *[1 mark]*. Paper discs soaked with the antibiotics are placed apart on the plate, along with a negative control disc soaked in sterile water *[1 mark]*. The whole experiment is performed using aseptic techniques, e.g. using sterile equipment and working near a Bunsen flame *[1 mark]*. The plate is incubated at about 25 °C for 24-48 hours *[1 mark]*.
  b) Erythromycin *[1 mark]*, because it has the largest clear zone *[1 mark]*.
2   E.g. Hospital staff and visitors not washing their hands before and after visiting a patient *[1 mark]*. Hospital staff and visitors should be encouraged to wash their hands before and after they've been with a patient *[1 mark]*. / Equipment (e.g. beds or surgical instruments) and surfaces not being disinfected after they're used *[1 mark]*. Equipment and surfaces should be disinfected after they're used *[1 mark]*.
[Maximum of 2 marks, 1 mark for a description of poor hygiene and 1 mark for a code of practice.]

Topic 7A — Muscles and Respiration

Page 149 — Muscles and Movement

1   Muscles are made up of bundles of muscle fibres *[1 mark]*. Muscle fibres contain long organelles called myofibrils *[1 mark]*. Myofibrils contain bundles of myofilaments *[1 mark]*.
2 a) The quadriceps are the extensors and the hamstrings are the flexors *[1 mark]*.
  b) Antagonistic pairs *[1 mark]*.
3   A = sarcomere *[1 mark]*.
    B = Z-line *[1 mark]*.
    C = H-zone *[1 mark]*.

Page 151 — Muscle Contraction

1   Muscles need ATP to relax because ATP provides the energy to break the actin-myosin cross bridges *[1 mark]*. If the cross bridges can't be broken, the myosin heads will remain attached to the actin filaments *[1 mark]*, so the actin filaments can't slide back to their relaxed position *[1 mark]*.
2   The muscles won't contract *[1 mark]* because calcium ions won't be released into the sarcoplasm, so troponin won't be removed from its binding site *[1 mark]*. This means no actin-myosin cross bridges can be formed *[1 mark]*.

Page 153 — Aerobic Respiration

1 a) B *[1 mark]*
  b) C *[1 mark]*
  c) It goes into the mitochondrial matrix *[1 mark]* for use in the link reaction *[1 mark]*.

Page 155 — Aerobic Respiration

1 a) The transfer of electrons down the electron transport chain stops *[1 mark]*. So there's no energy released to phosphorylate ADP/ produce ATP *[1 mark]*.
  b) The Krebs cycle stops *[1 mark]* because there's no NAD/FAD coming from the electron transport chain *[1 mark]*.

Page 157 — Respirometers and Anaerobic Respiration

1 a) To make sure the results are only due to oxygen uptake by the woodlice *[1 mark]*.
  b) The carbon dioxide given out would not be absorbed and would replace some of the oxygen consumed / the change in volume of the air in the test tube would not be as great *[1 mark]*. Therefore it would not be possible to accurately calculate the oxygen uptake of the woodlice *[1 mark]*.
  c) Carbon dioxide/CO_2 *[1 mark]*.
2   Because lactate fermentation doesn't involve electron carriers/the electron transport chain/oxidative phosphorylation *[1 mark]*.

Topic 7B — Exercise

Page 159 — Electrical Activity in the Heart

1 a) The sinoatrial node acts as a pacemaker / initiates heartbeats *[1 mark]*.
  b) the Bundle of His conducts waves of electricity from the AVN to the Purkyne fibres in the ventricle walls *[1 mark]*.
2   E.g. the ventricle is not contracting properly *[1 mark]*. This could be because of muscle damage / because the AVN is not conducting impulses to the ventricles properly *[1 mark]*.
For this question, you're not expected to know the answer, but you should apply your knowledge — think about how the contraction of the ventricles causes the QRS complex and what could cause a reduction in this.

Page 161 — Variations in Breathing Rate

1   The breathing rate would go up *[1 mark]*, because carbonic acid lowers blood pH *[1 mark]*. This stimulates chemoreceptors in the medulla oblongata, aortic bodies and carotid bodies *[1 mark]*. The chemoreceptors send nerve impulses to the medulla oblongata *[1 mark]*. In turn, the medulla oblongata sends more frequent nerve impulses to the intercostal muscles and diaphragm *[1 mark]*.
2 a) C *[1 mark]*
  b) Any five valid points from: As the lungs inflate, stretch receptors in the lungs are stimulated *[1 mark]*. The stretch receptors send nerve impulses back to the medulla oblongata *[1 mark]*, which inhibit the action of the inspiratory centre *[1 mark]*. This means the expiratory centre is no longer inhibited *[1 mark]*, so it sends nerve impulses to the diaphragm and the intercostal muscles to relax *[1 mark]*, causing the lungs to deflate which results in air being exhaled *[1 mark]*. *[Maximum of five marks available.]*

Page 163 — Variations in Heart Rate

1 a) Heart rate = cardiac output / stroke volume *[1 mark]*
     = 5420 cm³ min⁻¹ / 72 cm³ **= 75 bpm** (2 s.f.) *[1 mark]*.
  b) Chemoreceptors in his aortic bodies, carotid bodies and medulla oblongata *[1 mark]* detect a low blood oxygen level, low blood pH and high blood carbon dioxide level *[1 mark]*. Electrical impulses are then sent from these receptors along (sensory) neurones to the cardiovascular control centre in the medulla oblongata *[1 mark]*.
  c) Sympathetic neurones release noradrenaline *[1 mark]* which binds to receptors on the SAN *[1 mark]*, causing it to fire impulses more frequently, which increases heart rate *[1 mark]*.

Answers

Page 166 — Investigating Ventilation

a) Tidal volume = 0.4 dm³ *[1 mark]*.
Breathing rate = 12 breaths per minute/bpm *[1 mark]*.
Respiratory minute ventilation = tidal volume × breathing rate
= 0.4 × 12 = 4.8 dm³ min⁻¹ *[1 mark]*.
To find the tidal volume, you need to find the average difference in the volume of gas between each peak and trough on the trace. The distance between each peak and trough is roughly the same for this example, so you can just measure the tidal volume between one peak and its adjacent trough. For example, the difference between the last peak and trough on the graph is 1.4 − 1 = 0.4 dm³.

b) E.g. they would consume all of the oxygen in the spirometer chamber *[1 mark]*.
Remember, the gas in the spirometer chamber is oxygen. You can see that when the person is resting for one minute the volume of oxygen in the spirometer decreases by approximately 0.7 dm³. When they start exercising their rate of oxygen consumption will increase as their body needs more oxygen for respiration, so the spirometer is likely to run out of oxygen within a minute.

Page 169 — Homeostasis

It is a mechanism that amplifies a change further away from its normal level *[1 mark]*.

a) Thermoreceptors/temperature receptors detect a higher internal temperature than normal due to exercise *[1 mark]*. The thermoreceptors/temperature receptors send impulses along sensory neurones to the hypothalamus *[1 mark]*. The hypothalamus sends impulses along motor neurones to effectors (e.g. sweat glands) to reduce body temperature *[1 mark]*.

b) Any two from: sweating *[1 mark]* / hairs lying flat *[1 mark]* / vasodilation of arterioles *[1 mark]*.

c) It makes metabolic reactions less efficient *[1 mark]* because the enzymes that control metabolic reactions may denature *[1 mark]*.

Page 171 — Exercise and Health

There is a negative correlation between the time the women spent doing physical activity and their relative risk of CHD *[1 mark]*. However you cannot conclude that physical activity causes the reduced risk of CHD as there may be other factors involved, e.g. women who exercise more may also eat more healthily *[1 mark]*.

Page 173 — Exercise and Health

a) Any three valid points from: e.g. keyhole surgery involves a much smaller incision than open surgery so the patient loses less blood *[1 mark]* and has less scarring of the skin *[1 mark]*. The patient usually suffers less pain after keyhole surgery than open surgery *[1 mark]* and the patient usually recovers more quickly *[1 mark]*. It's usually easier for the patient to return to normal activities after keyhole surgery than open surgery *[1 mark]* and their hospital stay is usually shorter *[1 mark]*. *[Maximum of 3 marks available]*.

b) A prosthesis could be used to replace his knee *[1 mark]*. This might make it possible for him to play sport again *[1 mark]*.
E.g. banning the use of performance-enhancing drugs makes competitions fairer *[1 mark]*. Athletes are less tempted to take drugs that can have serious health risks *[1 mark]*.

Topic 8A — Responding to the Environment

Page 175 — Nervous and Hormonal Communication

1 Light receptors/photoreceptors in the animal's eyes detect the bright light *[1 mark]*. The receptors send impulses along neurones via the CNS to the effectors *[1 mark]*. These are the circular iris muscles *[1 mark]*, which respond by contracting to constrict the pupils and protect the eyes *[1 mark]*.

2 Any three from: e.g. the nervous system sends information as electrical impulses but the hormonal system sends information as chemicals *[1 mark]*. / Nervous responses are faster than hormonal responses *[1 mark]*. / Nervous responses are localised but hormonal responses are widespread *[1 mark]*. / Nervous responses are short-lived but hormonal responses are long-lasting *[1 mark]*.

Page 177 — The Nervous System — Receptors

1 B *[1 mark]*

Page 179 — The Nervous System — Neurones

1 a) A stimulus causes sodium ion channels in the neurone cell membrane to open *[1 mark]*. Sodium ions diffuse into the cell, so the membrane becomes depolarised *[1 mark]*.

b) The first action potential fired at 0.5 ms. If the second one fired at 4.5 ms, this means an action potential is fired every (4.5 − 0.5 =) 4 ms.
Number of ms in one hour = 60 × 60 × 1000 = 3 600 000.
There is one action potential every 4 ms, so in one hour there will be 3 600 000 ÷ 4 = 900 000 = **9 × 10⁵** action potentials.
[2 marks for the correct answer, allow 1 mark for the correct calculation of 3 600 000 ÷ 4.]
There's a lot to do to get the marks here, but that's A-level Biology for you. Just take your time and make sure you write down your calculations — that way you might pick up a mark even if you don't get the final answer right.

c) The membrane was in the refractory period *[1 mark]*, so the sodium ion channels were recovering and couldn't be opened *[1 mark]*.

Page 181 — The Nervous System — Neurones

1 Transmission of action potentials will be slower in neurones with damaged myelin sheaths *[1 mark]*. This is because myelin is an electrical insulator, so increases the speed of action potential conduction/conduction velocity *[1 mark]*. The action potentials 'jump' between the nodes of Ranvier/between the myelin sheaths, where sodium ion channels are concentrated *[1 mark]*.
Don't panic if a question mentions something you haven't learnt about. You might not know anything about multiple sclerosis but that's fine, because you're not supposed to. All you need to know to get full marks here is how myelination affects the speed of action potential conduction.

Page 183 — The Nervous System — Synapses

1 A — presynaptic membrane *[1 mark]*.
B — vesicle/vesicle containing neurotransmitter *[1 mark]*.
C — (postsynaptic) receptor *[1 mark]*.

2 The action potential arriving at the presynaptic membrane stimulates voltage-gated calcium ion channels to open, so calcium ions diffuse into the neurone *[1 mark]*. This causes synaptic vesicles, containing neurotransmitter, to move to the presynaptic membrane *[1 mark]*. These then fuse with the presynaptic membrane and release the neurotransmitter into the synaptic cleft *[1 mark]*. The neurotransmitter diffuses across the synaptic cleft and binds to specific receptors on the postsynaptic membrane *[1 mark]*. This causes sodium ion channels in the postsynaptic membrane to open *[1 mark]*. The influx of sodium ions causes depolarisation, which triggers a new action potential to be generated at the postsynaptic membrane *[1 mark]*.

Answers

Page 185 — Responses in Plants

1   IAA is produced in the tips of shoots and is moved around the plant, so different parts of the plant have different amounts of IAA *[1 mark]*. The uneven distribution of IAA means there's uneven growth of the plant *[1 mark]*. IAA moves to the more shaded parts of the shoots, where it is able to regulate the transcription of genes related to elongation and growth *[1 mark]*. This makes the cells there elongate, causing the shoot to bend towards the light *[1 mark]*.

2 a) P_{FR} is a phytochrome molecule in a state that absorbs far-red light/light at a wavelength of 730 nm *[1 mark]*.
   b) An iris would flower in the summer/June to August *[1 mark]* because it's stimulated to flower by high levels of P_{FR}, which occurs when nights are short *[1 mark]*. Daylight contains more red light than far-red light, so more P_R is converted into P_{FR} than P_{FR} is converted into P_R *[1 mark]*. When nights are short in the summer, there's not much time for P_{FR} to be converted back into P_R, so P_{FR} builds up and genes involved in flowering are transcribed *[1 mark]*.

Topic 8B — The Brain, Behaviour and Disease

Page 188 — Brain Structure and Function

1 a) E.g. control of breathing *[1 mark]*. Control of heart rate *[1 mark]*.
   b) Lack of coordinated movement / balance *[1 mark]*.
       You know that the cerebellum normally coordinates movement, so damage to it is likely to cause a lack of coordinated movement or balance.
2 a) Any two from: e.g. the extent of the bleeding *[1 mark]*. / The location of the bleeding *[1 mark]*. / What brain functions might be affected by the bleeding *[1 mark]*.
   b) A functional magnetic resonance imaging/fMRI scan *[1 mark]* and a positron emission tomography/PET scan *[1 mark]*.

Page 189 — Habituation

1 a) The birds' behaviour is habituation because they showed a reduced response (they didn't fly away as much) to the unimportant stimulus of the birdwatcher after repeated exposure for an hour every day *[1 mark]*.
   b) Habituation means the birds don't waste time and energy responding to unimportant stimuli *[1 mark]*.

Page 191 — Development of the Visual Cortex

1 a) i) Hubel and Wiesel stitched shut one eye of very young kittens for several months *[1 mark]*. When they unstitched the eyes, Hubel and Wiesel found that the kitten's eye that had been stitched up was blind *[1 mark]*. They also found the ocular dominance columns that were stimulated by the open eye had become bigger and had taken over the ocular dominance columns that weren't visually stimulated/for the shut eye *[1 mark]*.
       ii) Hubel and Wiesel's experiment showed that the visual cortex only develops properly if both eyes are visually stimulated in the very early stages of life *[1 mark]*.
   b) Yes, their experiments give evidence for a critical period in the development of the human visual system because our visual cortex is also made up of ocular dominance columns *[1 mark]*. The critical period is the period of time in very early life when it's critical that you're exposed to the right visual stimuli for the visual system to develop properly *[1 mark]*.
   c) During the critical period, synapses that receive visual stimulation and pass this onto the visual cortex are retained *[1 mark]*, whereas those that do not receive any visual stimulation are eliminated *[1 mark]*.

d) Any two from: e.g. animal research has led to lots of medical breakthroughs, e.g. antibiotics *[1 mark]*. / Animal experiments are only done when necessary and scientists follow strict rules *[1 mark]*. / Using animals is currently the only way to study how a drug affects the whole body *[1 mark]*. / Some people think humans have a greater right to life than animals *[1 mark]*.

Page 193 — Studying Brain Development

1 a) 'Nature' means your genes *[1 mark]*.
   b) A newborn baby's brain hasn't really been affected by the environment *[1 mark]*. This means scientists can see which aspects of brain development are more likely to be due to nature than nurture *[1 mark]*.
   c) Any two from: twin studies *[1 mark]* / brain damage studies *[1 mark]* / cross-cultural studies *[1 mark]*.
       The question asks you to suggest two types of study to directly investigate the effect of nature and nurture on brain development in <u>humans</u>, so don't go writing about animal experiments.

Page 195 — Drugs and Disease

1 a) Dopamine transmits nerve impulses across synapses in the parts of the brain that control movement *[1 mark]*.
   b) **5-6 marks:**
       The answer describes and explains fully the effects that Parkinson's disease has on the brain.
       The answer has a clear and logical structure and ideas are well-linked. The information given is relevant and detailed.
       3-4 marks:
       The answer attempts to describe and explain some ways in which Parkinson's disease affects the brain.
       The answer has some structure and attempts to link ideas. Most of the information given is relevant and there is some detail involved.
       1-2 marks:
       The answer describes some of the effects of Parkinson's disease on the brain, but there is little or no attempt made to explain them. The answer has very little clear structure and ideas are not well-linked. The information given is basic and lacking in detail. It may not all be relevant.
       0 marks:
       No relevant information is given.
       Here are some points your answer may include:
       The neurones in the parts of the brain that control movement are destroyed. These neurones normally produce the neurotransmitter dopamine, so losing them causes a lack of dopamine. A lack of dopamine means that less dopamine is released into synaptic clefts and so less dopamine binds to the receptors on the postsynaptic membranes. Fewer sodium ion channels on the postsynaptic membrane open, and so the postsynaptic cell is less likely to depolarise. Fewer action potentials are produced in neural pathways controlling movement, leading to symptoms such as tremors and slow movement.
   c) L-dopa is a drug that's used to treat Parkinson's disease *[1 mark]*. L-dopa is absorbed into the brain and converted into dopamine by the enzyme dopa-decarboxylase *[1 mark]*. This increases the level of dopamine in the brain *[1 mark]*, which causes an increase in the transmission of the nerve impulses involved in movement *[1 mark]*.
2   Scientists use databases that store the information from the Human Genome Project to identify proteins that are involved in disease *[1 mark]*. Scientists are using this information to create new drugs that target the identified proteins *[1 mark]*. The Human Genome Project has also highlighted common genetic variations between people *[1 mark]*. It's known that some of these variations make some drugs less effective *[1 mark]*. Drug companies are using this knowledge to design personalised medicines that are effective in people with these variations *[1 mark]*.

Answers

Any three from: e.g. personalised medicines will be more expensive to make and so will only be available to people that can afford them *[1 mark]*. / People may be refused a drug if their genetic information suggests that it is not very effective for them, but it may be the only drug available *[1 mark]*. / Genetic information may be used against people e.g. by insurance companies *[1 mark]*. / Knowing that a drug may not work because of a person's genetic information may be psychologically damaging for that person *[1 mark]*.

ge 197 — *Producing Drugs Using GMOs*

The human insulin gene is isolated using enzymes called restriction enzymes *[1 mark]*. The gene is then copied using PCR and the copies of the gene are inserted into plasmids *[1 mark]*. The plasmids are transferred into *E. coli* *[1 mark]*. The modified *E. coli* are grown so that they divide and produce lots of human insulin *[1 mark]*.

The hepatitis B vaccine in the plant tissues won't need to be refrigerated, which could make the vaccine available to people in areas where refrigeration isn't available *[1 mark]*. Herbicide resistance is a benefit because the plants will be unaffected by herbicides, so they will thrive after weeds are killed by herbicides, which will give a high yield of the vaccine *[1 mark]*. However, the transmission of genetic material between the genetically modified plants and wild plants could occur, which could create superweeds that are resistant to herbicides *[1 mark]*. There may also be currently unknown long-term impacts, as a consequence of using the genetically modified plant *[1 mark]*.

The question asked you to discuss the benefits and risks of growing the plant — make sure you write about both.

actical Skills

ge 200 — *Planning an Experiment*

5-6 marks:
The answer gives a full description of a valid investigation, which is fully supported by scientific knowledge.
The answer has a clear and logical structure and ideas are well-linked. The information given is relevant and detailed.
3-4 marks:
The answer gives some description of a valid investigation, which is sometimes supported by scientific knowledge.
The answer has some structure and attempts to link ideas. Most of the information given is relevant and there is some detail involved.
1-2 marks:
The answer attempts to describe an investigation.
The answer has very little clear structure and ideas are not well-linked. The information given is basic and lacking in detail. It may not all be relevant.
0 marks:
No relevant information is given.
Here are some points your answer may include:
A study should be carried out using two groups of participants. Give one group of participants the same daily dosage of fish oil (the independent variable) and give another group a placebo, to ensure that only the fish oil is having an effect on the clotting ability of the blood (the dependent variable). Control other variables by selecting participants who eat a similar diet/are not on any medication, as these could affect the validity of the results. The groups should have the same mix of ages/genders as these could also affect the validity of the results. Use a large sample size to increase the reliability of the results. Before the test begins, take a small blood sample from each participant and time how long it takes for the blood to clot, recording the result in seconds. The same volume of blood should be taken from each participant as this could affect clotting time (affecting the validity of the results). After a set period of time on the trial, test the participants' blood clotting time again.

Acknowledgements

Cover image © duncan1890/iStockphoto.com

Top graph on page 16 from 'Alcohol, tobacco & breast cancer – collaborative reanalysis of individual data from 53 epidemiological studies, including 58 515 women with breast cancer and 95 067 women without the disease.' Reprinted by permission from Macmillan Publishers Ltd on behalf of Cancer Research UK: British Journal of Cancer © Nov 2002

Data used to construct the bottom graph on page 16 reproduced with kind permission from Oxford University Press. P. Reynolds, et al. Active Smoking, Household Passive Smoking, and Breast Cancer: Evidence From the California Teachers Study. JNCI 2004; 96(1):29-37

Data used to construct the graph on page 19 from Townsend N, Williams J, Bhatnagar P, Wickramasinghe K, Rayner M (2014). Cardiovascular disease statistics, 2014. British Heart Foundation: London. © British Heart Foundation, December 2014

Data used to construct the graph on page 26 from P.M. Ridker, et al. Comparison of C-reactive protein and low density lipoprotein cholesterol levels in the prediction of first cardiovascular events. NEJM 2002; 347: 1557-65.

Data used to construct modelled temperature change graph on page 116 from IPCC, 2013: In: Climate Change 2013: The Physical Science Basis. Contribution of Working Group I to the Fifth Assessment Report of the Intergovernmental Panel on Climate Change, Box TS.5, Figure 1(b) [Stocker, T.F., D. Qin, G.-K. Plattner, M. Tignor, S.K. Allen, J. Boschung, A. Nauels, Y. Xia, V. Bex and P.M. Midgley (eds.)]. Cambridge University Press, Cambridge, United Kingdom and New York, NY, USA.

Instrumental temperature record graph on page 116 © Crown Copyright 2009. Used under the terms of the Open Government Licence V3.0 https://www.nationalarchives.gov.uk/doc/open-government-licence/version/3/

Data used to construct carbon dioxide and methane graph on page 118 adapted from IPCC, 2013: In: Climate Change 2013: The Physical Science Basis. Contribution of Working Group I to the Fifth Assessment Report of the Intergovernmental Panel on Climate Change. Figure 6.11. Stocker, T.F., et al. Cambridge University Press, Cambridge, United Kingdom and New York, NY, USA.

Data used to construct graphs of average global temperature on pages 118 and 119 adapted from IPCC, 2007: In: Climate Change 2007: The Physical Science Basis. Contribution of Working Group I to the Fourth Assessment Report of the Intergovernmental Panel on Climate Change. Figure SPM.3. Solomon, S., et al. Cambridge University Press, Cambridge, United Kingdom and New York, NY, USA.

Data used to construct graphs of average CO_2 concentration on pages 118 and 119 adapted from IPCC, Climate Change 2014 Synthesis Report, Summary for Policymakers, Figure SPM.1, part (c).

Data used to construct modelled global average surface temperature change graph on page 119 from IPCC, 2013: Summary for Policymakers. In: Climate Change 2013: The Physical Science Basis. Contribution of Working Group I to the Fifth Assessment Report of the Intergovernmental Panel on Climate Change. Figure SPM.7 part (a). Stocker, T.F., et al. Cambridge University Press, Cambridge, United Kingdom and New York, NY, USA.

Data used to construct table showing BMI and physical activity on page 170 reproduced with permission from Obesity and Physical Activity © 2011 National Heart Foundation of Australia.

Graph showing the incidence of CHD in elderly men according to distance walked daily on page 170 from Amy A. Hakim, MS; J. David Curb, MD; Helen Petrovitch, MD; Beatriz L. Rodriguez, MD, PhD; Katsuhiko Yano, MD; G. Webster Ross, MD; Lon R. White, MD; Robert D. Abbott, PhD. Effects of Walking on Coronary Heart Disease in Elderly Men. Circulation 1999; 100:9-13

Graph showing the prevalence of diabetes according to physical activity and BMI on page 170 from American Diabetes Association, Diabetes Care, American Diabetes Association, 2005. Copyright and all rights reserved. Material from this publication has been used with the permission of American Diabetes Association.

Data on exercise and the immune system on page 171 from L. Spence, W.J. Brown, D.B. Pyne, M.D. Nissen, T.P. Sloots, J.G. McCormack, A.S. Locke, P.A. Fricker. Incidence, Etiology and Symptomatology of Upper Respiratory Illness in Elite Athletes. Medicine & Science in Sports & Exercise 2007; 39:577-586.

Data in the exam question on page 171 from T.Y. Li, J.S. Rana, J.E. Manson, W.C. Willett, M.J. Stampfer, G.A. Colditz, K.M. Rexrode, F.B. Hu. Obesity as Compared with Physical Activity in Predicting Risk of Coronary Heart Disease in Women. Circulation 2006; 113:499-506.

With thanks to Science Photo Library for permission to reproduce the images on pages 62, 67, 91, 93, 187 and 188.

Every effort has been made to locate copyright holders and obtain permission to reproduce sources. For those sources where it has been difficult to trace the originator of the work, we would be grateful for information. If any copyright holder would like us to make an amendment to the acknowledgements, please notify us and we will gladly update the book at the next reprint. Thank you.

Index

Index